# The GLASS GIANT
## of PALOMAR

# The *GLASS GIANT of PALOMAR*

By

## DAVID O. WOODBURY

ILLUSTRATED WITH DRAWINGS BY THE AUTHOR,
SKETCHES BY RUSSELL W. PORTER,
AND PHOTOGRAPHS

DODD, MEAD & COMPANY
NEW YORK          1966

*THE GLASS GIANT OF PALOMAR*

PRINTED IN THE UNITED STATES OF AMERICA
BY THE VAIL-BALLOU PRESS, INC., BINGHAMTON, N. Y.

TO
INDIA RUYL WOODBURY
THE BEST COLLABORATOR
OF ALL

THERE are two distinct ways of approaching the story of a great scientific undertaking. One is simply to record fact, in the narrow sense of accurate dimensions and procedures, relying principally on the various tenses of the verb "to be." The other is to penetrate deep into the flesh and blood of the story, using facts merely as building blocks, cementing them together with the verb "to do." Here the whole is greater than the sum of its parts, and facts are exchanged for truth.

To the engineer this second approach is indefensible. Fact and truth are synonymous. Any element which does not conform to the rules of arithmetic is palpably unfit for use. To force human drama into the scientific account is to falsify it, to pander to the popular mind. If a statement is so, it is *so,* and, like the velocity of light, permits no enhancement.

Every lover of literature and art is familiar with the fallacy of this argument. He knows that a fact is the most unreliable performer in the world. It refuses to maintain a steady relationship to other facts; it is modified by everything that goes before it, with it and after it. And, taken alone, it thinks nothing of telling a plain, unadorned lie. But he knows that the truth, if one can attain it, can be counted on to remain the truth through thick and thin.

A year and a half ago, as I began the research which has led to *The Glass Giant of Palomar,* it seemed essential to present the story on the basis of the larger truths, subordinating the factual details to the great swing of the whole project. Here was the most magnificent engineering undertaking of our age, an unparalleled example of scientific courage and resourcefulness, a twelve-year adventure in pioneering which included every kind of genius, every shade of persistence, every degree of discouragement and triumph. Only through the recording of these human

emotions against the background of the great telescope could
the real story of modern science be told. In them lay buried the
typical portraits of the men who are bringing knowledge out
of the surrounding darkness. To have described the 200-inch
Giant in terms of mere facts would have been trivial and in-
sulting.

The literary purpose was large and the job correspondingly
difficult. To make a scientist tell about his work in terms of himself is well-nigh impossible. Early in the game an editor said to
me: "You'll never come anywhere near the real story unless
you go and live with those fellows—gain their confidence—
catch them off their guard." I took his advice, and *The Glass
Giant of Palomar* is the result.

But to be in possession of a scientist's confidence is only the
beginning of the battle. What follows is something like this:
Scientist A tells me a story—a good one, beautifully describing
his colleagues and himself and the work in hand. I repeat it to
Scientist B for verification and he denies it categorically. To
avoid backstairs politics I do not mention the source of my
story and so am accused of making it up myself out of whole
cloth. So far so good. I am better off than I expected. My story
is already fifty per cent substantiated. So I approach Scientist C,
who tells me that it's all right, because A is reliable and B is not.
Besides, he hints, B occasionally grinds an ax. Fine; now I am
up to sixty-six per cent.

I go on to D, who says, go ahead and print your story. It has
the essence of truth whether it is fact or not. But E begs me to
drop it entirely. Fact notwithstanding, it is better not to put
in anything that might offend anybody. And F brushes the
whole thing aside as true but unimportant and presents me with
a story of his own. So I catch the merry-go-round and make
the circuit again. I am satisfied. Story No. 1 is eighty-three per
cent perfect and that should be good enough for anybody.

So it goes; gradually I collect notebook after notebook of
those elusive atoms of information that my scientists like to call

facts, and in the meanwhile a true picture of a hundred great men at work building a great telescope. About the dimensions and cost of the vast machine they may agree, but about nothing else. Each in his own way has subtly suggested (quite unconsciously, of course) that I bias the account ever so slightly in favor of *him*, or of his estimate of the truth.

Not only do individuals invariably do this; each of the large corporations involved does it too (and not quite so unconsciously); each asks for a special break, a slight additional coloring of its own part in the proceedings so as to give a favorable picture of that particular institution. Not in so many words, mind you, but by coyly suggesting the omission of remarks tending to lessen its glory.

This is not merely a fact, it is the truth. In the course of offering the manuscript for criticism and approval, no group has ever objected, even in the mildest way, to statements about the others; on the contrary has often highly commended them. But about his own portrait no critic has failed to be irritable, and has occasionally become quite excited. To subject oneself to this criticism is a subtle form of literary sacrifice in the pursuit of accuracy. But the reward is the proof that human nature does exist, even among the scientists.

There is only one way to solve these constantly recurring dilemmas: first, to make sure of the engineering facts, then to weave them together according to one's own best judgment into a balanced pattern that is not inconsistent in any of its parts, *regardless of the critics*. In other words, frankly to dramatize literal fact till it takes on a universal meaning larger than any mere telescope.

I am aware that none of the characters in my story will be wholly satisfied with the result. To each of them the 200-inch telescope means something a trifle more specialized than I have made it. *The Glass Giant of Palomar* is a composite—a general solution to an intricate problem which has a thousand partial solutions, all inadequate. This is the scientific way of dealing with any complicated situation, as even the most technical among my friends will admit.

For the rest, I am sincerely grateful to them all for the hours and days of time they have given me—time frequently ill-spared from the absorbing task of building the Giant. Not one of all the scores of engineers and scientists I have approached has ever been stuffy or short; not one too busy to bother with an outsider whose thirst for information must have seemed uncommonly stubborn. From the lowliest mechanic to the head of the Project they have all accepted my presence for just what it was—the necessary preliminary to presenting their great story to the public.

And if, in the following pages, I have succeeded in making them live in flesh and blood, I shall have rendered them the best payment I can for their co-operation.

For they *do* live, even if they are scientists.

DAVID O. WOODBURY

Ogunquit, Maine,
May 22, 1939

# CONTENTS

## PART I

## ANCESTRY

## PART II

## THE GIANT IS BORN

xi

# PART I

# ANCESTRY

# CHAPTER I

## JULES VERNE BECOMES A PIKER

SEVENTY years ago the great romancer Jules Verne told of a gigantic reflecting telescope which was to follow the flight of a projectile fired from the Earth to the Moon. This fanciful instrument, which he described in full detail, was equipped with a mirror sixteen feet in diameter, weighing fifteen tons. It was to magnify 48,000 times and bring into sight an object nine feet in diameter on the Moon's surface. It was altogether the most powerful engine of sight that fiction's greatest visionary could conceive and was to cost the magnanimous Americans of that day four hundred thousand dollars.

Verne's characters built this giant on the 14,000-foot summit of Long's Peak in "the Territory of Missouri," and it worked, as any imagined instrument must, to perfection. With it the astronomers saw the projectile as it crossed the face of the satellite. Through its eyepiece they learned with horror that the intrepid adventurers had missed the Moon altogether and had plunged into the eternal void behind it, perhaps never to be seen again.

Eleven years ago Dr. George Ellery Hale, founder of the Mount Wilson Observatory in California, not only bore out Verne's prophecy but improved upon it, and began actual construction of a new telescopic giant on Palomar Mountain. Its mirror was to be seventeen feet in diameter, weighing twenty tons; its cost, six million dollars. Not the Moon, but the very boundaries of space, were its objectives. With it Hale hoped to attack such tremendous problems as the shape and size and origin of the Universe itself.

Today, a mile above the Pacific, on the flat top of an isolated mountain in California, the Glass Giant of Palomar is nearing

3

completion. Scarcely a year more and its great aluminum-coated mirror will be turned upon the heavens—a mirror ten thousand times as powerful a gatherer of light as the little lens with which Galileo discovered the moons of Jupiter in 1610, and more than a million times as keen as the human eye. It will reach twice as far into space as the present world's largest telescope, dragging billions of now invisible stars out of obscurity. It will settle the physical and chemical nature of stars that have been mysteries since astronomy began. It may even settle the question of Eddington's Expanding Universe. It began as one man's dream, but it finishes as the culmination of a thousand arts and inventions and the finest instrument that science and engineering can devise.

From all over the world glass and steel, manpower and brainpower and money are converging upon Palomar. Seventy men are working on the mountain today, living there with their wives and children, hammering, sawing, welding, pouring concrete, painting, lining up the huge beams and girders and aluminum sheets which will soon make the observatory shell, higher than a 15-story building. Up the twenty-mile paved road which the county supervisors built especially for the telescope the largest tractor-trailers in the world are creeping day by day with the parts of the telescope body, shipped into San Diego from eastern factories by way of the Panama Canal. A hundred miles to the north of Palomar, segregated in a laboratory of its own, the seventeen-foot disk of "Pyrex" glass is gradually being smoothed and polished and tested under the expert hands of twenty-one young men who have "grown up" with the job. Near by, in another laboratory, a dozen men and women, many of them young, all of them technical experts in every branch of science, are keeping ahead of the Giant's progress with pencil and slide-rule and drafting board, solving construction problems, inventing new methods, new machines, new approaches to a job the very magnitude and intricacy of which defies the best engineering practice of the day.

But this is not all. In every part of the world, where men

gather in laboratories or technical groups, the 200-inch telescope is known and discussed. Every day it inspires the world's foremost scientists to fresh ideas, fresh discoveries. Never before has a scientific undertaking so completely drawn the technical brains of the world together into a united front. Yet for most of these men there is no monetary reward; instead, the far higher pay which comes from a contribution, large or small, to the sum of the world's knowledge and understanding of itself and its cosmic environment.

Many of the scientists who have co-operated will not live to see the new telescope in service; many more will, in the course of their work, never come into actual contact with it. But in some strange way the instrument is moving surely toward the goal Hale's vision set for it: the rallying point for all brilliant men, the symbol of that magnificent spirit of research once so ably described by Willis R. Whitney: "The impossible is that which we have not yet learned to do."

The 200-inch telescope was impossible when Hale undertook it ten years ago; many of its minor details are still impossible—and will remain so until the time comes to make them fact. Then they will be fact, one can be sure of that.

For us outside of science there is also something to look up to in this symbol. Here in a world of warped philosophies, of ignorance and terror and impotence, of little men yelling large defiance, we see quiet men going about a job—not an easy job, not a cut-and-dried job, not a job that can be accomplished out of books or by the weight of money alone. But a job they think worth doing in spite of its impossibility, in spite of its tediousness, its demands for self effacement, sometimes at the risk of life itself. Men facing things that can't be done and doing them; for no other reason than that some men are made that way and always will be.

Such a monument could not be rising if it were not for one man: George Ellery Hale. Dr. Hale gave his life for astronomy and died just when men hate most to die—on the threshold of his greatest achievement. But the story of the world's largest telescope began a long time ago, when Hale began, as a child, to exhibit scientific genius. And that is how the story must be told, beginning in Chicago in 1881.

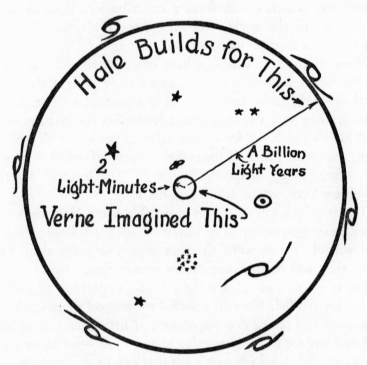

BUT THE SCALE IS INACCURATE. THE OUTER CIRCLE SHOULD
BE TWENTY BILLION MILES ACROSS.

## CHAPTER II

## DESIGN FOR GENIUS

In that year—1881—George Hale was thirteen years old. He decided to build a telescope, and asked his father for the money. His father gave it to him willingly. George hurried off and bought a small lens and mounted it in a home-made tube. It was a pretty crude affair and the images it made were fuzzy and indistinct. But it decided his career. Boys of his time who had telescopes used them to look at objects down the street. But Hale began at once gazing at the stars. He was fascinated with the telescope's marvelous ability to make faint stars bright and bring out hidden details on the Moon and demonstrate that Venus was nearly always a crescent instead of a disk.

In books his mother had given him he had read of how Galileo had discovered the moons of Jupiter with a telescope no bigger than the one he had now. But the old Italian professor could have felt no greater delight than this boy of thirteen, looking eagerly through an instrument almost identical with the first ever invented. But life was ahead of George, not behind him; and the dawning age of invention stretched out before him. He would be an astronomer, that was settled.

A little while later George heard of a telescope with a 4-inch lens that was for sale second-hand. He went to his father and explained that he wanted to begin scientific researches on the spectrum of the Sun; the elder Hale put up the money at once, and George bought the instrument and mounted it on the roof of the family residence in Chicago.

There were not many fathers of the Nineteenth Century who would have consented to a son's dabbling in science, much less furnishing them with the money to do it. But William Hale was different. He was a manufacturer of elevators, a well-to-do man of wide vision and important social connections. He understood perfectly that his son had mechanical ability. If George was headed for an engineering career the thing to do was to promote it in every possible way.

This is not the typical up-from-the-gutter success story that America loves. George had everything that he needed to give support to his talents: a sturdy New England background, plenty of money for education, sympathetic and intelligent parents, a host of influential friends and associates. In short, the very same equipment which leads thousands of good citizens straight into eclipse as nonentities for sheer lack of economic necessity. But George Hale rose above this level, for his necessity came from within. It was of the spirit. If he did not need wealth, he scorned inaction more.

His father decided to send him to the Massachusetts Institute of Technology. The boy accepted eagerly. In his freshman year there he made an arrangement with Director E. C. Pickering of the Harvard Observatory so that he might take care of some of the instruments and use them when the astronomers did not want them. There he got his first actual training in the observation of the heavens. Astronomy, he found out, was not only a question of enlarging the images of stars and planets so that you could see what they were. It was mainly a matter of increasing the diameter of the eye artificially so that it could see objects too faint to be seen alone, and so study them in detail. Astronomy was the pursuit of Light.

We see the same comparison today between a Brownie camera and a Leica: a difference in "speed" and "definition." The big lens and the tiny film of the Leica record in a flash the subtle lights and shades of a picture that are utterly lost to the snapshot camera. Once caught, the miniature pictures may be enlarged enormously, to bring out the finest of detail. But the Brownie's pictures are only approximations, and enlargements of them yield little. In the same way the great lens of the fifteen-inch refractor at Harvard revealed to George's eager eye a wealth of detail that he could hardly believe the heavens contained. Then and there he dedicated himself to Light. And Light meant not only the images of faint stars to George but the revealing of the secrets of the bright ones, too.

With his vigorous young mind he struck off at once into pioneering territory. "The Sun is our nearest star," he contended. "We must study it in detail; then we must prove by observation that the stars are like it. Thus we shall begin to understand the evolution of the Universe."

Sir Isaac Newton started the world's quest for light when he split the Sun's rays into a colored spectrum with a prism of glass, and went on to construct a theory of the nature of light itself. By the time Hale had reached M.I.T. the spectra of the Sun and of some of the brightest stars had been under scrutiny for some twenty years through a simple instrument called the spectroscope. This was the same arrangement of prisms Newton had invented; it had been in use for a century aiding chemists in the analysis of unknown compounds by splitting their light up into bright bands of different colors. Astronomers also had found the spectroscope a valuable tool. Installed at the eyepiece of a powerful telescope it had enabled them to investigate the chemical composition of the Sun and a few stars, and to measure their motions and study their temperatures. It had helped Lockyer to discover the strange new element helium in the Sun in 1868. And now, in the 1880's, it was rapidly becoming the most valuable instrument in astronomy, paving the way for the photographic analysis of stars and displacing the observer's eye at the telescope.

But the spectrograph (or photographic spectroscope) was still in its infancy when George Hale arrived on the scene. It was not fully adapted to the detailed work he was anxious to do on the Sun. So he very soon proposed a new instrument which he called the "spectroheliograph," for taking pictures of the Sun by the light of one chemical element at a time. It was based on an idea which Professor Young of Princeton had tried and discarded as unworkable in 1870. It operated on the principle of building up a photographic image of the Sun by "scanning," or adding hundreds of little elements together to make the whole.

The bright colored band of the solar spectrum is crossed by some 20,000 thin dark lines. They divide into groups which represent the absorption of light by various elements in the Sun's atmosphere. Actually, these lines are dark only by comparison and give enough light to affect a photographic plate. Hale's machine selected a single dark line and scanned the whole face of the Sun a little at a time, building up a picture of the distribution of one element. He proposed to take photographs with many common elements in this way and so determine the actual geography of the solar surface.

George invented the spectroheliograph when he was a junior in college. When the term ended he hurried home to the laboratory he had built in his back yard and spent the summer improving the machine.

In the fall he took it back with him to the Harvard Observatory but couldn't make it work. The principle seemed all right, but the blue lines of the element hydrogen which he was using did not affect the crude photographic plates enough to give a strong image. George had no time to trace down the difficulty, for Technology was clamoring for his attendance at classes if he were to graduate. Reluctantly he shelved his experiments and went back to his books, determined to get them out of the way in the shortest possible time.

Hale got his degree in 1890, packed up the spectroheliograph and went back to Chicago, free now to develop his invention. The astronomers at both Lick and Princeton observatories had heard of his work and offered him the use of large telescopes to aid in his researches. But George decided that he needed an instrument of his own—more than that: a whole observatory which he could devote exclusively to the work on the Sun. Again he went to his father and again succeeded in gaining his support. It was some thousands of dollars the elder Hale put up this time—still cheerfully—and the result was a solar laboratory erected in a separate building on the Hale estate in the suburb of Kenwood. Its principal boasts were a 12-inch refracting telescope and a machine shop, small but complete.

George lost no time in going to work on a carefully planned schedule of investigation. Little by little he collected equipment or built it himself with the aid of a nineteen-year-old photographer named Ferdinand Ellerman. He began all over again with his invention, this time using a violet line of calcium light to scan the Sun. The instrument was an immediate success. Putting a black disk over the face of the Sun's image at the end of the Kenwood telescope, he was able to photograph for the first time in history the towering flames of the prominences which were shooting as much as 500,000 miles up from the solar rim. It was a genuine contribution—the first step in his long struggle to "find a way of combining physics and chemistry with astronomy." His lifework was definitely under way.

Hale married now and on his wedding trip visited the Lick Observatory in California, where another young astronomer, James Keeler, had succeeded in making spectroscopic studies of the nebulous matter splashed across the night sky. Hale left with the firm conviction that the spectroscope and the photographic plate were the great coming instruments by which the stars could be brought to earth. It was then that he coined the term "astrophysics" to describe the union of astronomy and earthbound science.

When Hale went to Europe soon afterward, the fame of his spectroheliograph preceded him. At twenty-three he was already considered an authority on the Sun. Immediately he set about interesting the great authorities of the Old World in the new science of astrophysics. Crookes, Janssen, Huggins and Dewar took him into their councils and offered him their support in starting an international journal of astronomy and spectroscopy.

But Hale's immediate popularity did not turn his head. He

used this year abroad principally to study in Berlin under Helmholtz, Planck and other famous physicists. He had no thought of establishing himself as an authority until he had learned all that the older men could teach him.

Back in Chicago Hale very soon found that the little 12-inch telescope at Kenwood was not powerful enough. It revealed the Sun pretty well for a preliminary study but gathered far too little light for the great detail he needed. Nor could it support his intended program for the stars. The whole vast promise of astrophysics lay out there locked in a million dim suns, awaiting only the man who could capture enough of their light to understand. Hale wanted to be that man. He had been deeply impressed with the 36-inch telescope at Lick, then the world's largest, and with what Keeler and Campbell had made it reveal of the nebulae. He had come home from California with an ambition to own an instrument like it. Once provided with a *large* telescope he could indeed lead the world to something new.

The young astronomer was now only twenty-four, but his friend President Harper of the newly founded University of Chicago so admired him that he gave him the post of associate professor in astrophysics. William Hale contributed his son's salary. Both of the older men realized, however, that a mere professorship and an observatory with a 12-inch telescope could not keep pace with the young man's ambitions. Soon George Hale and the President were deep in plans for an observatory big enough and complete enough to carry Hale's researches to their logical conclusion.

One day Hale attended a scientific meeting in Rochester, N.Y. Purely by chance he overheard somebody talking to the great lens-maker Alvan G. Clark of Cambridgeport. Clark was in a quandary. The University of Southern California, at that time more ambitious than important, was sponsoring a grandiloquent scheme for outdoing Lick and building a telescope even larger than the 36-inch. Through Clark two huge glass disks had been ordered from the optical firm of Mantois in Paris. No sooner had the disks arrived in Clark's workshop than word had come from California that the expected gift of money to pay for the new lens was not to be forthcoming; Southern California would have no telescope. The University, said the regents, was sorry, but it couldn't even pay the Frenchmen for the glass. Clark was out of pocket about $20,000 and as there was no one else in America who could possibly afford such a telescope the great disks were on his hands, orphans.

Hale rushed back to Harper with the news. Ready to their very hands, he said, were glass disks large enough to make a 40-inch telescope—the most powerful in the world. With such an instrument the Sun, the stars, the planets—all could be studied as never before. It was the opportunity he had dreamed of. Harper's imagination soon caught fire. He could see his University made important by a department of astronomy where great pioneering work would be done. He could see a chance to give Hale the scope he needed.

But where was the money to come from? That question had burdened every scientist since Archimedes. Thousands of productive hours must always be sacrificed to the heartbreaking task of coaxing money from the world's rich that discovery and invention might continue. Of all the sciences astronomy was perhaps the most expensive. Only the finest instruments and workmanship would do. A first class job cost a fortune. And at that time—1892—not more than three men in America were skilled enough to shape large astronomical lenses at all.

The Lick Observatory had cost $610,000. Where indeed was the University of Chicago to get funds of this caliber?

Harper was an able organizer. He had great influence in the Middle West as the man who had built a first-class university single handed. But he couldn't find any such sum as this. He had often persuaded rich men to endow education in general, for that was something they understood. But astronomy was another matter. It was far too technical and its value too obscure to inspire a large gift. Harper did not know which way to turn.

But young Hale was not dismayed. He was already adept at obtaining funds for scientific research. He had been getting money from his father since boyhood—a task that was not as easy as it seemed. William Hale was hard-headed and sane. He never gave George a penny for sentimental reasons. He had to be convinced first that his son's objectives were sound and that he knew how to reach them. So George had learned to plead well and logically; more than that, he had learned to avoid blind alleys of experiment. His father's friend, Daniel Hudson Burnham, the great city planner, had said to George: "Make no small plans, my boy." George agreed. Long afterward, at sixty-seven, he had never made a small plan in his life. And with his big plans men were invariably fascinated. So, now, Harper.

"What are you going to do?" he asked Hale.

"See Charles T. Yerkes," said Hale.

"It's impossible," the President told him. "I've tried him many times. He gives away no money."

Yerkes was one of Chicago's most wealthy men—and most influential. He was said to own the principal streets of the city, for he held long-term trolley-car franchises on them. Anyone who remembers the lurid days of the traction magnates knows what that means. But Hale decided to tackle him.

He got himself invited to a dinner that Yerkes was to attend and contrived to sit next to him. Then he began talking astronomy. Yerkes was inattentive at first but soon became fascinated. This young man with his vivid interest in the stars was worth investigating. Before he knew it he had sheepishly admitted to Hale that he had dreamed since boyhood of building the biggest of all telescopes. Hale left the dinner with Yerkes' check for $20,000 in his pocket to buy the Clark glasses, and his promise of enough more money to make them into a 40-inch lens.

Next day he jubilantly told Harper what he had accomplished. Harper was delighted but his delight was tempered with a practical note. "How about a telescope to mount the lens in?"

he asked. "And an observatory to house it?"

"I'll go back to Mr. Yerkes and ask for the money," said Hale, confidently. He did, and was refused. He tried several times and still Yerkes refused.

"Now what?" said Harper.

"I'm going back, and keep on going back till I get what I want."

Then began one of the most discouraging periods in Hale's life. With the greatest prize in astronomy almost within his grasp he could not raise the money to possess it. Yerkes turned him down, for the last time. Hale tried others—friends, strangers, anybody with money to spare. They all admired him but none could help him. Finally, a year later, he visited Yerkes once more, on the chance. The magnate confronted him sternly.

"Confound it!" he said. "You're as bad as a delegation of aldermen."

"Worse," Hale grinned, "for I can wait longer." This time he went away with a check for the whole telescope. But the old financier absolutely refused to put up the money for the buildings.

# CHAPTER III

## HOW OLD THE STARS?

THE Yerkes Observatory was begun in 1892 and five years later it was dedicated at Williams Bay, Wisconsin. Hale, at twenty-nine, became its first director.

Soon after Yerkes first capitulated to the young astronomer's enthusiasm, Hale telegraphed Alvan G. Clark to come to Chicago to write a contract for the lens. Clark came at once and the papers were drawn up. Hale returned with him to Cambridge-port. The two men examined the great disks minutely. They were not perfect, but by long odds they were the finest pieces of crown and flint glass ever cast. However, it would be no simple task to make these slabs into a single objective lens three-and-one-third feet in diameter and less than five inches in combined thickness.

Clark was probably the only man in the world at the time who could do it successfully. His father, Alvan Clark, had been the greatest glass craftsman in America, but he had just died at eighty-three. The son, over sixty himself, had spent a lifetime learning the art, and had trained an assistant, Carl Lundin, to almost as great a skill as his own.

First the disks must be carefully cut to size, then each one ground down to a highly accurate curved surface, front and back. After this they must be polished to take out every faintest scratch that the grinding had left behind. And finally, the opticians' skilled and sensitive fingers must add the final "figure" —that exact, smooth contour at every point of the four surfaces, which would enable them in combination to focus star-light to a single spot 62 feet down the telescope tube. And all of this with the full knowledge that the smallest slip, the slightest lapse into carelessness, or even a moment of ill luck, might gouge the glass too deeply and send them back to do the work all over again.

Clark and Lundin hovered over the job constantly for three years, shaping, calipering, polishing, testing, rubbing minutely here and there to correct every infinitesimal "mountain" or "valley" which vitiated the smooth curves. It was not merely skilled workmanship; it was a kind of genius. The best glass blank in the world is not wholly homogeneous. There will always be slight variations in its density and composition, and these will bend the tiny starbeams and blur the image. It is the optician's final task to seek out these bad spots and to compensate for them by slight modifications in the true figure. Only thus can a huge refractor like the Yerkes telescope be made successful. Only men like the Clarks could do it at all, and they mostly by some feat of manual intuition—one of the rarest possessions in all the world of science.

By 1895 the work was done. The world's largest lens was ready. The total cost of the objective alone had reached $55,000.

But Hale was not out for rivalry. He was out for more light. He invited Keeler to come East from Lick and help him make the final tests. The two men went over the new lens with the greatest care and found it excellent. They were delighted. The science of astrophysics was about to get a mighty engine of sight. The men at Lick, at Harvard, everywhere, would benefit from its work just as much as the men at Chicago.

By this time Yerkes had given the funds for the telescope itself and Warner & Swasey were building it in Cleveland. But the observatory was still unobtainable. Yerkes rebelled at being bled for any more money and it got so that he would not even admit Hale to his house. Hale decided to go ahead piecemeal. A friend gave a tract of land and he himself, with his father's help, donated instruments and equipment from Kenwood. By picking up a few hundred dollars here and there, he gradually collected the makings of a whole observatory—all but the buildings. Then, unable to move another step, he went to Europe to study and bide his time.

Why Yerkes finally capitulated is not known. It is said that his architect worked upon his vanity and his conscience by urging him to square himself with the people of Chicago by erecting the Yerkes Observatory complete. At any rate, the magnate's sales resistance suddenly collapsed and within six months the buildings were going up. Cheerfully he signed check after check until at the end his investment had reached a total of $349,000.

The wedding of physics and the stars was to be no cheap affair.

In 1922 Dr. Hale went to Italy in the hope of regaining a measure of the health he had lost in the intense pursuit of astronomy. He and his friend James H. Breasted, the archaeologist, spent some time in Florence, and went to see Galileo's first telescope in the museum there.

"I wonder," Hale mused. "Do you suppose we could see anything through it now?"

"Let's borrow it and find out," Breasted proposed.

Hale was like a boy again; his perennial enthusiasm burst through and enveloped the timid officials of the museum. With the help of the Italian astronomer Abetti, the authorities were won over to the plan. As happy as a pair of kids the scientists tenderly took up the world's first astronomical telescope and hurried with it to the observatory at Arcetri, where they attached it to the side of the equatorial mount, and waited impatiently for the night.

Jupiter was high in the south—the same Jupiter Galileo Galilei had seen three hundred years before on his pioneer voyage through space. Their hands grasped the tube where his had grasped it; their brows pressed the eyepiece as his had done. And there were the four moons of Jupiter still; that bright silver string of little satellites, riding the heavens with their giant parent-planet, all amazingly clear and beautiful. Hale turned away and bowed his head.

"We should feel very humble, Jim," he said.

Well did Hale understand that modern achievements have not dimmed the great discoveries of the past. He never lost his reverence for the ancient men of genius who solved nature's first riddles without previous knowledge, with crude instruments, with nothing to help them but their own ingenuity and persistence.

For the five thousand years before Christ, for example, the Chinese, the Egyptians, the Babylonians and the Greeks had been observing the stars and the planets, naming them and studying their motions. They had learned how to tell time and they

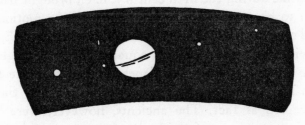

JUPITER WITH MOONS

understood the rotation of the seasons. In 200 B. C. Eratosthenes of Alexandria had measured the curvature of the Earth with a peg of wood and the Sun's shadow and computed its circumference within fifty miles of the right value. Seventy years later Hipparchus, comparing his own crude observations with those of another astronomer made two hundred years earlier, had discovered that the whole heavens had shifted a little, and reasoned that the Earth was wobbling like a top as it spun. It was an extraordinary thing for him to accomplish without precision instruments, for this "Precession of the Equinoxes" causes the Earth to wobble only a few degrees in a full cycle of 26,000 years.

But Hipparchus did something more important: he made a methodical tabulation of the sky, as much of it as he could see winter and summer in Greece, and published the world's first star catalogue. It had 1022 entries, carefully indexed according to brightness, or magnitude, from the first, Sirius, to that host of stars of the sixth, just visible to the naked eye. Later on Ptolemy amended and improved the catalogue somewhat, and it was handed on into the Christian era for the use of sailors at sea. It was so accurate, indeed, that it survived 1600 years of ignorance and darkness and helped Columbus to find America. As for Hipparchus' scale of magnitudes, it was so well conceived that it is still in use, and will soon become a part of the scheme of operation of the 200-inch telescope.

But we are getting ahead too fast. Pythagoras the traveler, at some time during the fifth century, B. C., brought back from Babylon to his native Greece knowledge of the motion of the Sun and the planets. He had been told abroad that the Earth was a revolving sphere and that its equator lay at an angle to the plane in which the Sun and planets seemed to move through the sky. He soon had many followers and presently the theory was accepted as fact. The ancients, however, were without optical instruments to furnish proof; moreover, they had no reason to suppose that the Universe was more than large enough to clothe the Earth with a decent envelope of space. So the opposing "geocentric" theory soon came into vogue. This made the Earth stationary in the center of a hollow sphere colored blue on the inside, with the Sun, planets and stars slipping around smoothly and regularly on its inner surface.

The idea soon developed embarrassing complications, for the Greeks were too mathematical a people not to notice that the planets failed to follow the stars in a simple regular course month after month, but would sometimes slow up perceptibly and even go backwards for a time. Eudoxus of Cnidus saved the geocentric theory by picturing the various heavenly bodies as if pasted on the insides of many huge spheres instead of only one. He explained that the spheres were geared to one another in some invisible way and that the whole conglomeration ran continuously, like a gigantic perpetual-motion machine. For the time being the reasoning seemed adequate and was not damaged in the least because it required twenty-seven interconnected spheres to do the trick. But twenty-seven did not long remain enough. By Aristotle's time the number had risen to fifty-five, and the theory, still in solemn repute, was receiving additions every year, as keen observers charted further vagaries of the skies.

Aristarchus of Samos, meanwhile, advanced another theory. The Sun, he contended, was the center of the Universe and the Earth and everything else revolved around it. The idea was soon outlawed by Ptolemy, who favored the geocentric view, and was in a position to back it up with political force.

Before long, however, the whole matter sank into oblivion as the interpreters of Christianity, with their cast-iron ideas of right and wrong, drove all independent thought into the black night of the Dark Ages.

Alchemy and astrology claimed many a generation for their own, then, and it was not till the Sixteenth Century that the courageous Polish monk Copernicus revived the subject in his dogged teachings that the Sun was the center of things and that the Earth, with a great many other bodies, revolved around it in comparative unimportance. The theory earned for Copernicus the undying enmity of the Church, but that did not deter him from publishing his hypothesis and circulating it throughout Europe.

For fifty centuries now, men had been studying the stars with their eyes alone. They had no way of seeing more than the two thousand-odd that were easily visible to the naked eye, nor any reason for thinking there were ten million times as many fainter ones beyond. But concerning that two thousand they had learned a good deal, especially about the planets. Though they knew nothing of them as worlds they had learned, by the Sixteenth Century, a great deal about them as bodies moving in space. It was in 1543 that Copernicus published his great theory of a planetary system moving around a central Sun. Three years after that was born the greatest of the world's naked-eye astronomers,

Tycho Brahe, the Dane.

Here was a George Ellery Hale of the Renaissance. As a youth he had opportunity to study astronomy all over Europe. His family were friends of the King of Denmark. In his twenties he persuaded his uncle to give him the money to build an observatory, which confirmed his interest in the stars and made him an astronomer for life. When he was just thirty Tycho built the world's largest and most complete observatory on the island of Hveen in the Baltic. The land and money for it had been given him by the King.

Brahe had no telescopes but he invented the most accurate instruments it was possible to devise for sighting the positions of heavenly bodies. To him the whole problem was the measurement of angles subtended by pairs of stars at the position of the observer. Without even a magnifying glass to study the calibrations on his instruments Tycho was able to read these angles to the sixtieth part of a degree, or about a thirtieth of the diameter of the Moon. A very fine accuracy when you remember that the Moon, as Pendray happily puts it, can be eclipsed completely by a green pea held at arm's length. Tycho Brahe was observing celestial angles with an error smaller than the thickness of the skin on the pea. Thus was born the science of precision measurement.

By 1600, when Shakespeare was at his zenith, the Church had reached the nadir of its intolerance. Enraged by the subversive teachings of the Polish monk, the Holy Inquisition began a purge of scientific ideas not unlike the political purges of our own day. Giordano Bruno, trying to expound the Copernican theory in Rome, was seized and burned at the stake. Copernicus' great work itself was seized and burned too and its author, happily dead, removed from Purgatory and thrown permanently into hell.

Like King Canute, however, the Church rumbled in vain. For men will find out and believe new things even if it kills them. There are brave spirits in every generation who do not count the cost of knowledge, or balk at the price of truth. Apparently by mistake a Dutchman, Jan Lippershey, looked through a combination of spectacle lenses he was making one day and beheld an enlarged image of a distant kirk. Instantly he saw the principle of a useful military instrument revealed, and hurried off to file a patent on it.

Soon there was great confusion among the spectacle makers, for the spyglass arrangement was dead simple: merely a convex spectacle lens at one end of a tube and a concave one at the other. All sorts of people hurried forward to claim priority, and Lippershey was soon lost in the shuffle, though he did get 900 florins from the Dutch government.

While the fight for credit raged the flame of the invention swept Europe. It soon reached quiet Padua, in Italy, where Galileo Galilei, a professor of science at the University, was just settling down to old age and honor after a lifetime of teaching. Galileo (to adopt his first name as the world has done in affection or ignorance)—Galileo came out of retirement in a jiffy and inside of a few days had constructed a spyglass of his own, exactly as George Hale did 300 years later, by buying lenses and mounting them in a home-made tube. But he did more. Unsatisfied with a meager magnification of three times, which the Lippershey instrument could give, Galileo studied the optical theory behind the phenomenon and saw that spectacle lenses were not high enough in power nor large enough in diameter: if he should make his own he might get far more magnification. This he did, and before long had constructed an instrument that would enlarge objects thirty times. To this he gave the name of telescope.

Galileo realized at once that the great value of the invention lay in what it could tell him of the stars. And so he began, methodically, to sweep the heavens, night after night in the soft clear winter air of the south. Literally thousands of stars sprang into being in the vivid dome above him. Wherever he pointed it, his instrument gave a sudden power to light that had been for all civilization's long youth too faint to be noticed. Then, on the night of January 7, 1610, he trained his telescope on Jupiter, and discovered the moons.

This at last was the beginning of modern astronomy, and Galileo must have realized it. With care and patience he followed the planet night after night, saw the moons approach the

WHERE HIPPARCHUS SAW ONE STAR, GALILEO FOUND 200.

parent body, disappear, and come out again on the other side. He understood that here was the keynote of the entire heavens —the principle of revolution about a central body. Turning to Venus, Galileo found more proof. In his telescope the bright evening star was a star no longer, but a crescent, changing steadily in phase as she revolved around the Sun, just as our Moon changes and for the same reason.

Galileo hastened to publish his discoveries and the scientific world rejoiced. But not the Inquisition. The heretic was summoned before it and told to recant publicly. On pain of imprisonment he must deny his teachings and re-establish the authority of the Bible. For had not Joshua said that the Sun moves, and the Earth stands still? Galileo saw the rest of his life ruined and his researches brought to an end. Sullenly he recanted and was set free. For seventeen years he held his peace, carrying on his investigations under cover but never publishing them. Finally, at the age of seventy the fire of his spirit burst through; he published a theory of the tides which not only championed Copernicus but crisply denounced the Inquisition in Rome.

Galileo was instantly haled before the tribunal again and ordered to recant on pain of death. The old man had grown too feeble to withstand such pressure. With tears in his eyes he denied the discoveries of a lifetime.

Then, under his breath he muttered defiantly: "Yet the earth does move!"

He was released, then thrown into prison. His friend the Duke of Tuscany interceded for him and Galileo was allowed to return home, where he was kept under guard for eight years in his own house, blind, ill and discouraged. But to the outside world he was a genius and the great men of Europe flocked to see him. That he had recanted was unimportant. He had brought forth the telescope, whose little beam of light would never recant and whose power would bring a new era of tolerance. With this man the Age of Science had begun.

Immediately there was a tremendous rush to improve the crude little instrument and to expand its discoveries. The Sixteenth Century began with Kepler, who invented a much improved eyepiece and then worked out the laws of planetary motion for the solar system. These he based on the splendid observations of Tycho Brahe and confirmed by Galileo's work. Newton soon placed them on so firm and rational a basis with his Law of Gravitation that even the contributions of Einstein in the Twentieth Century have added only slight refinements.

Next came Descartes with his improved telescope lens in hyperbolic form, then Huygens with a still better eyepiece and huge instruments from 200 to 600 feet long, with which he discovered that Saturn's rings were actually thousands of little moons strung together. Then came Gregory with the principle of the reflecting telescope, then Cassegrain with improvements on it, and finally Newton, with the corpuscular theory of light and the first reflecting telescope that worked. But Newton's greatest contribution was the Gravitational Theory, and he withheld it for twenty years because he was unable to make it fully consistent with observed facts.

The two types of telescope—the refracting and reflecting— soon began a race, which lasted well into the Twentieth Century. First one would be improved and then the other; for a few years science would abandon the lens and concentrate upon the mirror; then, as some new discovery gave the advantage back to the refractor, the reflector would fall behind. Little by little the intricate optical principles of both were disclosed, and all the while men plugged ahead doggedly, discovering secret after secret of the skies.

The speed of light was measured in 1680 by Roemer within a few per cent of the correct value. Just after that Halley, then Royal Astronomer of England, computed the path of the great comet of 1682 and predicted its return. Cassini saw and counted the satellites of Saturn about this time, and the true distance of the Sun and the diameter of the Earth's orbit followed soon after. Laplace came forward with the celebrated Nebular Hypothesis to explain the origin of the solar system.

Then came the great William Herschel, the first of the men with an intuition for shaping astronomical mirrors. Herschel was an oboist in an English orchestra but when he found that he could make a telescope of his own he abandoned music and devoted his life to astronomy. His was the true spirit of the discoverer; it was his intention to cover the entire heavens with a methodical survey which should bring order out of chaos and point to the explanation of the whole Universe. His first discovery was the planet Uranus, for which he was made the King's private astronomer. His next, the invention of that vital branch of astronomy called the star count.

With an 18-inch reflector of his own making, Herschel studied the Milky Way and perceived that it was made of thousands upon thousands of stars. In certain typical areas he actually counted them, averaged the figures, and arrived at an estimate of their total number. With the aid of his son John, who took the great telescope all the way to South Africa to complete the survey, Herschel finally determined that there were at least five million stars within the reach of his instrument. More, he drew a picture of their general distribution: "The stars of our firmament," he wrote, "instead of being scattered in all directions indifferently through space, form a stratum of which the thickness is small in comparison with its length and breadth, and in which the Earth occupies a place somewhere about the middle of its thickness."

This was the greatest discovery of all, for it gave the first true conception of the galaxy in which we live. Herschel's stratum of stars has long since been confirmed, and modern astronomy has measured it and found it to be one among millions of the same design.

And so into the Nineteenth Century, with Lord Rosse discovering the existence of the spiral nebulae; Fraunhofer the dark lines in the Sun's spectrum; Kirchhoff and Bunsen the chemical composition of the Sun; Foucault the method of testing a truly parabolic mirror; Steinheil the secret of the silvered reflecting surface; Bessel the actual distance to a near-by star; Daguerre the photographic process; and finally Alvan Clark the method of making the first fine telescopic lenses in America in 1864.

The future of astronomy was prepared for now. And in the United States Clark and his son soon formed the nucleus around which the great observatories of the present and future: Lick, Yerkes, Mount Wilson and Palomar, were rapidly to grow.

Hale and Breasted were right to be humble in the presence of the first of all telescopes, that night. Without three hundred years of intense work—defeat, discouragement, faith, patience, success—the astronomy of the Twentieth Century would not be. More than any other science, perhaps, astronomy is founded on the triumphs of many men; and builds for the glory of all, obscure and prominent alike.

## CHAPTER IV

## THE WORLD'S LARGEST—1900

FROM the moment George Hale got the money from Yerkes he lost no time in driving ahead the plans for the observatory. While the Clarks nursed the lens along at Cambridgeport, Hale set about giving the new telescope a home worthy of its great expected power.

In Europe he began on the plans for the building, but not until he had visited every observatory he could reach on the Continent, and, as he described it, "borrowed freely." The Imperial Observatory at Potsdam, Germany, gave him the most valuable ideas. Without knowing it, Hale was removing to safe ground in the Western Hemisphere the fruits of German genius so soon to be engulfed in the cataclysm of a new Dark Age. When at last he had gathered all the valuable ideas he could, he sent the sketches home, and Yerkes' architect went to work on them.

Next in importance was the choice of the best site for the observatory. When news was published in Chicago that the University was to have the world's largest telescope, dozens of people hastened forward to offer land for it. Twenty-six sites in the state of Illinois alone were tendered. And one as far away as Mount Wilson in California. It was an amusing coincidence that the very glass for the 40-inch refractor had originally been ordered for installation on Mount Wilson. But this had no connection whatever with the mighty observatory which has since risen there.

Hale at that time did not like mountains. He had spent a week on top of Mt. Etna in the Bellini Observatory trying to imitate an eclipse of the Sun with his spectroheliograph. It had been a failure, partly because the fire and brimstone of the near-by volcano made an eclipse more or less permanent anyway. The atmosphere, too, was in perpetual turmoil, with updrafts, downdrafts and cross currents which made the "seeing" about as good as if one were clinging with his telescope to the mouth of a factory chimney. Hale came home.

He and Keeler had also clambered to the top of Pike's Peak with a good sized telescope and the spectroheliograph. They stayed up there two weeks, studying the Sun and trying to estimate the conditions for seeing in America's "clearest" atmos-

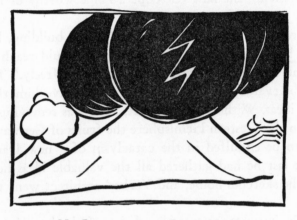

No Place for an Observatory

phere. They came down disillusioned. The roaring elements had made it abundantly plain that man could expect no cooperation from them. Every noon heavy cumulus clouds enveloped the summit and straightway a violent thunderstorm would begin, which lasted the rest of the day. The wind would rise to 70 miles an hour, bringing with it a blinding blizzard of snow and ice. The astronomers and their instruments were soon parted and they could only find them again with the help of the incessant lightning which leaped about in every direction. "The electrical effects," the scientists said mildly, "were very remarkable." Then would come the mountain sickness and the nosebleeds. Altogether it was not the right place for an observatory.

Jules Verne, with his imaginary giant telescope on top of near-by Long's Peak had made another slip. It was Hale's considered decision to put the Yerkes Observatory down on flat land, and near home.

The location finally chosen was at Lake Geneva, Wisconsin, seventy-five miles northwest of Chicago. It seemed ideal, but for a long time Hale was worried about the city's smoke. Before accepting the site he wrote to every astronomer of importance in America to find out what they thought of observatories near big cities. The consensus was that a city at least ten miles away gave no trouble, either from smoke or reflected light at night, and that it might be very handy for repairs and to give those little doses of civilization that astronomers need to offset their lonely vigils. So Lake Geneva became the final choice.

GAWKED AT BY THOUSANDS

Warner & Swasey had long since completed the telescope mount and tube and had set it up at the Chicago World's Fair of 1893, where it was gawked at by thousands and seemed such a glowering mass of gears and steel that it caused some peaceful people to fear that the University was installing a giant cannon to shoot the astronomers themselves to the stars. Hale's preoccupation was now with the architecture of the buildings themselves.

It was his delicate task to soften Yerkes' grandiloquent ideas to the point where the buildings would not only serve science but avoid doing too much violence to the aesthetic sense of the chance visitor. What he got in the end was a compromise. The

ornate terra cotta exterior on which his benefactor insisted had
to be supported by heavy brick walls. Hale knew that telescopes
perform well in proportion as they can adjust themselves quickly
to the vagaries of outdoor temperatures. Encased in three feet
of brick, it was a question whether the 40-inch refractor would
ever be at night temperature, winter or summer. In this he was
fortunately too pessimistic, for Yerkes still has its brick walls
after forty-two years, and is still giving fine results.

The great year of 1897 finally arrived and the whole observatory was ready. In May Clark and Lundin tenderly loaded the
lens on a private parlor car and took it, with the aid of a special
engine bravely displaying the white flags of a preferred shipment, the thousand miles to Williams Bay, Wisconsin. There,
in a few days the two thin glasses, unmatched in all the world,
had been hoisted into place and bolted firm. The lenses and the
metal rings that held them weighed half a ton, yet the assembly
was so rigid and at the same time so frictionless, that the whole
mechanism, weighing many tons, could easily be turned by hand.
A clockwork motor, under the control of an astronomer's
fingers, could then hold it on a single star all night.

Hale had spent twenty-eight years subordinating his emotions to scientific requirements, but with what suppressed eager-
ness must he have awaited the slow coming of that first night
of observation—he and Keeler and Professor Barnard, and the
others who had gathered around! The Sun went down and the
stars came out—and then went in again. Wisconsin was buried
thousands of feet in a dense blanket of cloud! How Pike's Peak
and Etna must have exchanged laughs across the world!

But on the next night—the evening of May 21st—nature
was ready. Rapidly the little band of scientists trained the giant
tube up through the slot in the 140-ton dome above and out
upon the vaster dome of stars beyond. Sirius, Vega, the double-
double star Epsilon Lyrae, the Great Nebula in Orion, the Ring
Nebula in the Lyre—there they were, the old familiar friends
of many a night's work, but now in such a wealth of fire and

brilliance as never before seen by any of them. These modern Galileos must have tightened their grip on each other's arms in the soft darkness, and though they uttered not a word among them, there must have been a tightening in their throats, too, as with every human being in the presence of great achievement. Down inside they must have muttered: "Thank God! It works!"

Then Barnard took a peek again—Edward Emerson Barnard, the keenest visual observer of his day. He trained the telescope

EPSILON LYRAE

back on Vega, for in his first momentary look he thought he had seen something unusual.

"There's a new star here," he cried after a moment. "Faint, but I see it well. It looks like a companion to Vega."

The others looked, and saw what Barnard saw. Keeler, who had used the 36-inch at Lick for years, finally straightened up from the eyepiece. "I've studied that area time and again," he said, humbly, "but I never saw that star before."

Thus was the history of the Yerkes Observatory so auspiciously begun. There was a note of sadness, though, too. Three weeks after that memorable night Alvan G. Clark died, at the age of 65. Only Carl Lundin was left to carry on the Clark tradition.

That fall the Observatory was dedicated with ceremonies befitting, and a co-operation which betokened the true brotherhood of science. There was a quiet splendor about the affair, for many of the great of the profession were present: Pickering, Simon Newcomb, Michelson, Charles T. Yerkes and the skilled lens-maker Brashear; Lord and Lady Huggins from England, Professor Ricco from Italy, Dr. Carl Runge from Berlin. The 29-year-old Director addressed them modestly and gave credit to all but himself. But his plans were far from modest; they covered practically every field then known to astronomy.

The Sun, the Moon, the planets; the constitution and temperatures of the brightest stars; the measurement, by parallax from the two opposite points of the Earth's orbit, of the distance to the nearer stars; the computing of the masses and behavior of the double stars; the analysis of the Milky Way and the dark shadows that cross it so mysteriously; the observation of the nebulae and the inquiry as to why so many of them are spirals and whether or not they belong to our own galaxy. All that grand cosmic display, said Hale, stretching billions of billions of miles and years into space and time, should yield up, little by little, its secrets through the fine-polished disks the Clarks had made. And there was to be no question of rivalry here, no vying between great telescopes for results or credit. Rather must it be corroboration and help and humility, each in support of the others.

With this point firmly established, Hale bid them good-by. The real work of the observatory must begin.

He had gathered around him some of the finest astronomers of the time, and some of the keenest hands with glass. Besides Barnard there were now and in the next ten years such names as W. S. Adams, Frank Schlesinger, Edwin Frost, S. W. Burnham, Edison Pettit and Edwin Hubble—every one of them skilled observers and all as keen to pioneer in astrophysics as their Director himself.

Hale had insisted on an instrument shop for his observatory. That had never been done before; the making of astronomical instruments had always been farmed out to commercial firms. But Hale said no; his astronomers should design their own auxiliaries and his shops should build them, for how better could the intricate problems of interpreting the stars be attacked than by cutting and fitting every instrument to its specific need directly on the spot? The shop was a masterpiece and the man he put in charge of it, one of those rare experts with glass upon whom astronomy has depended for every telescopic advance. The man was George W. Ritchey, a former manual training teacher in the Chicago schools.

The well-oiled schedule of the Yerkes Observatory was soon under way. None was more inspired in his attack upon the heavens than Barnard. This man was in a way the relic of an older astronomy. Like Percival Lowell and Schiaparelli before him, Barnard relied mainly upon his own two eyes, harking back to the days when telescopes were built to look through, and records of the heavens, when kept at all, were in the shape of sketches by the astronomers themselves. The photographic plate was changing all that now. Not only could it eliminate the personal equation, sadly demonstrated in the controversy over the canals of Mars, but it could also *accumulate* light, rendering the invisible easily seen, if given time enough. What the eye saw, with or without a telescope, it could see at once or not at all. But the photographic plate saw more the longer it looked, integrating hour after hour, till its total stored response might be thousands of times stronger than the eye's momentary one. So Barnard, the last of the great visual observers, was passing.

But in the passing he made a grand effort; he adapted himself and his eyes to the uses of photography and Hale turned him loose on that thick-strewn greensward of the skies, the Milky Way.

Barnard brought with him from the past an almost godlike intuition in the interpretation of what he saw. To the casual outsider, he looked and acted a good deal like an unoffending mouse, softly padding about in the shadows under the big dome, rarely seen in the daytime, never at home at night. But to his colleagues he was a Prometheus, riding the splendid reaches of the Milky Way with his telescope to his eye, bringing back to them thousands of vital messages of worlds unknown. And he was an artist, too, and a saint. "Whatever they may mean," he said of his early photographs, "they are singularly beautiful as simple pictures of the stars."

Even before the 40-inch telescope had been dedicated, Barnard had explored the entire summer heavens with it and had made a solid beginning upon a great program of exploration which kept him fastened to his telescope for the next twenty-five years. There he died, in his prime, still clinging to the controls, overcome by an affliction which he would not take time to notice. Many is the brave captain who has gone down clinging to the bridge of his ship; but how many are the Barnards who have dragged themselves, dying, to their telescopes, to be borne forever into the skies they loved and understood?

As for Hale himself, it was the Sun he wanted most to study, for the flaming solar disk was unquestionably the key to the systematic study of stellar evolution. For the five long years while the Yerkes Observatory was in construction, Hale had been mightily busy with the Sun at Kenwood, making the best of the inadequate equipment. In 1895 a flurry of excitement ran through the scientific world. The mysterious element helium, long ago discovered in the Sun's spectrum, had been found on Earth by Ramsay in England, unexpectedly cropping up in a spectrographic analysis of the mineral "clevite." At least, Ramsay thought it might be helium. Its spectrum exhibited the well known "$D_3$" line that had led Lockyer to identify it as a new element. But Ramsay also found another line—a faint green one, which seemed to belong to the same group as the $D_3$. Lockyer had said nothing about this. Evidently he had not seen it with his crude instrument.

Imagine the state of excitement in a mining town when someone brings in a lump of rock that may be rich in gold. Everything depends on the assay. Is it gold or is it rubble? No one can eat or sleep till the matter is settled. That is the state of tension for the moment as Ramsay discovers helium on Earth. Everything depends on that one faint green line that Lockyer had failed to see. Is it in the Sun, too, or has Ramsay made a mistake?

Hale receives the news of the find from Runge in Potsdam by telegraph. He drops everything and dashes over to Kenwood, sets his spectrograph going and waits impatiently for the little photographic plate to record what it sees. Then to the dark room, while the chemicals deliberately build up the spectrum image. Then out into the light with the dripping plate in his stained fingers.

There it is! The green line of helium—in the Sun!

What Lockyer had missed Hale had found. Thus Hale, the young astronomer, had a hand in a tremendously important discovery—one destined to aid geologists in determining the age of the Earth; one that has had a profound influence on aviation; one that even today seems about to set a new standard of safety in deep sea diving.

No better proof could be asked of the value of astronomy to man in his everyday life.

As soon as the 40-inch telescope was in service, Hale transferred his investigations on the Sun to Williams Bay. A new and much larger spectroheliograph was the first requirement, but as usual he lacked funds to build it. Yerkes had reached the limit of his capacity to give and no other money was readily available. So Hale again embarked upon the discouraging task of begging for funds here and there wherever he could get them, postponing the work he was impatient to begin until he should find new backers generous enough to fit him out. He had to wait six years.

Gradually he added one small gift to another till at last the construction of the new instrument could be begun in the observatory shops. But an expensive lens was necessary and this he could not afford. So he fell back upon a device which has saved many a scientist in the past (and still does): he went to a Chicago hock-shop and bought an old Voightländer camera lens for a song, took it up to Wisconsin and had Ritchey fit it into the spectroheliograph. It worked, and is still working today.

There were two principal uses to which Hale proposed to put

the new instrument. First, and most important, the detailed mapping of the Sun's surface by the light of calcium, sodium and
perhaps hydrogen, to see what the actual topography was and
how each of these elements was distributed. Then, a study of
the Sun's rim, including the famous prominences and the faint
but beautiful corona, which shoots millions of miles into space
in all directions. The corona had never been seen before without
a total eclipse, nor could the prominences be studied properly,
and astronomers had traveled to the outposts of the world for
many years to view them, content to get what they could in the
brief moment the Moon held sway.

This moment rarely lasted longer than seven minutes, and
was never more frequent than twice a year. It usually took place
in the Arctic wilderness, the tropical jungle or the middle of
the ocean. Hale's spectroheliograph gave promise of changing
all that. With it the prominences could be photographed at
home, any day the Sun shone, for as long as desired. He hoped
eventually that it might even take pictures of the corona in the
same way.

George Hale came to be considered the world's greatest authority on the Sun. But his friends used to joke him on the fact
that he was the only astronomer in two hemispheres who had
never seen but one eclipse, and that one by mistake.

The story goes that he was crossing Siberia on an important
mission some years ago when his train came to an abrupt stop
and everybody began piling out into the snow in great haste.
Hale grabbed a passing conductor by the sleeve.

"What's up?" he demanded.

"Didn't you know?" returned the official. "There's an eclipse
of the Sun going on out here."

In the interest of accuracy I checked that story and regret
to say that it isn't true. Hale saw several eclipses, quite by intention. But it *should* be true, for it beautifully illustrates the
concentration of the man. If an eclipse of the Sun didn't happen
to bear on the problem Hale had in hand, then he wasn't going

to waste time chasing across half the world to see one.

He felt that the time devoted to preparing and carrying out eclipse expeditions could be better spent in research which would make them unnecessary. He was right. Lyot in France has at last done what Hale tried to do for forty years. He has photographed the spectrum of the Sun's corona in full daylight.

## CHAPTER V

## A CHAPTER OF FIGURES, LARGE AND SMALL

THE Earth had now spun itself onto the threshold of a new century and the Yerkes Observatory began to turn out astronomical history.

Besides the 40-inch main telescope there were two others: a 24-inch reflector which Ritchey had made himself, and the 10-inch Bruce star-camera. Some time after the dedication a New York star enthusiast named Catherine Bruce became so enthralled with Hale's projected voyages of discovery that she gave the Observatory ten thousand dollars to buy an instrument —whatever instrument was needed most. Hale decided on a star-camera. Warner & Swasey constructed it and fitted it with lenses by Brashear, and it became an admirable exploring instrument to support the huge refractor. It could take photographs of whole sections of the sky at once and prepare the way for the more detailed investigations of its big brother.

The Bruce camera was Barnard's special instrument. Night after night he stood from dusk till dawn "guiding" it as it followed some portion of the Milky Way. He took hundreds of pictures, and soon they began to reveal those same strange dark clouds that had made Herschel exclaim: "Surely this is a hole in the heavens!" Barnard did not agree. They were not holes but dust—great clouds of obscuring dust.

This was a most important discovery if it could be substantiated. If the "dark nebulae" were indeed matter instead of empty space, then the Universe was more thickly settled than had been supposed. What could the dark material be? Was it dust from the graves of dead suns? Or elemental particles awaiting the approach of some cosmic force to organize them into new suns and solar systems? The poet and the scientist in Barnard united to give him the imagination and the patience to begin this great research. He spent twenty years on it, and the final answer is not yet.

Meanwhile everyone else had been doing fine work, too. Frank Schlesinger (now Director of Yale Observatory) began the

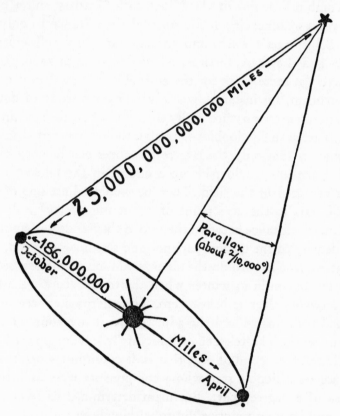

PARALLAX OF THE NEAREST STAR

measurement of the distances from the Earth to the stars. This he did by photographing some near star such as Sirius or Vega, and then carefully studying the plate to determine its exact position against the background of more distant stars. Six months later, when the Earth had traveled 186 million miles to the opposite end of its orbit, Schlesinger photographed the same star again.

The "shift," if any, across the background, could be used to compute the star's distance away. It was a most exacting task. Not only must the astronomer sit up all night taking pictures, but cramp himself all day over the plates measuring tiny star images with microscope and micrometer. But it was splendidly fruitful. The combined genius of the Nineteenth Century and a hundred years of observing had estimated the distance to only 60 stars. Schlesinger's work, and that of his many colleagues at Yerkes and elsewhere, in time, raised that total to 2200.

There was more work for the 40-inch telescope than it could do. Burnham, for instance, was advancing the study of double stars and their true nature. Fully a quarter of all the stars in the heavens are actually doubles or triples, though most of them are so far away that only the largest telescopes can separate them at all. Burnham would pick up a double in the telescope and get it centered in the field. Then he would adjust one of the pair of stars to the zero point of a fine micrometer scale and measure the distance between the two in thousandths of an inch. This demanded the utmost patience and steadiness of hand, and was often cruelly hard on the observer. Much of the best seeing came in Wisconsin in winter when the temperature was often ten or twenty degrees below zero. The micrometer screws demanded bare fingers and the adjustments many hours of continuous work. The telescope's limit of "resolving power" was one-tenth of a second of arc; that is, it could just separate into two images a double star whose components were as little as $\frac{1}{36,000}$ of a degree apart. Burnham determined to reach that limit, and by long practice did so, although he had to learn to measure distances only $\frac{3}{10,000}$ of an inch in size.

But Burnham was tenacious and he had remarkable eyes. In former days he had been a court reporter in Chicago and a zealous amateur astronomer. When Yerkes was opened he joined the staff and worked for a long time without pay. But his discoveries became so important that Hale at length began paying him a salary out of his own pocket. It is men like this and situations like this that give science its sincerity and its value.

Ritchey, too, contributed an important invention about this time in the double-slide plate holder for taking direct telescopic photographs. Formerly it had been necessary to swing the whole instrument in order to "guide" it and keep it accurately on a star. With Ritchey's invention the plate was moved instead, in a framework by means of simple handscrews, and the results were vastly improved. The device soon became standard throughout the world.

It was in this early period, also, that Walter S. Adams made a start on his spectrographic study of the stars, measuring their "radial velocity" toward or away from the Earth and laying the groundwork for his brilliant method of determining how bright they actually are and hence how remote. Years afterward at Mount Wilson, Adams and his assistants developed this method, which depends upon a study of the relative brightness of the spectral lines of a star, and so gives a clue to the temperature and pressure within it. The scheme has added thousands of stars to those whose distances we know and has enabled us to sort out big and little stars like eggs in a basket, out to distances of thousands of light-years from the Earth.

The light-year? A distance of six million million miles, more or less. Yet Adams measured such quantities to a decent degree of accuracy by the aid of photographic images not more than three inches long.

Young Professor Hale, meanwhile, had his hands full, administering, correlating, organizing, keeping everybody reasonably patient and happy, and the instruments busy but not overcrowded. And most of all in raising money to keep the project going. His great goal of uniting physics and astronomy was coming closer every minute, and to further it he had taken an excursion into the publishing business. In 1895 he had started the *Astrophysical Journal,* hoping to bring together reports of astronomical and spectroscopic researches from everywhere. The response of scientists had been overwhelming. The *Journal* had soon become the meeting ground for researchers throughout the world. It steadily lost money but just as steadily gained in prestige. The Pear's Soap advertising which it carried on its inside covers neither prevented the one nor hindered the other. Hale, as editor, found himself in the vanguard of the whole attack upon the Universe.

Hale's own beloved researches on the Sun were not forgotten. But they were dragging sadly. Not through any fault of his, nor even through lack of time, for the 40-inch refractor was his all day to work with as hard as he wished. It simply was too soon. Science was not ready. The spectroheliograph alone could not win the battle.

It had done its best. It had taken remarkable pictures of the Sun's disk in calcium light and with the violet lines of hydrogen. Great clouds of these elements proved to be massed across the solar surface, driven hither and thither as if by tornadic winds. By beautiful refinements of technique Hale had even reached many thousands of miles below the surface layer, discovering how the Sun's atmosphere moved. And he had studied the prominences and was on the way toward an explanation of their origin.

But in the meantime he had run solidly up against the real clue to the mystery—the one clue which the spectroheliograph of that day was not powerful enough to solve: the ancient and honorable phenomenon of sunspots.

Those were banner years—the early 1900's—for the appearance of the strange disfigurations on the solar disk. The sunspot minimum had been passed at the turn of the century and the markings were appearing more extensively every day. The spectroheliograph had convinced Hale long ago that the spots were not mere blemishes on the solar countenance; they were huge "holes" in the outer envelope of incandescent gases, created from below, marking in some yet unintelligible way the inner conflict of the star. But how? What titanic forces created the vast wells of low pressure which extended to the depth of thousands, perhaps tens of thousands of miles? Wells into which the Sun could easily swallow the Earth, or a dozen earths for that matter, without the slightest inconvenience.

Apparently sunspots had no general form; they were random, scattered hither and thither without plan. This is not like nature, said Hale. A phenomenon that has been appearing regularly since the dawn of history must have a single steady cause. Therefore, there must be a scheme, a standard structure for sunspots that will reveal that cause. Where shall I look for it?

With calcium light he tried; with the new green lines of carbon which he had discovered, and with hydrogen. The spectroheliograph could show him nothing but apparent chaos. There was something he had not tried, however: the *red* line of hydrogen, associated with this gas in its cooler state. Perhaps sunspots were not so hot as the rest of the conflagration up there, for they certainly were thin and hence areas of lower pressure and lower temperatures. The analogy of the tornado in the Middle West struck Hale then: tornadoes are "holes" in the earth's atmosphere. And, he asked himself, what happens? The surrounding air rushes headlong toward these holes, can't stop in time when it gets there, and so goes into a spin—a vortex. It was an exceedingly interesting thought. Sunspots—holes in the Sun's atmosphere—gases rushing in to fill them—vortices, whirlpools, maelstroms. The comparison seemed undeniable. But the spectroheliograph showed nothing, just a jumble. It was up to that red hydrogen line to tell the story.

Brilliant reasoning, but it could not be checked—then. Photographs could not be taken in the red light of hydrogen. The photographic plates of 1902 were entirely insensitive to it. Much promising work was being done, Hale knew, to overcome this, and in time red-sensitive plates would be available. But not yet. He must try another tack. He must drop the spectroheliograph for the moment and fall back upon its older companion, the spectrograph.

The two instruments are similar but not identical. The spectrograph splits up sunlight (or starlight) which is concentrated upon it by the main lens of the telescope, and spreads it out on a photographic plate as the familiar spectrum, the bright and dark lines of which represent the elements in the conflagration being studied. The spectroheliograph, on the other hand, picks out a single one of these bright spectrum lines and with its aid scans the whole of the Sun's disk bit by bit, building up on a photographic plate a picture of the orb in monochromatic light. It is similar in principle to the movie camera. Hale later invented the spectrohelio*scope*, which scans the Sun or a part of it 20

PHOTOGRAPHIC SPECTRUM OF THE SUN

times a second and gives an actual motion picture of it in the midst of its stupendous activities. But for the problem Hale now had in hand, neither of these inventions was of use. The spectrograph must do the job.

So the most up-to-date possible instrument was built by Brashear and installed on the 40-inch telescope. Results were more mysterious than conclusive. The sunspot areas showed that extraordinary things were happening to the usual spectra of the gases. Many of the dark lines, normally narrow, were widened. Sometimes they were double, or even triple. These effects were not original observations of Hale's, for Lockyer and others had already puzzled over them thirty years before. But they were intensely disquieting. Here he was, a third of a century farther along the road, yet as unable to answer the riddle as a former generation of astronomers had been. In the old days at Kenwood his 12-inch telescope had given him a Sun's image two inches in diameter and this had been far too small. He had planned the 40-inch telescope to give 7-inch images and had assumed that they would be adequate. They were, but the telescope itself was not. The Sun was blazing away up there, bursting with a secret if only he could scrutinize it minutely enough to make out what that secret was. But the 40-inch could not carry on its back instruments large enough and delicate enough to solve it.

Sunspots, which anybody can project on a piece of white paper with an ordinary field glass, were beyond his power to analyze. Hale might have preferred to start out at once in quest of a new instrument, but that was impossible. After all, he was the director of an observatory dedicated to all the uses of astronomy. The Sun problem was only one of them. In the design of the 40-inch instrument he had deliberately sacrificed his own special field for the good of the rest, and to get an all-round telescope that could be worth to the world what Yerkes had paid for it.

The limitation that blocked him was magnification—not in the telescope itself but in the spectrograph. A telescope magnifies according to the ratio of the focal lengths of its lens and eyepiece. A spectrograph magnifies directly in proportion to its focal length, measured from prism to photographic plate. Thus the actual size and detail of the spectra Hale could obtain depended upon the size of the spectrograph. And that, in turn, depended upon the ability of the telescope to carry it.

The largest instrument he could use was several feet long and tremendously cumbersome. It weighed 700 pounds. Every morning it had to be fastened rigidly to the lower end of the Yerkes refractor, while an attendant had to climb up into the dome and load 700 pounds of iron weights on the upper end to counterbalance it. After the day's work on the Sun all this had to be removed and put away again, so that the night men could use the telescope for the stars.

To overcome this limitation Hale had two alternatives: to build a *fixed* telescope especially designed to carry a much larger spectrograph which could be fastened firmly to the floor; or to build a larger moving telescope which could support the weight of such a spectrograph in the air. Neither alternative was possible at the moment.

He now did the hardest thing that a man of energy ever has to do. He sat down to wait. That is inaccurate; Hale always did his waiting on his feet. At any rate, he submerged his primary interest for the time and went about widening the background of his knowledge, to prepare for the day when adequate instruments would be available. He began an exhaustive study of the spectra of metals when heated to incandescence in the laboratory, and was soon able to show that their spectral lines were exceedingly sensitive to temperature and pressure. This was data of the utmost value in the coming study of the stars and tied itself in immediately with the observational work Adams had begun.

Then he joined the group of night watchers around the 40-inch telescope and began to unravel for himself the mysterious and mighty question: what are the stars made of?

But it was waiting for all that. Fortunately, the delay was not long.

SUNSPOTS

## CHAPTER VI

## MOHAMMED TO THE MOUNTAIN

DURING the year 1902 Andrew Carnegie, feeling more than a little grateful for the way the world had treated him, decided to endow Science. He had seen the metallurgists and chemists in his own laboratories open up vast new fields of application for steel. He felt that Science deserved a reward and a good sized wink to spur it on to further achievements.

At first Carnegie thought he ought to endow individual professors in universities so that they might work unhampered by knotted purse strings; then it seemed wiser to establish a general fund from which worthy lines of research might be subsidized. Accordingly, in this year of 1902, he established the Carnegie Institution of Washington and put it under the charge of Daniel Coit Gilman. The grant, amounting to ten million dollars, had few strings attached. The old steel magnate stipulated only that it must be used "to encourage in the broadest and most liberal manner investigation, research and discovery, and the application of knowledge to the improvement of mankind."

Gilman set about organizing the Institution at once. The subject of plant biology interested him, so he established a desert laboratory in Arizona first. A Bureau of Historical Research soon followed, then a Department of Terrestrial Magnetism and a Genetics Laboratory. Fifth on the list came Astronomy.

One day Professor Hale up in Chicago happened to pick up a newspaper and on an inside page came upon a small item explaining what Carnegie had done and what he hoped to accomplish with his millions. Hale's imagination, as usual, was instantly fired. Here was a rich man after his own heart—one who had not waited to be dunned; one who understood the value of research on his own account. Here at last, after five discouraging years of fighting for small gifts, was the promise of substantial funds. A plan began to take shape in his mind.

Within a few months Hale was made a member of a Carnegie committee for studying the needs for astronomical endowment. The group included four famous older men: E. C. Pickering, Simon Newcomb, Samuel P. Langley and Lewis Boss. Hale was only the secretary, but he soon became the source of power. From childhood he had always been the motive force for everything he touched. The vigor of his mental energy, which his father had called his "desire to do everything yesterday," invariably permeated a project and colored it and made it Hale's own. Only a few years before he had invaded the National Academy of Sciences, becoming virtually a child member among graybeards the first year and one of its governing council the second, completely demolishing its antiquated viewpoint overnight and substituting his own. And now he was ready to do the same thing again. Until the committee got busy and did something he would not let it rest.

The astronomers took action at once, and recommended the establishment of a solar observatory at some point where the climate was especially favorable. The Institution tentatively accepted the plan and provided $5000 for an investigation of possible sites. The trustees let it be understood that the Institution itself could not furnish the endowment for so large a project but hinted that Mr. Carnegie himself might provide a special grant. For the moment everything seemed bright.

During the first part of 1903 the Committee sent Professor Hussey from Lick on an extensive reconnoitering expedition with a nine-inch telescope to study the "seeing" in subtropical latitudes. Hussey covered southwestern United States and even went to Australia, but his choice soon narrowed down to five mountain tops in Southern California, where the weather was good and the seeing steady over long periods of time. One of these was Mount Wilson. Another was Palomar Mountain a hundred miles to the south.

Hussey got very poetic in his description of Palomar; it was the perfect mountain retreat, buried deep in the wilderness with a wealth of scenery and a charming climate. Its very isolation, though, influenced him to drop it as an observatory site. Mount Wilson was his final choice.

It was not his discovery, of course. As already mentioned, the gaudy University of Southern California had tried to put a telescope there and had failed. Professor W. H. Pickering had done some observing there also, in years gone by. And the mountain had been inhabited for several years before that.

Hussey's findings were transmitted to the trustees of the Institution and Hale waited confidently in Chicago for a telegram from them confirming the grant for the observatory. The telegram did not come. Next day he found in the newspaper an account of the trustees' meeting and a list of the grants they had authorized. There was not a word in it about Mount Wilson or a solar observatory.

For a moment Hale did not know what to do. For months he had been building his plans around the near certainty of that grant of money; Yerkes was a going concern; he needed new fields to conquer; everything was in readiness for the start. And now there was to be no start.

He fell back upon a plan of action which he had used many times with his father, when grants of money dragged. He would go out to Mount Wilson on his own and demonstrate to the Institution that a solar observatory *must* be established there. Somehow he would raise the money for this new expedition himself.

Hale arrived in Pasadena just before Christmas and quickly settled his family there for the winter. Within two months he had met a wealthy Los Angeles businessman named John D. Hooker and had persuaded him to donate a thousand dollars to the project for the purpose of bringing Barnard and the Bruce camera to California. He had also raised enough money in addition to pay for moving a small solar telescope out from the

Yerkes Observatory. And the property owners on Mount Wilson had kindly given him the use of a small log cabin known as the "Casino" on top of the mountain. He was up to his old form again.

In the early days Hale had had some tough experiences with mountains. This one was not going to prove any easier, as he soon found. Some thirty years earlier, according to local accounts, three amateur explorers named Martin, Wilson and Strain had climbed to the summit and established camps there. Strain built his cabin on top and the others settled near by. The three never got along, and Martin amused himself by running Wilson's pack trains off the mountain and isolating him for days at a time. But Wilson was the most persistent of the three and finally bought or drove his neighbors off, taking possession of the whole region in his own name. Later, he turned his camp into a sort of primitive wilderness hotel and established a company to operate it. To get up to it he improved an old Indian trail which the Spanish padres of the Eighteenth Century had used to get lumber down to build the missions.

By the time Hale arrived there were two trails up the mountain: the old Wilson trail, which Hale described as "steep and irregular," and the "New Trail," which climbed the mountain for nine miles through Eaton Canyon. This he regarded as a great improvement. Its grades ran from ten to thirty per cent and its width was an even two feet all the way up. For most of the distance it clung to the nearly perpendicular wall of rock and rubble and dirt by whiplashing back and forth in a perpetual series of hairpin turns. A man could stay on it by digging his feet in and holding onto the bushes; only the native donkey felt at home there.

On Leap Year day, 1904, the young astronomer was ready to make the first ascent. Accompanied by a carpenter and a couple of burros loaded with tools and food, he started, and by evening had reached the Casino. The trip Hale described as uneventful, with only a few minutes' delay while he fought off a rattlesnake coiled in the center of the trail.

The Casino was considerably less than its name implied. The night breeze drifted easily through the chinks in the logs as Hale and the carpenter lay in their blankets that first night and gazed up at the stars through a great hole in the roof. There was not a light of glass in any of the windows and the floor was rotten and

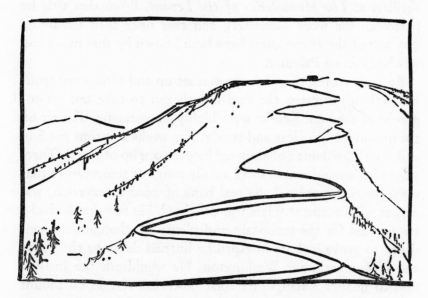

treacherous. Hale decided that his hosts' generosity was rather less than he had supposed.

In the morning he set off down the mountain, "shooting the slides" of loose gravel that swept downward toward the valley. Arriving at the bottom he leaped on his bicycle and pedaled off to Pasadena to shop for repair materials, then rode back again and legged it up the mountain for supper, bundles of nails, putty and glass on his back. But he was happy. He knew that this was the beginning of a great pioneering job.

As soon as the Casino had been calked and repaired against the winter winds, Hale sent to Williams Bay for Ellerman and the solar telescope. Ellerman packed up and took the first train in high anticipation of California's sunny skies. But when he arrived and started up the mountain with Hale a blizzard closed down on them and they were instantly lost, and did not get into camp till late at night, exhausted. Ellerman was inclined to be skeptical but Hale soon reassured him. He had built a fireplace in the cabin and they spent the long winter nights very snugly indeed, planning their program and reading such oldtime thrillers as *The Monasteries of the Levant*. From that title he borrowed the word Monastery and ever since then the living quarters of the astronomers have been known by that name and will be again on Palomar.

By early spring the telescope was set up and after some trouble with adjustments the two men began to take test photographs of the Sun. Results were highly encouraging. The air on the mountain was clear and steady. For weeks at a time the Sun and stars blazed out unhampered by even a wisp of cloud. There was so little wind and so small a daily range of temperature that atmospheric "wobble," the real bane of good observation, was almost wholly absent. Hale was delighted. He felt that he had a strong case for the mountain and plenty of photographic evidence to prove it. Late in April he hurried down to the valley and took a train for Washington. He would ask the Institution to finance a temporary solar observing station on Mount Wilson.

The trustees were amazed at what he had done. They had evidently shelved the whole project and were not prepared for the fight talk Hale gave them. Overnight they capitulated and made him an appropriation of $10,000 to continue the work.

Hale decided to borrow from the Yerkes Observatory a large solar instrument which had been the gift of a Miss Helen Snow of Chicago. It had never performed well at Williams Bay but he believed that it would on Mount Wilson. With the new funds he would bring it to California and set to work to prove definitely that a permanent solar station was justified. If $10,000 was not enough, he would borrow more on his own security.

By the summer of 1904 the project was in full swing. Taking

Adams, Barnard and Ritchey with him, and turning over the directorship of the Yerkes Observatory to his assistant, Edwin B. Frost, he arrived in Pasadena with the Snow telescope and began the work of installing it on the mountain.

The instrument was designed to lie flat along the ground, and had a focal length of sixty feet. Its heart was a spectrograph of 18-foot focus—nearly three times as long as the best portable instrument that the 40-inch Yerkes telescope could carry. It could also accommodate a spectroheliograph of almost any desired size and power. With everything solidly anchored to the ground on concrete piers Hale was confident he could obtain the high magnification and detail he needed for his beloved search into the nature of sunspots and other solar phenomena.

But this telescope, weighing tons in the storehouse in Pasadena, was a very different thing from the same instrument installed six thousand feet above the valley on Mount Wilson. How was it to be got up there?

With characteristic courage Hale began sending up the parts lashed to the backs of burros and mules. Steel beams, cement, nails, tools, food, and supplies for the erecting crew, all went up the same way. It was all right as long as the donkeys were not too fat; if they were their stomachs rubbed the sides of the trail and were apt to start an avalanche, or else push the precious loads askew and send burro and all over the edge for a long roll back down the mountain.

When it came to the heavy steel base-castings for the telescope, donkey transport failed. A single beast could not begin to carry them. So Hale devised a truck made of four automobile wheels with a low platform slung between the pairs and perched a man on the front of it with a steering wheel similar to a hook-and-ladder apparatus. Then he hired the largest horse he could locate in Pasadena and dispatched the castings. During that summer and fall this outfit made the ascent sixty times, carrying half a ton each time. The speed was about one mile an hour and the only way the truck got around the bends at all was to have a man walk along behind it, steering the back wheels with a tiller. Nevertheless there was not a single accident.

Meanwhile Hale, on top, had started the new "Monastery." It had been his idea all along that the astronomers would be better off at their work if their wives and families were safely established at a distance in the valley. Lick Observatory operated on the other scheme, with a complete colony on Mount Hamilton surrounding the telescopes winter and summer. Hale thought he would try the opposite. So the Monastery was being built to house the scientists and the artisans needed to run the instruments. Before winter had set in the building was finished and comfortable quarters were provided for everyone. The telescope had arrived complete and was being set up. A 15-horsepower gas engine and dynamo were in service for light and heat and a good clear spring had been found for abundant water. The little band of celibates was ready for the newest adventure in the sky.

Nature set out at once to see what these new invaders would be willing to put up with, and immediately produced a long, cold winter. The astronomers were virtually marooned in the Monastery. For months there was no getting up or down the mountain except by fighting a blind course along the edge of the precipices through the white wilderness. The men remained on top and occupied their time with tests.

Barnard began taking photographs with the Bruce 10-inch which was already in service, and was rewarded with striking results. Pictures of the Milky Way could be taken in three hours which were the equal of ten-hour exposures back in Wisconsin. The air, even in the rainy season, had a transparency far surpassing the best in the East.

Hale spent his time planning the installation of the Snow apparatus. He had an idea that the solar mirrors would work better if installed well above the ground where the irregular "heat waves" could not get at them. To test this he climbed up a pine tree and lashed a small telescope in its upper branches, observing the Sun from a perch on a lower limb. The results were just what he had expected. The Snow mirrors would have to be up in the air.

The installation of a horizontal telescope some 100 feet long "well above ground" would be an expensive thing. Hale puzzled over this for much of the long winter months, but by the time the snow had gone he had his solution. He had discovered a spot on the edge of the mountain where the slope of the ground would permit the instrument to be installed with its mirrors suspended thirty feet over the brink. At the earliest signs of spring he began the work of hauling in supplies for the construction.

Winter had made a wreck of the trail up the mountain and there were weeks of work to be done on it before even the sure footed burros could be trusted to carry up freight. By Herculean labor the road was repaired, the supplies hauled up and the telescope finally set up in place. The first photographs were taken. Though they were not perfect, Hale was delighted. There would of course be many troubles to iron out, many months of work to do before the Snow would be a going concern. But there was only one real obstacle to final success: money. The Carnegie grant had given out.

All other sources of funds were dried up for the present; Hale decided that he must go to Washington once more and persuade the Institution to give him permanent support. The trustees were about to hold their annual session. He must present them with his evidence before it was too late. So, with the blessings of his colleagues he started off, taking along what few photographs the Snow had produced.

The rest of the story is legendary, and may even be apocryphal. But it gives a true picture of the founding of Mount Wilson. According to it, Hale was not heard from for weeks. The others were worried. If only they could send him more photographs—better ones—more ammunition. There was hardly any time left. They calculated the last possible moment that new material could be sent and still be of help to Hale in his battle with the trustees. To get the photographs, they needed one new part for the telescope. It had already been ordered from the East. If it would only come in time. . . .

The final day arrived. Word was brought up the trail that the telescope part had come, and was waiting down in Pasadena. The deadline for the photographs was six o'clock, when the Sun went down into the Pacific. Tomorrow would be too late.

Hale's associates did not hesitate any more than he himself would have done. One of the young astronomers started off down the mountain on the run, shouting back over his shoulder that he would be back later. Then he tackled the nine miles of whip-lashing trail, leaving a cloud of pebbles and dust behind him. At the bottom the telescope part was waiting, with a burro to take it up. But the young man was not going to risk it that way. He couldn't depend on burros. Sometimes they stopped for no reason at all and were stalled for hours. Sometimes they lost their footing and rolled for miles.

The new instrument was heavy, but the astronomer was young. He got a couple of the burro drivers to lift the load onto his back. Then he started up the trail on foot.

Along toward the middle of the afternoon he got there. Eighteen miles of mountain climbing, half of it weighed down like a pack-horse. But he got there. The part was installed, the photographs were taken, sent down the mountain and mailed.

By and by Hale returned. The group was anxiously awaiting him on top. "Well?"

"I don't know," Hale said. "They still aren't convinced, though those pictures of yours were certainly an improvement." He puttered around a moment. Then, resolutely:

"I've got to raise some more money and try again."

Without ado he got on a burro and started down the mountain.

At the half-way station he saw a rider coming up. As it was impossible to pass anybody except at the station, Hale had to wait. He was impatient. Finally the rider arrived, and Hale leaped on his donkey and without a word started down.

"Wait a minute," the man called after him. "I've got a tele-gram for you."

Hale tore it open.

"Washington, D.C. Mount Wilson made full department of Carnegie Institution. Initial grant of $150,000 allowed."

Hale probably embraced the rider and gave him five dollars. Anyway, he turned and went back up to the stars.

# CHAPTER VII

## THE SUN AND THE STARS

THE Snow solar telescope soon took up permanent quarters on the southeast edge of the mountaintop and opened up for Hale the field of research he had been aiming at for fifteen years.

It was an innovation in astronomical instruments. A carefully leveled pair of rails ran as nearly north and south as possible for about 150 feet, protruding out over the edge of the precipice at the south. These were fastened permanently to massive concrete piers bedded on rock. At the south end, supported so they could be turned, were two circular mirrors, coated with silver on their *front* surfaces. Both were as flat as Ritchey could get them, which meant that they were not more than a millionth of an inch or two out of true. Both were ground on disks of glass, one thirty inches in diameter, the other two feet.

The first mirror, which faced southward, had a clockwork drive to keep it pointed toward the Sun. The second mirror, facing the first, only needed adjustment once a week, as the seasons changed. Sunlight, striking the "coelostat" mirror, was reflected to its companion and thence sent down the length of the rails in a beam which never varied in direction from hour to hour or day to day. At the farther end of the telescope the beam fell upon a concave mirror inside a shed, which brought it to a sharp focus sixty feet away and formed an image of the Sun seven inches across. Another concave mirror could be substituted which would increase the focal length to 143 feet and produce a picture of the Sun sixteen inches in diameter. These images fell upon the slit of a spectrograph or a spectroheliograph, depending on the work in hand.

The two instruments were installed side by side and were the largest ever built. They too were solidly established on concrete and rock. The whole arrangement gave an unmatched opportunity for the accurate study of the 20,000 lines in the Sun's spectrum, any one of which was worthy to be singled out and analyzed alone.

Hale's first troubles were with the mirrors themselves, which could not face the Sun for more than a few minutes without beginning to warp from the heat. There were several ways to

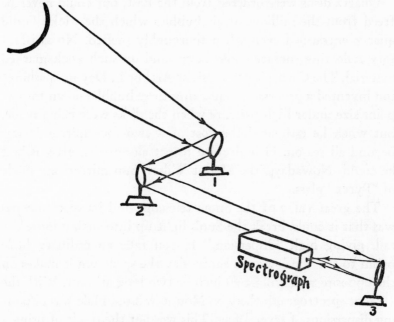

SCHEME OF THE SNOW TELESCOPE

cure this difficulty. The telescope could be used when the Sun was low on the horizon, with more of the Earth's atmosphere to cool its rays, as at dawn and sunset. Or the mirrors could be cooled with fans and kept carefully covered except for the occasional moments when photographs were being taken. A third, and more satisfactory way was to keep them *heated* on the back. They warped because the Sun warmed them on the front only. Hale hit upon the idea of installing electric resistance coils behind them and so adjusting the temperature that the mirrors would expand evenly. It worked fairly well. But the best way of all, he found, was to arrange extra mirrors to shine sunlight on the backs, too, thus letting the expansion take place from a single cause. None of the arrangements was quite satisfactory and at one point the astronomers tried to replace the glass with fused quartz, which has virtually no expansion at all over a wide range of temperature.

Quartz disks were ordered from the East, but could never be freed from the millions of air bubbles which the sticky liquid quartz entrapped even when thoroughly melted. No satisfactory reflecting surface could be ground on such pock-marked material. The Carnegie geophysicist Arthur L. Day in Washington invented a process for squeezing these bubbles down to pinpoint size under high pressure when the disks were being made, but when he estimated the cost of a two-foot mirror it was beyond all reason. Hale decided to get along with glass as best he could. Nowadays, the Mount Wilson Sun mirrors are made of "Pyrex" glass.

The great value of the Snow telescope and its spectroscopes was that it could break the Sun's light up into such minute detail, giving high "dispersion." If you take an ordinary little prism to the window on a sunny day the spectrum it makes on the opposite wall will be an inch or two long at most. With the 18-foot spectrograph there on Mount Wilson, Hale was obtaining dispersions of several feet. This was not the result of using a bigger or better prism, but because prisms had been replaced with an extraordinary little thing called a diffraction grating.

For the past twenty years Professor Henry A. Rowland had been working at Johns Hopkins University on an idea originated long before by Lewis Rutherfurd of New York. Tiny scratches on a polished metal plate, Rutherfurd had found, if arranged parallel and close together, would break up sunlight just as prisms would, only with much greater dispersion. The more scratches the more the dispersion. Rowland set himself the task of cutting fine lines on metal with a diamond point and for that purpose invented a "ruling engine" which drew the lines so close together and so accurately that even the best microscope could not show any unevenness. He spent most of his life on it, for in dealing with light inaccuracies must be only a small fraction of the average wavelength, which is $\frac{1}{50,000}$ of an inch. After years of work he turned out a ruled grating which had 90,000 lines in the space of six inches. It is upon the outcome of such magnificent devotion as this that astronomy and every other science must depend for its advance.

A six-inch grating was not the last word, however, though it was the largest Rowland was ever able to cut accurately. An eight-inch or even a ten would have been better, and Professor Michelson in Chicago later on set himself the task of making one, and finally succeeded. But Rowland, with pardonable pride, always maintained that his own should be good enough for anybody.

When George Hale was a boy in high-school someone gave him a small Rowland grating and he soon became adept in its use. A long while afterward he and Rowland met for the first time. The old inventor began boasting a bit incautiously about the excellence of his workmanship. "Any grating of mine should be good enough for an infant," he said.

"I made one work when I was sixteen," Hale told him.

Rowland looked at him a moment. "I stand humbled," he said, bowing. "Go on, my boy, from where I left off."

So now, with this powerful addition to the Snow telescope, Hale and his associates began the attack upon the true nature of sunspots. The campaign moved forward on many fronts at once. While hundreds of spectrograms were being taken of the spots themselves, an experimental laboratory was established down in Pasadena and Adams, King and others began the work of duplicating, as nearly as they could, the conditions of pressure and temperature on the Sun. It was not easy. The coolest part of the solar atmosphere is at about 10,000 degrees Fahrenheit. No temperature anywhere near this can be reached on

Earth except in the electric arc or spark.

The work was done by burning various metals and other elements in an intense electric discharge under closely controlled temperature and pressure, and then studying the spectra which resulted. Whenever there was a suspicious similarity between laboratory results and actual Sun spectra, there would be great excitement, and a redoubled effort to reproduce the experiment again and again till there remained no room for doubt. Then would come the process which Faraday once called "guessing by hypothesis"—trying to explain by pure reasoning what the discovery might mean.

One such adventure was started when Adams and Hale made a long series of experiments with a carbon electric arc. Having tried almost everything else, they finally burned some titanium oxide one day. Its spectrum closely resembled the one that was always present in a certain part of every sunspot. Back and forth they hurried from laboratory to telescope, up and down the mountain for weeks, photographing, experimenting, calculating. At length they were sure of it. There was no doubt whatever that titanium oxide existed in sunspots. Now for the guessing. Oxygen was known to exist on the Sun, but in far too excited a state, at the average temperature of 6000 degrees Centigrade, to combine with anything and make an oxide. If it combined with titanium, then, it must be cooler than that; therefore the sunspots themselves must be cooler, too. Here was the first link in the chain of proof they were after.

The next was not forged overnight. Nothing in astronomy can be done in a day, or a night; little enough in a lifetime. It is the gradual accumulation of thousands of days and nights, of tens of thousands of painstaking observations, experiments, computations, measurements. Once in every blue moon enough certain knowledge will have been gathered to give a definite answer to a single problem. The rest is waiting—and surmise. So it was not till 1908 that Hale and the others could fit the next big link into the chain. In June of that year photographic plates were for the first time rendered sensitive to deep red light.

Hale's old friend the red hydrogen line was at last available to the spectroheliograph! He lost no time in setting up and making the exposures—getting the photographs of the turbulent clouds of hydrogen that held the secret of the sunspots. There they were—the peculiar wisplike lines of vapor converging toward the dark holes of two spots close together, precisely as if they were the flow-lines of the wind on a weather map! Suspicion was corroborated at last. Unquestionably the spots were whirling vortices in the Sun's atmosphere. More than that—the two spots seemed to be rotating in opposite directions; more still, they looked strangely like the patterns that iron filings make around the poles of a magnet. Hale now made a long jump and landed squarely in the midst of a brand new hypothesis.

"Is it possible," he said to Adams, "that sunspots can be magnetic?"

"Let's find out," said Adams.

Brilliant experimental work in England just prior to this time had established beyond doubt that elements at high temperatures broke down into tiny constituent particles smaller than atoms. These were demonstrated by Sir William Crookes to carry electric charges. Eventually they had come to be called "electrons," or particles of negative electricity. Similar, though larger, particles were found to carry positive electric charges. Rowland himself had shown that if a group of these charges were whirled around rapidly enough they generated a magnetic field. Hale was on the threshold of the next great step; the new science of electron-physics was about to unite with astronomy.

"If for any reason," he wrote, "there should be a sufficient preponderance of positive or negative charges in the sunspot vortex, the magnetic field might be of considerable intensity. But how can it be detected at the distance of the Earth?"

The question could only be settled in one way: if sunspots were magnetic, the light from them must bear some mark to prove it. Was there, Hale wondered, such a mark that could be detected by analyzing the sunspot spectrum?

Here he was down on the bedrock of science. Nothing is more fundamental in the Universe than the nature of light. Ever since Michael Faraday's time it had been called "electromagnetic vibration." The great pioneer of electrical science had managed to show, after years of experimental failure, that polarized light under some circumstances is slightly affected by a magnetic field. From this he reasoned that a *source* of light, invaded by magnetic forces, should be influenced too. "I believe," he wrote in his notebook, "that the various forms under which the forces of matter are made manifest have one common origin, or, in other words, are so directly related and mutually dependent that they are convertible one into another." But try as he would he could never prove it by experiment.

He died still believing, still trying to devise a conclusive test, well knowing that only the crudity of his apparatus had kept him from his goal for half a lifetime.

Thirty-four years after that a Dutch spectroscopist named Zeeman discovered the thing Faraday had missed. When he subjected a flame saturated with common salt to tremendous magnetic force and then looked at it with a spectroscope, he found that the spectral lines, ordinarily very narrow, were widened. Zeeman jacked up the power on his magnet till it almost blew up, and looked again. The lines had separated into doublets and triplets. He put on more power and still more; the lines became a family of thin bands, some with as many as 21 components. This was the thing Faraday had been looking for—the mutual dependence of magnetism and light.

Hale's job now was to find these split lines in the spectrum of the sunspots. How well, he said to himself, this demonstrated the soundness of his contention that astronomy and the laboratory must combine to solve the problems of physics! Here was Zeeman, a laboratory man, shuttling the question over to him, an astronomer, knowing that the next phase of the matter must be settled not in the laboratory but in the Sun.

In the four years the Mount Wilson Observatory had been going it had acquired many new instruments. One was a successor to the Snow telescope—a solar tower-telescope 60 feet high. It had a 30-foot spectrograph suspended in a well underneath and was almost twice as powerful as the Snow apparatus had been.

All the intricate machinery of this new device was set in motion at once. On the first day the results were a muddle. The spectrum bands were widened but confused. Hale sat up most of the night figuring improvements and variations in the technique. On the second day he tried again, and succeeded. There on the photographic plates were the double and triple lines Zeeman had said should be there. That simple little row of hieroglyphics proved it. The whole chain of evidence was forged at last. Sunspots are regions of low pressure; therefore they are cool; moreover, they are whirlpools on the Sun's face. Therefore they are magnetic. Observation had checked theory at every step. Faraday, Zeeman and Hale had won by a team play spread over fifty years.

A complicated fuss, it may seem, over so minor a detail as the nature of a sunspot. But this was only the beginning. What the Mount Wilson men were wondering now was how much this new knowledge would help them in their study of the stars. How typical was the Sun? Where did it fit in the cosmic picture? How many kinds of stars were there? What were their relative sizes, temperatures, pressures, ages? What were their motions, masses and chemical constitutions? Answer these questions, said Hale, and you will be well on the road to an understanding of the secret of the Universe.

The discoveries about the Sun had come at a psychological moment. Astrophysics everywhere was beginning to advance with great strides. Brilliant work was being done abroad in the physics of the atom. Einstein had just published his first important contribution—the Special Theory of Relativity. Michelson was in the midst of devising new experiments to disclose the nature of light and the medium it traveled in. Millikan was preparing for his famous measurement of the actual electric charge on the infinitesimal electron. Observatories in every part of the world were joining in the drive to combine physics and astronomy and prove the truth of Faraday's unity of nature. To Hale and Adams and their colleagues the time had come to put all their energies into the study of stellar evolution.

As anyone knows who has given the heavens more than a casual look, some stars are white, some are green and some are definitely red. Arcturus is distinctly yellowish, for instance, and Betelgeuse, in Orion, is red. There had been much speculation as to the temperature of these ruddy stars. Were they cooler than ordinary? Perhaps old suns that were dying? Adams thought if he could photograph the spectrum of such a star with the Snow telescope he might find out.

It was a daring thing to do—photographing a faint red star with a telescope meant for the Sun. About as daring as starting out across the ocean in an open boat, and infinitely more worth while. To the unthinking the astronomer may seem comfortable and safe and unadventurous. Only those who risk their lives are heroes, so the convention goes. But how about the man who risks his health day after day and night after night, summer and winter, regardless of weather, sickness and everything else for the sake of finding out something that a whole scientific world is waiting for? Disregarding his feelings, disregarding failure, disregarding the impossible; yet being honest and humble and unbiased about his results all the while. Those, as history may write some day, are the real heroes of civilized progress.

Adams took a sporting chance on Arcturus. The ruddy light was so faint in the Snow telescope that a single night of exposure was not enough. It took five; five nights of five hours each to make that one photograph. During the entire period the Rowland grating in the spectrograph had to be kept at precisely the same temperature; any change would have meant slight distortions and a meaningless record at the end. This was done with an electric thermostat, which had to be watched day and night. When the star had gone down and Adams could snatch a little sleep somebody else had to take charge to see that nothing about the telescope was disturbed by even a hairsbreadth. Then in a few hours Adams would be back again. That week everyone tiptoed about on the top of the mountain. Much hung in the balance.

When it was over and the plate was developed, there was the spectrum of Arcturus—the largest ever obtained—on which many hundreds of lines could be identified by close scrutiny. The star and the sunspot were similar. A red sun was a cool one!

Much more was at stake than taking Arcturus' temperature. In fact, to the astronomers Adams' discovery was only a minor thing. Yet it was typical of a hundred dogged experiments as they felt their way along toward an understanding of the heavens. Then at last they stood in the open, with the whole promise of astrophysics spread out before them, wondering whether the results of four preliminary years warranted fitting out a whole new expedition into space. To a man like Hale there was no question about it. They *must* go ahead. The Mount Wilson Solar Observatory must expand into the spearhead of the attack upon the stars.

It was time to install a big reflecting telescope.

## CHAPTER VIII

## REFLECTOR OR REFRACTOR?

EVEN in the old Yerkes days Professor Hale realized that he needed an instrument far more powerful than the 40-inch refractor to make the study of stellar evolution effective. But at the moment there was neither time nor money to build it.

William Hale saw this. Quietly he wrote to a famous French glassmaker and ordered the largest glass disk he could turn out. When it came, he presented it to his son with a twinkle in his eye. "It's always a good idea," he remarked, "to provide for the future."

"It would be still better," George Hale replied simply, "if more astronomers had fathers like you."

The disk was sixty inches in diameter, a great slab of clear green glass eight inches thick and as big as a table top. It was to be made into an astronomical mirror. Ritchey stood it up in a corner of his instrument shop and admired it; once in a while in a spare moment he got it out and worked on it, planning how he could make a machine big enough to grind its surface to the right shape. The problem was a tremendous one. The largest mirror Ritchey had ever made was only two feet in diameter. This new one was five, and it weighed a ton.

Several years went by and the disk still stood in a corner, waiting. Then Hale built the Mount Wilson Observatory and persuaded the Carnegie Institution to buy the Snow telescope. They offered to make the 60-inch disk into a telescope. So here it was now, in the Laboratory at Pasadena, patiently awaiting its turn. Ritchey began planning for it in earnest.

But why was Hale turning to mirrors so suddenly? What could they do that lenses could not? Why was he starting on the line of great reflecting telescopes that was to culminate forty years later in the Giant of Palomar? Let us examine the two types of instrument and see.

The purpose of any telescope is to bring the light from a distant object to a focus and make an image of it. If a lens is used to do this the instrument is called a "refractor," because the incoming light passes through the glass and is bent or refracted in a narrowing cone of rays which meet at a point called the

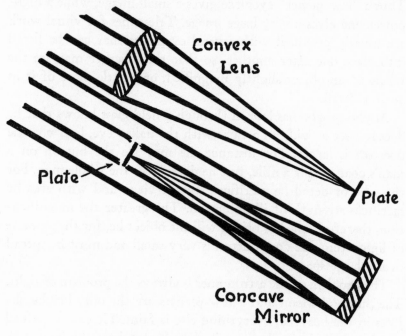

Convex
Lens

Plate

Plate

Concave
Mirror

LENS AND MIRROR COMPARED

"focus." If a concave mirror is used to do it, the light is bounced back to a similar focus by reflection, and the instrument is called a "reflector." In either case an image of the object is formed at the focal point.

If a piece of paper is held at the focus of any telescope an image will be cast upon it, and one may look at it and study it in detail. Regardless of which type of telescope it is, the size of the image depends upon the distance from the glass to the focal point. This distance is decided entirely by the curve on the glass.

Now the next question is magnification. When a telescope is used to look through, a small lens, or "eyepiece," is placed just back of the focal point and one views the image through that. The eyepiece is nothing more than a magnifying glass, and the size of the image depends upon the "strength" of this glass. Thus a "low-power" eyepiece gives a small image, while a high-power one gives a very large image. Telescopes for visual work are usually provided with several eyepieces that can be fitted into place one after another, so that the observer may see the whole of an object slightly magnified, or a little piece of it in greater detail.

Anybody who has looked through a field glass knows that he does not see as wide an area as with the naked eye, but what he does see is larger. For instance, he may see the button on a man's coat at half a mile. But he doesn't see the whole man. For the sake of detail he sacrifices area of view, and with area he sacrifices strength of illumination. The greater the magnification, therefore, the less bright will the object be, for the amount of light from one coat button is very small and must be spread over a large space.

The problem of the astronomer is always the problem of light. The Sun and Moon and a few planets are the only bright objects in the heavens; everything else is faint. He cannot afford much magnification because it so badly weakens the images he is trying to study. When it comes to the stars (other than the Sun), magnification is useless anyway. Even the nearest of them is so remote that the highest possible enlargement fails to give the star a measurable diameter. It simply remains a point of light, defying all efforts of the telescope to magnify it. So the astronomer proceeds in the other direction, concentrating all the light he can get on a very small space and making the star image as intense as possible.*

---

* Actual photographs of stars show them as disks or blurs. This is because of atmospheric "wobble" and the spread of light within the photographic emulsion.

The astronomer is something like the photographer who wants to get a picture on a rainy day. Both of them gladly sacrifice magnification for light; both get photographs that are very small but very sharp. When the astronomer points his telescope at the planets or the Moon he can of course use magnification, but even here he usually prefers small images, because, like the camera expert, he can take his pictures quickly in strong concentrated light and then enlarge them later as he sees fit. Light, not magnification, then, is the astronomer's goal. And the way to get light is to use the largest possible lens or mirror.

Galileo's little telescope was a refractor with a main lens about two and a quarter inches across. It brought him some eighty times as much light from a celestial object as he could catch with his unaided eye, and opened a new heavens of perhaps half a million stars. No one before him had ever seen much more than three or four thousand. But Galileo used his telescope as a magnifier also and with it examined the details of the planets and the Sun. It magnified thirty "diameters."

Three hundred years later, when Hale began work, the telescope had become almost entirely a machine to gather and concentrate light. Visual observation was rapidly giving way to astronomical photography which yielded permanent records and built up on the plates the delicate impress of stars far too faint to be *seen* by man even in a big telescope. Astronomers were all turning to photography now because the chemical plate could accumulate starlight as long as it could be held in position. And it never guessed or changed its mind about what it saw.

Barnard, it is true, still did much visual work on planets and special groups of stars and Burnham used an eyepiece and high magnification to measure the separation of double stars. There would always be work for the astronomer's keen eye in special fields. But Hale realized that to go deeper into space meant more light and always more light for photographic plates. That is why he devoted his life from the beginning to the building of larger and still larger instruments.

When the work with the Snow telescope on Mount Wilson showed that larger light-gathering machines would be needed, Hale had to decide between the lens and the mirror. He chose the mirror because it was evident that the lens of the 40-inch Yerkes instrument was about the limit of practical refracting equipment. Since the light had to pass *through* the lens at every point, the glass had to be of the most beautiful and even texture throughout. Only one glassmaker in the world had been able to cast a 40-inch disk of such optical perfection. None could make a larger. Even today it is unlikely that it could be done. And even if a larger lens were possible, Hale argued, it was doubtful if it could be used, since the weight of a thin disk supported only at the circumference would make it sag and thus destroy its shape.

Then there was the very important matter of efficiency in a large lens. When white light passed through a telescope objective it did not all focus at the same spot. "Chromatic aberration" spread the different colors down in slightly different planes. Thus the astronomer must either put up with blurred images or use colored filters and increase his exposure time. Besides this, much light was absorbed in passing through the glass, especially the blue rays which affected the photographic plates most rapidly. The larger the lens the thicker it must be and the more light it would absorb. Consequently increases in size would soon defeat themselves by cutting the gain in speed to zero.

With large mirrors Hale anticipated no such difficulties. A telescope mirror, being silvered on the front surface instead of the back, could be as thick as necessary without reduced efficiency. It need not even be made of high grade optical glass, for it acted only as a mechanical vehicle for the coat of silver on top. It could be supported in the telescope by the back as well as the rim so that there would be no problem of warping, even if it were very large. The only real limit to the size of a mirror was the ability of the glassmaker to cast it. Once that was done the surface, however huge, could be brought to the right "figure" within the necessary limits of two millionths of an inch.

This word "figure," by the way, runs through all astronomy and must soon be made familiar to anyone who is interested in that art. The figure of a mirror is rather like the figure of a woman—a curve that is not only beautiful but exactly adapted to its purpose. No sculptor ever smoothed the contours of a statue with more loving care than the optician who works a lustrous surface upon glass down to the perfect parabolic curve which will capture not only the admiration of his fellows but the secrets of the stars.

But as Hale well knew from experience, there was a drawback even to mirrors. To keep the silvered surface from warping, the glass underneath must be homogeneous and free from strains. Ordinary glass like a window pane is full of "crazy spots," as a glance outdoors will prove. Such unevenness in astronomical mirrors is not allowed. Hence the utmost care is needed in casting and annealing. Hence, also, the glassmaker who does the job must be an expert.

The 60-inch disk was of the best plate glass obtainable. It had been cast by the ancient glassblowers of the Forest of Saint Gobain in France—a firm which dated back to 1665, when it was founded at the royal command of Louis XIV. For nearly ten generations these artisans had been growing up with the telescope; the new disk was their masterpiece. It had been made according to a secret formula and annealed for a long time to make sure that the last vestige of internal strain was relieved. It held all the promise that Hale could desire.

## CHAPTER IX

## FIRST OF THE GIANTS

RITCHEY was soon installed at the Laboratory in Pasadena in a well equipped optical shop. It was up to him to put a perfect reflecting surface on the 60-inch disk. In every detail of the task his word would be law.

There is something about the astronomical optician which sets him apart from other men, even from his colleagues. He is round shouldered and taciturn, and apt to be a zealot. For generations men like him have been shaping glass for lenses and mirrors. They did not learn the art in books, or at school, or mainly from others. They drew their skill somehow out of their own blood; they were gifted with a sixth sense which told them through their finger tips how to make the glass behave.

George Willis Ritchey was a lonely man who kept his own counsel and did not have many friends. He was utterly absorbed with glass, as who would not be who could make it respond so beautifully. When he undertook a mirror his colleagues simply waited. They knew it would come out all right in the end. The long, back-breaking hours he suffered in silence. If he was discouraged he never spoke of it; successful, he was silent still. The finished mirror spoke instead.

Ritchey rough-ground the surface of the disk on a machine of his own devising. The big glass was slowly rotated as it lay flat on its back. A second disk, made of cast iron, rested on it and moved back and forth deliberately, turning as it went. Between the two Ritchey fed in a thin soup of emery and water and gradually, in the course of weeks, wore away a hollow in the glass. The machine was run by motors and belts and did not require much physical work. But it needed watching at every stroke, to be sure that the grinding proceeded evenly.

After a month or two of this preliminary shaping the hollow was about one inch deep at the center—hardly noticeable, but enough. Ritchey carefully washed the disk, the tool, the machine and himself, and changed to a finer grade of "grit," then began all over again. Day after day and week after week he kept up this routine, grinding awhile, inspecting minutely with a magnifying glass, washing, scrubbing, changing his clothes, shifting to a finer and finer size of abrasive. It was not that he was fastidious about his dress; but if a single grain of coarser grit dropped from his sleeve or out of his hair, maybe, onto the mirror, there would be a scratch which would force him to go back and grind the whole mirror over again.

At last all the work with grit was done and the mirror had in its face the satin-smooth spherical hollow that Ritchey had been aiming for. Now for the real work of polishing and figuring.

He cleaned out the shop entire; removed the mirror, pushed the machine outside, denuded the place of everything, large or small—everything that might harbor a single grain of emery. Then he scrubbed the room from top to bottom—every inch of plaster, every crack in every board. Next he nailed down the windows and plugged up the doors to keep out the dirt, then varnished the walls to make them smooth. And when he moved the disk and grinding machine back in again he had given them a cleansing that would have found grit in the conscience of a saint.

All this merely to *prepare* for the polishing.

Ritchey now became a recluse in earnest. He shut himself into his optical shop and locked the door. Donning a surgical cap and gown, and sprinkling water on the floor to hold down the dust, he uncovered his mirror and began. Not with grit now, but with jeweler's rouge of the finest grade. With a specially designed tool and a slow, short stroke on the machine, he commenced the weary task of removing that last few millionths of an inch of glass. Having consumed something like six months at the grinding, he now spent nearly *two years* in the polishing.

It was not that the glass came off so slowly with rouge. The danger was that it would come off too fast, and in the wrong places. The only safety lay in proceeding at a snail's pace and making sure of his position by incessant checking up.

Ritchey used the beautiful knife-edge test which Jean Foucault had devised nearly a century before and which even today is the only simple method capable of measuring a surface in millionths of an inch. After polishing for a little while he washed the mirror and turned it on edge. Then, in the darkened laboratory he flashed a tiny beam of light on it and watched its reflection in the glass from the other end of the room. Slowly he passed a fine-ground knife blade across the line of sight, sharp edge first. Just before the blade cut off the view, the disk would suddenly go mottled with shadows, and the hills and valleys in the glass would stand out in amazing relief, like a contour map of rolling country. Here he had in minute detail the picture of the mirror's curves; the shadows gave him directions for what he must do next.*

Only a few minutes at a time could Ritchey polish, for the heat of friction would warm the disk ever so slightly with every stroke and the surface would soon be minutely twisted out of shape and become impossible to test. Not until hours later could he turn on his little beam of light and be sure that the mirror, at last cooled to normal temperature, would give him a true account of itself.

It was exacting work. This silent man in his white cap and gown bending over his silent glass was like a surgeon in the hush of an operating room, carrying life or death in his swift skilled fingers. But Ritchey could not go home at the end of the day with his task done and his patient out of danger. There would be more of it tomorrow and for innumerable other tomorrows; always more delicate and more critical as time went on. A wrong interpretation of one little shadow, a single false move,

---

* A more detailed explanation of the Foucault test will be found on p. 298.

and the entire mirror must be ground again and a new surface started.

He had been making mirrors for many years, and yet the strain and responsibility of this one and the next which soon followed, so burdened his mind that he was never quite the same again. Let any man devote two years of his life to a single small area five feet in diameter—in glass or in any medium—and see how well he fares!

Hale wisely left Ritchey alone; interference could not help; advice was superfluous. Besides, there were many other things to think about. Possession of a finished mirror did not mean a telescope. There were the mountings, the control devices, driving engines, foundations, dome and buildings. Every beam and bolt and plate of all this had to be designed, ordered, built and paid for before the telescope could see a single star.

Ritchey himself made the drawings for the delicately balanced tube and framework that was to carry his beloved mirror —a spare-time job that he fitted in while waiting for the glass to cool down for tests. He was an engineer, too, it seemed, and a most clever man. Hale contributed the ideas for the dome and foundations. Adams and everyone else on Mount Wilson added their thoughts on the auxiliaries and the various optical arrangements. It was team play straight through and no one asked for credit or desired it.

Hale was still acutely sensible of the troubles he had had at Yerkes with the massive brick buildings which absorbed the day's heat and sometimes so affected the air inside that the telescope would be erratic for hours in the evening. This must not happen on Mount Wilson. There were too few dark hours in a lifetime of nights to waste any of them in waiting. Precision engineering, not architectural grandeur, was the criterion. The dome and walls should be of thin steel that could hold no heat; the telescope should stand high on a massive concrete block to be clear of the sun-warmed ground.

The mirror, including all of Ritchey's long years of work on it, probably cost not more than one-tenth of the whole, yet so firmly had Hale convinced the Carnegie Institution of the need for a large reflector that the money was easily forthcoming—to the tune of some two hundred thousand dollars. Orders for the steel-work and cast iron parts were soon placed with California firms and the work of constructing the observatory got under way.

Early in the spring of 1907 an amusing young man came to work at Mount Wilson. This was Jerry Dowd, an electrician who had helped Thomas Edison test his first trolley car at Llewellyn Park, N.J. Jerry had a brother-in-law at the Mount Wilson optical shop and through him got a job on the staff under Ritchey's command. He could do almost anything, though electricity was his forte, and for a start they gave him charge of a new and rather cantankerous electric truck that the Observatory had bought to haul the heavy supplies up the hill.

Dowd had been in California for his health since 1903 and was no stranger to the spectacular things they were doing on the mountain, especially since the more hair-raising adventures were being luridly reported in the newspapers. These very stories, in fact, had tempted him to apply for the job. He had read, for instance, how, in the days of the old horse-drawn wagon which had hauled the Snow telescope to the top, it was never possible to use one animal for more than a mile at a time; how the driver always "towed a spare along behind," and stopped every hour or so to change. He had read, too, of the hairpin turns on the trail which continually caught the loads and upset the pack animals and rolled them down the mountain; how one mule with a load of plasterer's lime lashed to his back had been caught in a thundershower and so badly burned by the sudden slacking of the lime that he had leaped overboard and rolled for miles. And he had heard the story of how they got the first bath tub up to the Monastery, by driving the mule on the run all the way. "If he'd ever once stopped," Jerry remembered vividly thirty years later, "he'd have gone over, sure. Tub was right side up, too," he grinned. "Lucky it didn't start raining that day."

All this appealed to the enthusiastic young Yankee and he quickly got himself introduced to Ritchey and wangled a job. The astronomers were always doing this sort of thing: hiring men for their spirit instead of their knowledge. They were pioneers; what they needed was more men like themselves. "I guess," said Jerry, "if I can fix a trolley car for Edison—" and onto the payroll he went.

The two-foot trail up Mount Wilson, thanks to Hale's ingenuity, had served for transporting the Snow telescope, but no amount of scheming could make it answer for the massive 60-inch reflector. So in 1906 the Observatory widened the trail to a road eight feet "in the clear." It seemed to Jerry like a boulevard.

The truck they gave him to drive had a big gas engine in it, connected to a dynamo. Each of the four wheels had its own electric motor and the thing worked like a trolley car, dead man's handle and all. It would carry several tons, so the makers said.

"That first year—Ought Seven," Jerry remembered, "there was no rain on the last three miles of the trail and the dust and loose rocks were four inches deep—just like sugar. I would get up there with a load of beams or cement or something and stall every time. Then I would have to dig my way out. I took a man alongside of me on the seat with a shovel. He didn't do anything else but dig. He was worn out all the time.

"It took us ten days to make a round trip—fifteen miles up, fifteen back. I made them give me a team of mules, too. We hitched them to the front of the truck and then started. They were pretty near human. They would just walk along, not doing a lick of work till they heard the engine begin to grind and labor. Then they'd take a strain on the chains and pull. When the engine calmed down they'd stop in a jiffy.

"Every once in a while, up in Fern Canyon, we'd go off the road into a soft shoulder. Then I'd send my helper back down the mountain for more mules and sit and wait for them to come up and pull me out. We carried a load of wood blocks and I would lay these down in the dirt for a corduroy road. We'd never have got out at all without that. Wherever we were when night came, we'd stop and lay down in the road. We'd be too all-in to care.

"The second year I carried a cook and lived in style. We made ten round trips, five tons to the trip, and 'caved off' the edge at least once to every trip. But we got the 60-inch up there, lock, stock and barrel, mirror included. I never lost a piece. When it was all over they sold the truck for junk and I got a job as janitor down at the Laboratory. I was glad to take it easy for a while."

That is what it takes to make an observatory.

Gardiner W. Sherburne was another young fellow who joined the group about this time. He was a trained mechanic, but he'd had no sort of experience erecting observatories. No one had. But he learned fast—so fast that he was soon in charge of erecting Mount Wilson's largest—the 100-inch Hooker—and made it work. It is still working.

So are Dowd and Sherburne. Both of them have gone back to pioneering again, on the Glass Giant of Palomar.


While all this was going on, Hale's old admirer, John D. Hooker, became so enthralled with the whole idea of Mount Wilson that he offered Hale the money to buy a mirror for a larger telescope still.

"How large a mirror would be good?" he asked.

Hale couldn't answer that. The 60-inch was not yet finished. It wasn't at all certain how it would behave.

"How about a 7-foot mirror?" Hooker suggested. "Eighty-four inches."

Hale pointed out that there was no way of telling whether the "seeing," even on Mount Wilson, would permit a large telescope to be used efficiently. The bigger you made a mirror the more a prey it became to that unfortunate "wobble" of the atmosphere which sets the star images dancing in the field. He

THE 60-INCH TELESCOPE

*thought* they were safe in assuming the 60-inch would perform, but couldn't tell for sure till he tried it. An 84-inch would be a pure shot in the dark.

But Hooker insisted, and Hale finally said he would accept the gift.

A little while later, Hooker came back. He said he'd been thinking it over and wasn't satisfied with an 84-inch telescope after all. He'd make it 100 inches instead. He didn't want to be a piker.

"I told him it was highly problematical whether any such gigantic machine would be effective," Hale said afterward. "But Mr. Hooker still insisted. He was experienced enough to know, too, what a chance he was taking. He had designed and built machinery himself."

What Hale didn't mention was that Hooker had fallen under the astronomer's spell, as many a rich man had done before him. He was expressing his faith, not in what a 100-inch telescope might do, but in what he knew Hale would do.

He backed his faith to the tune of forty-five thousand dollars.

# CHAPTER X

# THE 100-INCH TELESCOPE

THE 60-inch reflector went into service in 1908. The work that lay ahead of it was enormous, but it is characteristic of the astronomers of Mount Wilson (as it is of astronomers everywhere) that they did not rush into it with the idea of obtaining quick and spectacular results. Instead, they began gradually and methodically, as explorers in any field must, with the modest assurance that if they kept on long enough they were sure to find out something.

Adams started at once on a long series of spectroscopic researches into the temperature, composition and motions of a large number of stars. The great efficiency and light-gathering power of the new telescope brought classes of stars within range which had never been recorded previously with the spectrograph. Problems developed rapidly and relationships between motion and distance and constitution began to unfold at once.

Only an infinitesimal portion of all the stars could be analyzed, of course, but the choice was carefully made so as to constitute a fair sample of the whole. In the first five years Adams, Pease and others together made over four thousand photographs with the 60-inch instrument, and studied every one of them in minute detail. Many hundreds of long nights they spent, holding the telescope accurately on a star for hours at a time. And many hundreds of days as well, poring over the little smudges on the plates which the spectrograph had made—analyzing, interpreting, making courageous guesses as to what they might mean.

For every result of importance there were months and years of routine analysis—the same kind of routine as in any office or factory. The only difference was that here men found the work exciting because it held such promise.

Seares, meanwhile, was working with direct photography at the main focus of the 60-inch, taking picture after picture of single areas of the heavens to further a quest of his own. William Herschel and his successors had long ago established the general cartwheel shape of our island home in the Universe. But Seares now wanted to discover the distribution of the stars which composed it. His first job was to establish fundamental standards of brightness for stars in selected areas in certain parts of the sky, following the work already begun by the famous Dutch astronomer, Kapteyn. Out of this came the Mount Wilson Catalogue of Selected Areas, giving the magnitudes, on a uniform scale, of 67,941 stars. Kapteyn himself came all the way to California to collaborate in the work.

With the preliminary data collected, Seares was ready to tackle the problem of star distribution. His procedure was to take a series of photographs of an area, each picture a longer exposure than the one before. Then he would count the stars on each one, finding that the first would be nearly blank, while the last would contain thousands. The relation of the number of stars to the length of exposure would give him the data he needed.

Long periods of study and measurement followed. It was a well known fact that if the stars were evenly spread over the whole Galaxy, they would appear more thickly on each successive plate as the exposure was increased. But Seares found that they did not. The fainter the stars the fewer there seemed to be. There was only one conclusion: they must thin out as they became more remote. If he went far enough, then, he would come to the edge of the Galaxy. But how far was far enough?

Seares could not answer that at once. But Adams was developing a method which seemed promising. The spectrum of a star, he said, when we know enough about it, will tell us how bright that star actually is. We know how bright it *looks*. The ratio of these two brightnesses should give us a measure of its distance.

It is a simple thing to describe here, but it was a vastly diffi-cult thing to do on Mount Wilson. Nor could it be done en-tirely with the 60-inch telescope, powerful as it was. "Over the whole sky," said Hale, "the 60-inch will probably record more than a billion stars." That was not enough; there were probably thirty or forty billion more beyond. At least, so Seares's plates seemed to indicate. These were the important ones; they held the key to the size of the Galaxy. But they were out of reach.

At this point Hooker came forward with the money for the 100-inch mirror. Though Hale and the others were doubtful of its success they were delighted. If the atmosphere permitted the new telescope to make good the full gain in power that its size implied, half a billion more stars would be theirs. Hale left his colleagues to go patiently on with their program and put all his energy into solving the problems of this new giant.

The disk for the mirror was the first serious consideration. There was only one group of glassworkers in the world who could cast a disk nearly nine feet in diameter—the French firm of Saint Gobain. Hale got in touch with them at once and they said they thought they could do it, provided they were given time. The first disk was poured from three huge pots of molten glass, one after another, and where the layers met great clouds of air bubbles were trapped and could not escape. It was a fail-ure.

The worried glass men wrote to Hale, asking what to do. Then they buried the huge slab outside in a manure pile for an-nealing—the time honored method in use for generations. Hale soon replied, instructing them to send the disk to America for inspection. Perhaps it was not as bad as they thought.

Without much hope they dug it up, scraped off the manure and shipped it to California. Then, one after another, they poured three more disks by the same process, trying by every trick they knew to avoid the air bubbles between the layers of clear glass. It was useless; each one was worse than the last. They were discouraged. They had three five-ton slabs of glass on their hands and another in America. Not one of them was satisfactory. A 100-inch telescope, they said, was impossible.

When the great mirror blank was unpacked in Pasadena Hale too was discouraged. It certainly did look like a failure. The glass was as full of air bubbles as a layer cake is of frosting.

The disk was put on Ritchey's grinding machine and the top smoothed off flat with grit and then given a light polish. Hale meant to be sure. But one look into the glass at the layers of bubbles was enough. The disk would not do. If it were made into a mirror the surface might be all right but it would never remain true. The slightest temperature change in service and the layers of air bubbles, expanding at a different rate from the solid mass, would warp the mirror and make the surface worthless.

It was Ritchey's influence particularly that brought the decision against the Saint Gobain disk. He did not want to devote many years to making a fine reflecting surface only to find that it wouldn't hold its shape. The disk was put aside and Gardiner Sherburne captured it and moved it into his machine shop in another part of the Laboratory. He needed a large flat surface to assemble the parts of the instruments he was making, and this was just the thing. At any rate, the disk was better off in a machine shop doing useful work than lying buried at the bottom of a manure pile in France.

For a year the project was stalled. Hooker died, and Mount Wilson went on with its work on the 60-inch and Hale with his researches on the Sun. But he was never quite satisfied with his decision. Had he succumbed to Ritchey's pessimism too easily? Finally he decided to call in help. He wrote to Dr. Arthur L Day, who was still head geophysicist for the Carnegie Institution in Washington. Day had devoted his life to a study of glass. He would know for sure what to do.

The glass expert crossed the country at once and Hale took

him to the machine shop in Pasadena. Sherburne hastily cleaned off the disk and Day examined it minutely. The astronomers gathered around, waiting.

"You know," Day said finally, looking up, "my guess is that those bubbles are the best thing you could have to guarantee a perfect reflecting surface."

"The *best* thing—?"

"Go ahead and make your mirror. The give and take in those layers of air won't cause distortion. They'll *prevent* it!"

Ritchey was not wholly convinced. But however dissatisfied he may have felt about it, the others overrode him and in a very short time he found himself in his optical shop facing the hardest task of his career. He must put a true optical concavity on a disk of glass the size of a small room, with an area of nearly eight thousand square inches, every one of which he must polish true to within a couple of millionths of an inch. He took the task with dreadful seriousness, and devoted six solid years to its accomplishment.

The story of how Ritchey spent those six years is a scientific legend: how he locked himself into his shop, day after day, week after week, for months on end, with only the whine of the machinery and the crunching of grit for company; how from the very beginning he lacked confidence in the fate of the mirror and, over-conscientious scientist that he was, tried to compensate for it by being even more careful than was his wont; how the "figuring" of the final surface made so much friction that it quickly raised the temperature of the glass so that he could not work upon it for more than five minutes a day and still be certain of his knife-edge tests; how the strain of all this so told on Ritchey that he gradually became moody, then taciturn and at last totally at odds with his colleagues and assistants.

Here was a scientist making the supreme sacrifice of himself so that a single project might be fulfilled and all astronomy advanced. Ritchey no doubt did things the hard way—a fact only the more tragic because the price to himself was the ruin of his disposition and peace of mind for the rest of his life.

Ritchey did not do the work alone; no human being could have stood such a strain. He had several subordinates who actually ran the grinding machine and carried out the nerve-racking work of swinging the five-ton slab of glass about for tests. The strain these men were under is well illustrated by what happened to one of them—a nervous and high strung chap like Ritchey himself—a man unfortunately afflicted with a tendency toward insanity. This man was a carpenter who had been pressed into service because he, too, was utterly careful and conscientious.

Ritchey had always contended that the 100-inch disk was internally weak. The story goes that he used to stand over this particular man as he operated the grinder and say to him in a low, tense voice:

"Take care what you do, now. Any moment that disk may blow up if you're not careful. Take care, now. . . ."

The poor carpenter was nervous enough as it was, what with the awful responsibility of forty-five thousand dollars worth of glass on his shoulders. But to be told incessantly that it might explode in his face was too much. He grew to be afraid of it, then to dread it; finally to regard it as a bomb that was on the verge of going off and blowing him to pieces. Eventually he went mad, and had to be removed to an asylum.

Ritchey had not meant that it would literally explode, of course, but only that it might crack and smash, just as any glass object may do. But he was too overwrought himself to realize what he was doing to his workmen.

While disk and men were going through their travail, Dr. Hale was facing a greater problem: how to collect the sizable fortune necessary to complete the project. The many honorary degrees which had been bestowed upon him did not bring with them any new sources of money. He must fall back once more on his old talent for firing enthusiasm in rich men.

In 1910 Andrew Carnegie himself came to Mount Wilson to

see how things were going with the Observatory. He was delighted with everything, and especially with the new mirror disk and Hale's rising confidence in what it would do.

"But we are a long way from our goal yet," Hale told him. "We need easily half a million dollars for the telescope and buildings."

Carnegie was not dismayed. "Let the Institution supply it," he decided.

At once a series of discouraging negotiations began. The Carnegie Institution could not supply it. This sum of money represented almost the total annual income from the endowment. Mount Wilson's share was only a tenth of it. To discontinue the work of the entire Observatory for ten years merely to pay for one telescope was out of the question. For the moment even Hale was stuck. Not another rich man was on the horizon anywhere who could be approached to the tune of half a million for so abstract a thing as the exploration of space.

Hale's long experience in raising money, however, had taught him not to hurry. Confident that some way would ultimately be found to finance the 100-inch instrument, he went back to the program already in hand with the Sixty, devoting some time to writing books and articles describing what Mount Wilson had already accomplished. A year later he was on his way across Europe to get a rest. He had made up his mind that time alone could solve the financial difficulty. The seeds he had planted would have to germinate as they might.

"At Ventimiglia, on the Italian frontier," he wrote afterward, "I bought a local newspaper, in which an American cable had caught my eye. Mr. Andrew Carnegie, by a gift of ten million dollars, had doubled the endowment of the Institution."

In his letter to the Trustees accompanying the gift, Carnegie said pointedly: "I hope the work at Mount Wilson will be vigorously pushed, because I am so anxious to hear the expected results from it. I should like to be satisfied before I depart [this life], that we are going to repay to the old land some part of the debt we owe them by revealing more clearly than ever to them the new heavens."

The future of the 100-inch was secure.


It was not until 1917 that the new world's largest telescope first saw the stars. The moment was not an especially propitious one. Ritchey was pessimistic and predicted that the big mirror would not give good results. Nevertheless, the final tests in Pasadena were very satisfactory and showed that the figure of the disk had been brought to a high degree of perfection. But the question was, how would it behave in the telescope?

The story runs that when the mirror finally went up the mountain and into its cradle at the bottom of the telescope tube, Ritchey declined to go into the dome to help with the installation. Instead, he sat on the edge of the cliff and stared moodily into space.

Even without this the morale was not very high. It was America's first winter in the war and everyone was on edge, especially the astronomers, whose work seemed more remote than ever from reality.

Alfred Noyes, the English poet, was in California at the time and Hale had invited him to be a guest on the first night of observation. Noyes and the astronomers had come to understand each other deeply. At last on a night in November the mirror was trained on the stars. It was just as Ritchey had said it would be. There were images of stars that looked like daggers, and images that multiplied and became several. But there was none that was clear and sharp and small.

Was the difficulty with the mirror itself or with its support? Or could the trouble lie in the distortion of the great disk by temperature? The dome had been open all day, exposed to the Sun's heat as the machinists worked upon the final adjustments of the telescope. The answer would not be known for hours, for the five-ton mass of the mirror must first adjust itself to the temperature of the night.

The little group stood about in silence. Noyes, not comprehending in the least the technical matters involved, understood perfectly the poignancy of the moment.

The telephone rang. A message was on the wire from the valley below. The Italian army, it said, had just fallen before the Austrians in a disastrous defeat at Caporetto. It was one of the darkest moments of the war.

With one final look at the distorted star images in the telescope, the three men—Hale, Noyes and Adams—went back to the Monastery to find what sleep they could.

But in the last hours before the dawn the astronomers stole up the long steps to the observing floor again and pressed their eyes to the instrument. Rather hopelessly they swung the ponderous 100-ton mechanism to the bright star Vega, unwilling to make the test upon a fainter one on which there might be some doubt.

There to their amazement, in the center of the field, the bright object blazed out—a single, sharp, clear point of light, with a brilliance never before seen by the human eye. The distortion of the early evening was gone. From that moment the success of the great telescope was assured.

For George Willis Ritchey it was the last of his close connection with the Mount Wilson Observatory. Soon after this he left, to wander like a comet, silent and mysterious through the astronomical world.

## CHAPTER XI

## WHAT NEXT?

WHILE the 100-inch mirror was still in the shop a tragic change had come over Hale himself. The strain of twenty-five years of intense activity, day and night, had begun to destroy his health, bringing on a condition which grew steadily worse until his death.

The trouble came suddenly in 1910, and at a most unfortunate moment. Mount Wilson was host that year to the International Union for Co-operation in Solar Research, which Hale himself had organized long before. Besides many prominent American astronomers, thirty-five important foreign scientists had come to Pasadena for the meeting, many of them with their wives and families. The occasion was one of splendor and excitement as the visitors were taken in carriages up the precarious 8-foot trail to the Observatory.

Hale had been ill for some weeks but it was absolutely necessary that he welcome the visitors and start the meeting off. With tremendous effort he got himself up the mountain in time to receive his guests, and made them a short speech. That evening he presided at the official dinner in Pasadena and spoke again. Then he collapsed, and the rest had to be done by his colleagues.

But this was only a foretaste of what was to come. Before many years he had to abandon active astronomical work on the mountain entirely.

Dr. Adams' account of this crucial moment in the life of a great scientist gives a tender and forceful picture of the way Hale adjusted himself to his calamity. "In 1910 the first shadows of physical illness began to fall across Hale's life," he wrote. "After this time he was never completely free from attacks of a type of brain congestion which occasionally produced severe pain and almost complete mental exhaustion. He soon learned that such attacks were most apt to occur when his mind was occupied with his scientific work, and with profound courage he attempted to adjust himself to the situation. Without completely giving up his research, he devoted more time to writing, to executive work, and to the organization and development of projects he had especially at heart."

Here Hale began a pattern of life which seems so often to appear in the history of genius. For nearly thirty years after that he carried on as best he could, knowing that the solar research which he most loved to do openly invited collapse and suffering; deliberately running the risk of the penalty whenever he felt the thing he wanted to do was worth the price. The rest of the time he devoted his extraordinary energies to inspiring others, until even that exertion became too much. Finally, as his affliction descended upon him in earnest, he made the supreme effort of his life and drove through to completion the difficult negotiations which prefaced the birth of the Giant of Palomar.

Hale was, after all, quite as much a builder as an astronomer, and it was science's good fortune that when he had to leave the laboratory he could still plan and organize for others. Now that he had inspired and completed the world's largest and most perfectly equipped observatory, on Mount Wilson, he could withdraw for the time, at least, and let the science of astrophysics catch up with the opportunities he had made for it.

The 100-inch telescope made its debut early in 1918 and for twenty years thereafter remained astronomy's mightiest weapon in the attack upon the stars. While the men Hale had trained at Kenwood and Yerkes carried on the solar work with the most modern instruments in the world, his associates and many visiting astronomers and physicists began a steady march toward a knowledge of the Universe.

No profession has ever co-operated so completely, nor has any socialist dream of equality ever achieved such a combination of endeavor or brought about such a sharing of results as the world of astronomy and physics has done in these twenty years, under the inspiration of such men as Hale and the help of such observatories as Mount Wilson.

From the work of Adams and his colleagues came new and accurate methods of measuring the distances of stars; from the Michelson interferometer, applied to the 100-inch telescope, the first determination of a star's actual diameter; from Shapley's studies a true conception of the size and population of our Galaxy; from the painstaking photography of Edwin Hubble the mapping of ten thousand "island universes" which lie so remote in space that the light from the nearest of them takes nine hundred thousand years to reach the earth.

And from the inspired researches of Henrietta Leavitt at Harvard—one of the few great women astronomers—the discovery of the "Cepheid variables," and hence a method by which the vast distances to the outlying stellar continents could be accurately measured.

Eddington, Jeans and Einstein, all were visitors there at Mount Wilson; from the work of the staff there and of others inspired by them in all parts of the world, these geniuses of mathematical theory began to form a picture of the Universe as a whole, and raised a controversy as to whether in its larger elements it was still in chaos or was following some mighty plan. Out of that argument came the concept that these island universes were not random at all, but were systems like our own —billions of suns gathered together in obedience to one law. Eddington conceived of these galaxies as rushing away from each other at horrible speeds and called his conception the Expanding Universe; Einstein, on a different plan, saw space as "curved" and the Universe as a finite creation in the midst of a void so absolute as to be mathematically nonexistent. The world of science—physics, chemistry, astronomy and mathematics—became involved in what seemed a hopeless tangle; so much was argued, so little could be proved.

Hooker and Hale had started men on a controversy they could not end. The 100-inch telescope, from the day it went into service, asked more questions than it could answer. For every precise measurement that it took it demanded a dozen more it had not the power to make. As the years went by these questions piled up in Hale's mind. It was the old story he knew so well: build however large a telescope you will, there will always be need for a larger still.

But where was the end to be? Would it ever be possible to build one final instrument so large that it could see all the stars and all the galaxies, sweeping the cosmos clean? Would one more jump in size reach to the boundaries of the Universe—if boundaries there were—and solve all possible unknowns? Hale could not tell. But he seemed at last to have come out into the truly open spaces; this time he saw that he was facing the most fundamental mysteries of all, perhaps even, as Jeans maintained, the mystery of God himself.

To a man like Hale there could be only one course to pursue. More light! A larger telescope still!

# PART II
# THE GIANT IS BORN

PART II

PRICES

# CHAPTER XII

## ANOTHER VOYAGE BEGINS

"LIKE buried treasures, the outposts of the Universe have beckoned to the adventurous from immemorial times. Princes and potentates, political or industrial, equally with men of science, have felt the lure of the uncharted seas of space. If the cost of gathering celestial treasure exceeds that of searching for the buried chests of a Morgan or a Flint, the expectation of rich return is surely greater and the route no less attractive."

So wrote George Ellery Hale in *Harper's Magazine* early in 1928, when the greatest industrial boom in the history of America had made the future golden and all things seem possible.

"Starlight is falling on every square mile of the Earth's surface, and the best we can do is to gather up and concentrate the rays that strike an area 100 inches in diameter. I have never liked to predict the possibilities of large telescopes, but the present circumstances are so different from those of the past that less caution seems necessary. The question remains whether we could now safely advance to an aperture of 200 inches or, better still, to twenty-five feet."

It was not an inspiration of the moment created at a magazine editor's request. Hale had been cogitating the problem of a larger telescope for years. Since 1923, when his health had forced him to surrender the directorship of Mount Wilson to Adams, there had been much more time to dream of the future of astronomy. He would sit for hours with one astronomer or another, romancing about the great things that might happen in science in the next twenty years. "Telescopes are small affairs in comparison with battleships and bridges," Hale used to say. "Why shouldn't something be done to bring the tremendous post-war advances in engineering fully to bear on the problems of astronomy?"

Pease was a dreamer, too, and an engineer. He sat down one day and made a scale drawing of a 300-inch telescope. It was gigantic, but neither he nor Hale saw any reason why it could not be built during their lifetime. Hale wrote to Dr. Day in Washington and asked him for advice. Could a 300-inch glass disk be cast? Day replied by pointing out a serious problem. Supposing it were to be cast, how was it to be moved to the observatory?

"I told him," Day said afterward, "that I had every confidence that the advances in glass technology would eventually make such a disk possible. But I was quite sure that even if cast successfully it could not be transported by any means available in America. The disk would weigh some fifty tons and stand as high as a two-story house. Not a bridge nor a railroad tunnel on the continent would let it pass. Nor could a ship be found that could safely handle it."

The disk, he wrote Hale, would surely have to be manufactured on the mountain where the observatory was to be established. An entire glass plant would have to be built first, then experts brought in from outside to handle the job. Fuel and sand would have to be hauled up from the valley in vast quantities. Every problem of glassmaking would have to be solved in the wilds of a mountain retreat. The cost of the undertaking would be fantastic. Yet he supposed that it could theoretically be done.

Both Hale and Pease realized that Day was right. They had been thinking in terms of a future century; even if the Coolidge Boom kept on indefinitely it could not support such a project. They dropped the plan into the back of their minds and went on to the more immediate concerns of the present.

But Hale kept thinking about big telescopes and discussing them with everyone whose advice he thought would be worth anything. Everybody agreed with him that some kind of a gigantic instrument was needed to solve the fast gathering problems of the outer Universe. But few believed that it could ever be built. They reminded him of the difficulty Saint Gobain had had in casting even the 100-inch disk. Certainly no glassmaker would be willing to tackle an object three times as large and twenty-seven times as heavy.

As the years went by, however, Hale became more and more convinced that a larger telescope must be built. Everywhere men were taking advantage of the new engineering methods boom times had brought. An Empire State Building, a Boulder Dam, a Golden Gate Bridge, a *Normandie* were on paper already. Why not a Giant Telescope? So, when the invitation came to contribute an article on astronomy to *Harper's,* he chose the subject: "Possibilities of Large Telescopes," and threw into it every ounce of the great enthusiasm he possessed.

"I believe," he cried at the end of it, "that a 200-inch or even a 300-inch telescope could now be built and used to the great advantage of astronomy. . . . Lick, Yerkes, Hooker and Carnegie have passed on, but the opportunity remains for some other donor to advance knowledge and to satisfy his own curiosity regarding the nature of the Universe and the problem of its unexplored depths."

It was not merely a challenge to a wealthy man; he had thrown down the gauntlet to Croesus himself.

But where was the millionaire with sufficient enthusiasm to finance such a telescope?

Not so far off as he had feared, apparently. The old Hale formula was at work again, though the figures had jumped from thousands to millions. The man who now followed in the footsteps of Yerkes and Carnegie was Dr. Wickliffe Rose, President of the Rockefeller General Education Board in New York.

Hale knew Rose well. When the *Harper's* editors sent him proof of his article he sent a copy of it along to Rose, suggesting that here might be a philanthropy that would interest him. Would the General Education Board be willing to make a grant of money to determine whether a large astronomical mirror could be cast?

Rose was immediately impressed. More, he was inspired. Within two weeks Hale was in New York conferring with him. When a project of this magnitude captured his attention he did not put it aside; he investigated. Hale opened the conference with a vivid description of the work in progress on Mount Wilson with the 100-inch telescope. He described its achievements in detail and enlarged upon the opportunities that lay before it. Then he painted a picture of the vast cosmic spaces that the 100-inch could never reach: the billions of stars in the spiral nebulae that it would never see; the details of our own Galaxy waiting to be investigated; the diameters of stars yet unmeasurable; their densities and temperatures still unknown; the unsolved mystery of the Sun's age. Thousands of secrets lay untouched within these "cosmic crucibles." Jeans, Eddington, Einstein, all were trying to construct different worlds out of the dark; debating, arguing, groping for want of positive knowledge.

"Important differences of opinion still exist," Hale said. "The final test is that of observation and our present instruments are insufficient to meet the demand."

A larger telescope was the only possible solution.

"It will cost a lot of money," Rose interjected thoughtfully.

"Millions," Hale agreed. "For the thing must be done thoroughly or not at all."

The two men understood each other from the start. For the past twenty years they had been doing the same kind of pioneering in different ways. While Hale was establishing Mount Wilson Rose was leading the Rockefeller Sanitary Commission into the South to fight and conquer hookworm. While Hale was building the Hooker telescope Rose was busy eradicating malaria in the Southwest. During and after the war, when Hale was heading the National Research Council, Rose was adminis-

tering a five-million-dollar gift to the Red Cross and acting
as chairman of the War Relief Commission. And in the 1920's,
while the astronomer was planning new voyages to the stars,
the philanthropist was concentrating huge sums of Rockefeller
money in the programs of the General and International Education Boards to widen knowledge on every front.

It was Rose's policy to help the strong, to wage a ceaseless
campaign against human ignorance by subsidizing the most brilliant men he could find. He believed in science to the limit. And,
like Hale, he was in the vanguard of everything he touched. "He
was not interested," said a colleague, "in making a path out of
somebody else's footprints."

The day after his conference with Hale he left for California
to see the 100-inch telescope for himself. Meanwhile Hale set
out to collect all possible data on the cost of the instrument and
the best method of administering it when in service. It was his
hope that the new telescope—if it became a reality—might be
installed on Mount Wilson with the others. The Carnegie Laboratory in Pasadena was beautifully organized and at the peak
of its efficiency; it could profitably be enlarged with the new
gift.

He called Adams on the transcontinental telephone and talked
with him an hour about it. Adams had a different idea. This new
instrument, he thought, should become the property of all
astronomers, not of a single group. It ought to be presented to
the National Academy of Sciences. Like the Royal Society in
England, this group might administer the telescope in the interest of all, and develop a program which should be the composite of world-wide research. The observatory should have a
site of its own.

But, said Adams, Dr. Rose favored neither plan. He insisted
that the new instrument be given to some university as a definite
part of an educational scheme. He refused to consider any other
arrangement.

Hale was very anxious to launch the new project without encumbrances, maintaining a strong connection with the Carnegie Institution and the excellent organization on Mount Wilson. But if Rose insisted on his own plan, could he afford to go against his wish? Rose soon returned to New York and Hale began to sound him out. He saw at once that it was hopeless. While in Pasadena Rose had had several talks with the California Institute of Technology people and had decided that if Rockefeller money were given at all, it should be given to them.

Hale gave in—gracefully.

But Rose was not satisfied yet. He insisted further that the new organization should not conflict in any way with Mount Wilson. The California Institute had long had a reciprocal arrangement with the astronomers and a number of very fruitful co-operative researches were in progress. If there were any danger of damaging these friendly relations the Rockefeller trustees could not help with the new telescope.

Hale met President John C. Merriam of the Carnegie Institution in New York and put the proposition before him. Merriam agreed absolutely. He would do everything in his power to assist the project. The Mount Wilson staff would be available for consultation, and to co-operate in the use of the new telescope; it would throw open its files; it would so shape its program that there should be no duplication of work. Whatever was necessary to make this great advance a reality would be done.

All this time it had been understood only that the Rockefeller group would provide the basic endowment to begin the work. Hale knew that many a high financial hurdle remained for the future. He met with Rose again, hoping to seal the bargain, and make a start. This time the President of the General Education Board asked for figures. Hale was not caught napping—he had them, complete.

"How large a telescope do you contemplate?" Rose asked.

"Two hundred inches."

"And its cost?"

"Six million dollars."

Rose did not even blink. "Dr. Hale," he said, "I think you can count on Rockefeller support for the entire sum."

"*For the whole thing?*"

"For the whole thing."

Hale was not a demonstrative man ordinarily, but he burst out now with his pet quotation from Jules Verne's *Journey to the Moon.*

" 'A frightful cry was heard,' " he shouted gleefully, " 'and the unfortunate man disappeared into the telescope!' "

Then he seized the startled Dr. Rose's hand.

Hale hurried back to Pasadena to start the ball rolling. He had not been there a day when he got a telegram from Rose saying that the Rockefeller group had canceled the whole plan. It was the maddening story of Mount Wilson all over again.

The transcontinental wires hummed immediately. By telephone Hale threw General John J. Carty of the Radio Corporation into the breach, then rushed to New York himself. The blockade, he found, concerned the money that would be necessary to operate the telescope once it was built. The Rockefeller group knew that the California Institute could not support so vast a project. They did not want to saddle education with a white elephant.

Hale drew upon every important man he could find, even to Elihu Root, and together they revived the Rockefeller interest. Promises were finally obtained for a further endowment of several millions more from other sources. The project was saved.

It was Hale's greatest triumph in the politics of raising funds. And though he did not find it out till later, it was Rose's greatest triumph, too. This was the largest single grant that the Rockefeller interests had ever made.

Soon after this Dr. Rose retired.

"I am going to climb a mountain and fish," he said, with a wistful sigh.

Hale's fishing was over for some time to come.

CHAPTER XIII

THE MEN

THE first important step was to organize an Observatory Council. Men, not machines, were to be the fundamental of the project from the start.

California Institute of Technology was eight years old in 1928 when it fell heir to the six million dollars from the General Education Board. It possessed no department of astronomy whatever, nor had the trustees thought of establishing one. The arrangement between the Physics Department and Mount Wilson Observatory seemed sufficient. Suddenly the whole outlook changed. This huge sum would give it the most perfectly equipped astrophysical laboratory in the world. There was need for careful planning.

"Cal Tech" deeply bore the imprint of Hale's energetic personality. Since early Mount Wilson days he had been a powerful factor in its affairs, finding time in the midst of his innumerable activities to build it into a first-rate technical school. Originally it had had a purely local career as Throop Polytechnic Institute. But, as its dismally ornate little campus was within a mile of the Mount Wilson Laboratory in Pasadena, the trustees had had opportunity to watch Hale's organization grow to world-wide fame through the years. Finally they could sit on the side lines no longer; they went to Hale and asked him to help them make Throop important, too.

The astronomer readily agreed and at once set about reorganizing the school, bringing to bear all his energies and his genius for drawing great men and great fortunes to his support. By 1928 Cal Tech had become one of the best technologies in the country. Nobel Prizeman Robert A. Millikan headed the Institute's Executive Council and held the chair of Physics.

Arthur A. Noyes had become Professor of Chemistry. Thomas Hunt Morgan was in charge of the Biology Department. The faculty included men like Tolman, Bateman, Epstein, Von Karman, Buwalda and Monro—all authorities of world repute. And Hale had brought in such visiting lecturers as Einstein, Lorentz, Franck, Bohr, Michelson and Alfred Noyes.

For the Institute's Advisory Board he had gathered leading spirits from some of America's largest corporations and scientific institutions. Cal Tech had indeed become the scientific center which Hale had always longed to see on the Pacific coast. It was small and select; its students sat in small groups with leading authorities in the sciences and humanities, after the fashion of the great universities of Europe; considerable sums of money were available for new laboratory buildings and Hale was able to have his old friend Bertram Goodhue, the famous architect, enlarge and unify the campus.

The background for the world's most advanced department of Astrophysics was the best that men of genius could supply.

When Hale organized the Observatory Council within this galaxy of talent, he insisted on the principle of committee management. There should be no one man in a position of domination. Each voice should be equal to the others and the chairman should be only the executive head. Dr. Millikan concurred heartily in this; the system was working admirably in the Institute as a whole—an experiment in American education that had already proved its worth. Most universities in the United States, as Millikan pointed out, were run by one man who controlled the policy completely. When he died or resigned, his successor was pretty sure to have other ideas and other preferences and the institution frequently suffered a violent change. Nowhere else in the world was this done but in America. Under the committee system the evils of one-man rule could not occur. There were too many equal voices, too many varying points of view.

Such a system was entirely necessary for administering so huge a project as the building of the new telescope. Almost every problem would be new, and the solution of them must not be hampered by past convention; there should be no rigid ideas laid down at the start, to be outmoded at the finish. Like Ibsen with his plays, Hale wanted to keep the project fluid as long as possible, so that no new idea of worth should be missed.

Hale, Millikan, Noyes and Henry M. Robinson, the banker, formed the Observatory Council at the start. Robinson was an interesting addition from outside. He knew nothing of astronomy or engineering but almost everything about spending money wisely. He was a typical behind-the-scenes force—the man who had helped to write the Dawes Plan; who had occupied a seat at Geneva; who even now was doing important things for Herbert Hoover in the background at Washington. There were large questions of policy and matters of industrial co-operation ahead for the Giant of Palomar; Robinson was the man to settle them.

First of all the Council faced the question of outside advice. There was plenty of talent and technical experience on the Council and its committees to build a 200-inch telescope and make it work. The Rockefeller money had been given them without strings to spend as they saw fit. But none of the members wished to make the project a local affair. If there was any person in the world, technical or otherwise, who might have ideas to contribute, let him be consulted.

It was an imposing list of men who were soon concentrating their attention from all parts of America and Europe as the undertaking got under way: Ambrose Swasey and E. P. Burrell, veteran president and chief engineer of the firm that had built Yerkes and Lick; Gano Dunn of the J. G. White Engineering Corporation—another dean of the profession; Professor W. F. Durand of Stanford University, President Swope of General Electric, Dr. C. E. K. Mees, Director of the Eastman Kodak Laboratory; President Max Mason of the Rockefeller Foundation; Dr. Arthur L. Day and Dr. Frederick E. Wright of the Carnegie Institution; Sir Herbert Jackson of the Scientific Instrument Research Association in London, and Sir Charles Parsons, inventor of the steam turbine and grandson of Lord Rosse himself. And to these were added the foremost names from every observatory in America. Besides Adams, Anderson, Pease, Hubble, Pettit and Nicholson of Mount Wilson (and their colleagues), there was Harlow Shapley of Harvard, Frank Ross of Yerkes, C. G. Abbot of the Smithsonian, Henry Norris Russell of Princeton, Joel Stebbins of the University of Wisconsin.

Every one of these men had his own specialty; from the recommendations of them all would come the first definite plans for the telescope. Hardly a man among them was to be retained by the Council for an actual fee; all were invited to contribute their ideas for the good of science in general. It was scientific co-operation on a truly grand scale. No other man than Hale could possibly have drawn into the project so many authorities or induced them, without personal reward, to pool such a mighty array of engineering talent. It was the typical result of Hale inspiration all over again, this time with the whole scientific world for its background.

As executive officer and liaison man for all this Hale chose Dr. John A. Anderson, who for fifteen years had been the chief optical expert for Mount Wilson, and before that a physicist at Johns Hopkins and the man who took up the celebrated work on diffraction gratings after Henry A. Rowland had died. Anderson was a self-effacing man who loved the quiet of his laboratory, but he came out of it now and put his shoulder to the strenuous task of organizing the vast project and correlating everybody's ideas into an intelligible whole. But he was no mere executive; he was an astronomical physicist perfectly capable of designing the telescope's optical system single handed if need be. And although he consistently kept in the background during all the years of the building, it was John Anderson more than any other man who solved the intricate problems which came up at every turn, and took over the leadership as Hale in his illness gradually had to let it go.

It was not the Council's policy to confine itself to big names only. Lesser men, too, were to be drawn in from everywhere—men of ideas, vision and attack, most of them young. "There must be new blood constantly," Hale insisted. "Many of us will be dead before this work is finished. The 200-inch telescope cannot be entrusted solely to old men."

So began a policy of getting the best man for every job no matter who he was or where they had to go to get him. With it the Giant is rapidly being completed today, just as Hale knew it would be, after he himself and many others had died.

The first instance of this cosmopolitan spirit gives an amusing example of how the Council went about collecting its talent.

In the little hill town of Springfield, Vermont, in 1928, there was working a man of extraordinary Yankee ingenuity—an inventor, optician, architect, artist, Arctic explorer and typical close-mouthed New Englander—a fellow named Russell W. Porter. How the Council came to hire him, Porter never knew, for he had always thought that his obscurity was complete. For years he had drifted around from one thing to another and his only claim to fame was that he had started several thousand amateur astronomers to building their own telescopes. At the moment he himself was designing "optical comparators" for the Jones and Lamson Machine Company, whose owner, James Hartness, used to be the Governor of Vermont.

Porter, as a young architectural graduate from Massachusetts Tech, had gone off with Peary on his earlier Arctic trips, because he wanted to paint ice. He had drifted about in the North for ten years. He was an innocent participant in Dr. Cook's fictitious dash to the summit of Mt. McKinley and later got shipwrecked with that famous Arctic character in Greenland. Finally, he was marooned for two years with Fiala in Franz Josef Land and vowed that if he ever got out alive he would spend the rest of his days clinging to the equator. He wound up in the cellar of a Maine farmhouse with nothing to do but tinker and no money for that.

There he took up telescope making, because his fingers liked the feel of glass. He appealed to Hartness for help and the manufacturer sent him an obsolete automobile; Porter turned it into a successful telescope. That led him to Albert G. Ingalls of the *Scientific American* magazine, who was trying to get his readers interested in the stars. Porter agreed to head the movement to organize the telescope fiends of America. Soon he had designed and built "Stellafane," the first amateur observatory in the United States.

Porter had kept abreast of Hale's plans for the 200-inch from the beginning, but it never occurred to him to apply for a job on the project. Obviously it was not the place for an amateur. Nevertheless, he had a headful of ideas on telescope design and had even patented one instrument and marketed it. Ingalls had taken every opportunity to publicize this patron saint of the amateurs and finally brought Hale and Porter together in New York. But it didn't occur to Porter to ask him for a job even then.

Hale did not forget the restless Yankee inventor, however. In fact, he had been greatly impressed with his versatility. Casting about for the nucleus of his organization in 1928 he said: "I think this may be the man we need for our designer. At any rate he'll be useful for keeping us stirred up and alive. We'd better look him up again." So Anderson and Pease, who happened to be in the East at the time, took a train for Springfield and inquired for Porter at Jones and Lamson's shops. They were annoyed to find that their man had gone off on an all-day picnic with friends, no one knew where.

"You better go and see Mr. Hartness," a machinist advised them. "He knows Porter like a book."

"We have only a little time before our train goes," the astronomers objected.

"Well, go and see him anyway," said the man. "You'll be sorry if you don't."

They did; Mr. Hartness entertained them all day and they

THE TWO-HUNDRED-INCH TELESCOPE

*An Imaginative Drawing by Russell W. Porter*

POURING THE 200-INCH

MCAULEY AND HOSTETTER TEST THE RIBS ON THE BACK OF THE SUCCESSFUL
200-INCH DISK

ON THE MOUNTAIN

*Anderson*      *McDowell*      *Mason*      *Porter*

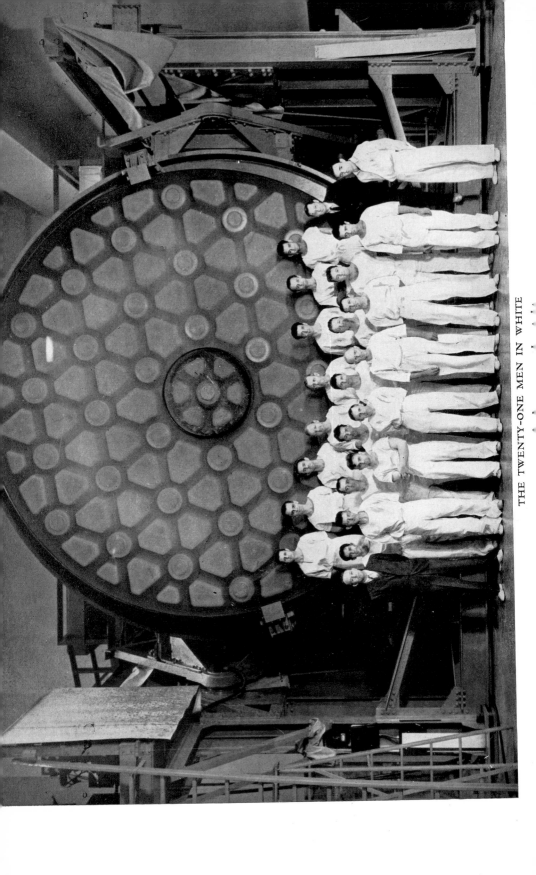

THE TWENTY-ONE MEN IN WHITE

DR. GEORGE ELLERY HALE

LIGHT PATH TO PRIME FOCUS, *f* 3.3
CASSEGRAIN *f* 16
COUDE *f* 30

APPROXIMATE SCALE

R. W. PORTER '38

### THE 200-INCH OBSERVATORY

*A special cutaway drawing by Russell Porter*

missed several trains without knowing it. Finally, just as they were leaving, Porter showed up in his Ford. "Don't tell him who you are," Hartness whispered to the Californians. "Just let him think you're friends of mine. You'll get a better line on him that way."

Porter was introduced in a casual way and presently offered to drive the visitors to the station on his way home. During the ride he told them all about the picnic and the virtues of Vermont, then branched off into a description of the Arctic and the iniquities of Dr. Cook and the limitations of being an artist. He talked steadily for half an hour. At last, as Anderson and Pease climbed aboard the train, they got a chance to ask him if he knew anything about astronomy.

"Not a great deal," Porter shouted. "It's a big subject. Some other time I'll be glad to tell you what little I do know, though." And he waved his hand at them as the train pulled out.

"Nice fellows," he said to Hartness. "Who are they?"

"Two of the head men on the 200-inch telescope job."

"Two-hundred-in—good God! Why the blazes didn't you tell me?"

"Didn't want you to spoil it," Hartness said. "I fixed it all up before you came, anyway."

"Fixed what up?" Porter demanded.

"I think they were up here to offer you a job," the ex-Governor grinned. "They didn't say so but I think they were. I acted accordingly."

Porter drove him home in silence.

Three months later he got word from Hale, inviting him to move to California for a steady job at a good salary.

"Russell," said Hartness at the train, "that was the luckiest picnic you ever went on in your life."

# CHAPTER XIV

## WHAT KIND OF MIRROR SHALL WE HAVE?

JUST six months after *Harper's Magazine* put Hale's article on the newsstands, Russell Porter arrived in Pasadena. Hale gave him an office and a drawing board and put him to work designing a small telescope for making "seeing" tests. This was soon finished and Porter began on preliminary sketches for the Astrophysical Laboratory to be built on the campus at Cal Tech.

This unit of the project, while only a small part of the whole, was the nucleus around which a start must be made. It was necessary to have quarters for the staff: office space and laboratories for them to work in. It was necessary, too, to have shops to build models in, and optical rooms for the grinding and polishing of preliminary mirrors, prisms and testing apparatus.

Everything was to be built around the one fundamental dimension—the seventeen-foot diameter of the future mirror. Therefore, spaces must be vast, ceilings high, clearances ample. The three buildings which Porter soon had on paper were all designed for double utility. The Astrophysical Laboratory was to act as the administration center; later become headquarters for the astronomers. The Instrument Shop would begin as a machine shop, "tin-knocker's" and welder's department, and end as workshop for the observatory. The Optical Shop would first offer a clean and quiet asylum for the mirrors, and wind up as a testing laboratory.

Porter reveled in the job. He knew more about telescopes than he would ever admit; he found he had been thinking about the 200-inch for a long time. Ideas flew from his pencil like shooting stars in a meteor shower. He soon became the project's "idea man."

But there was a greater problem than the design of three

moderate-sized buildings and the Council faced it squarely and at once:

"Can a successful mirror two hundred inches in diameter be cast?" they asked. "Until we are sure that it can; until we have actually made such a mirror, we will spend no money on telescope or observatory."

The problem was a serious one indeed. A seventeen-foot mirror would have a reflecting surface of nearly 30,000 square

As Big as a Two-Car Garage

inches—room enough to accommodate seventy-five people standing side by side. To be sure of the necessary rigidity the block of glass would have to be at least thirty inches thick—a single mass of material that would weigh some forty tons. Beside this giant the Hooker mirror was a mere toy—but a toy which itself had given Mount Wilson plenty of trouble in its time.

The uncertain factor about any astronomical mirror is what it will do when the temperature changes. The surface is so delicately attuned to the rays of starlight that the slightest distortion caused by expansion or contraction may render it temporarily useless. Thick glass does not respond evenly when it is heated or cooled. When night falls over the observatory the day's heat, trapped in the heart of the disk, begins to escape. But the heat on the surface gets away first, so that the outside becomes cooler than the inside. This causes complicated strains in the glass, which pull the mirror's face into a wild grimace many millionths of an inch out of true. While this is going on the images at the focus of the telescope are so badly distorted as to be worthless. If the temperature drop is considerable, it may take hours for the glass to "settle," and half the astronomer's night may be wasted.

Just how serious this effect would be with the new mirror the Observatory Council did not know. But they were certain that it would be much worse than in any former telescope. It had been serious enough with the 100-inch mirror, which was only thirteen inches thick and weighed five tons. Years ago, before the Hooker had been put into service, Hale had had Anderson calculate the time it would take the mirror to adjust itself to dropping night temperatures. Anderson had found that if the disk were as little as ten degrees warmer than the night air it would take twenty-four hours to cool, and would be useless during all that time.

To prevent this it was obviously necessary to hold the mirror at night temperature during the day, and elaborate means were provided to do it. A system of coils carrying cold water was installed at the back of the disk, connected through a rubber hose to a circulating pump. The astronomers were to make a wise guess as to the temperature of the coming night and all day long the mirror would be held at that point. Then when darkness fell the telescope would be ready to go to work at once.

The scheme was a failure for the astronomers could rarely guess the night temperature in advance. An error of more than a degree or two often resulted in hours of waiting while the mirror readjusted itself to make up for the mistake.

The first time they used the device Dr. W. H. Wright came all the way down from Lick to make some observations. Anderson took him up the mountain and showed him the cooling coils and explained how they worked. But at nightfall there was such a sudden change in temperature that Anderson was actually afraid to open the mirror for fear of cracking it. Dr. Wright had to wait till nearly dawn and even then the mirror was so badly distorted that it could not be used at all.

The cooling coils were soon abandoned. It was found better to keep the observatory tightly closed all day and the mirror heavily insulated in a cork-lined chamber. Thus the glass mass was held at the average night temperature constantly, and the time lost in waiting for it to settle became negligible.

Similar precautions, of course, would be planned for the 200-inch mirror. But it was certain that temperature troubles would be seriously aggravated because of the greatly increased mass of the disk. If the same kind of glass were used distortions eight times as severe as with the 100-inch were to be expected. To get a workable instrument it was perfectly obvious to everyone in Pasadena that the new mirror could not be made of ordinary plate glass. It must be of some special material with a much smaller sensitivity to temperature.

Advice on disk material began to pour in from every part of the country and abroad. Word had gone round that the 200-inch would be a convention breaker from the start. So every suggestion that had found merit in three hundred years of mirror making popped up again, and many new ones besides.

Up to the middle of the Nineteenth Century astronomical mirrors had been made exclusively of metal. Glass reflecting disks were unknown. The Herschels and Lord Rosse had used a special alloy of copper and tin called "speculum," which could be cast in a foundry and then given a high polish on its inner face. Such mirrors were not very good, for they had to be thin to save weight and so were likely to sag and distort. But they did escape the difficulty of warping for the very reason that they were so thin and such good conductors of heat. Rosse's mirror was six feet in diameter and it worked so well that he had discovered the first of the spiral nebulae with it. Hale had always admired that achievement and Herschel's, a hundred years earlier, and consequently was anxious to give metal mirrors a thorough study before going on to glass.

A number of alloys were quickly suggested: speculum, and various steels and patented products such as Invar, Stellite, stainless steel and others. A firm in Holland even proposed a combination of steel and glass: a metal backing with a vitreous reflecting surface welded to it. They sent Hale an 8-inch mirror of this design which gave such remarkable results under sudden heating in the Sun that the Council ordered a three-foot mirror for the Astrophysical Laboratory's solar telescope. But for a 200-inch disk the drawback of weight was considered too serious. There was no way to be sure that the needed rigidity could be obtained, and the cost of a patented disk of such huge proportions would be enormous. These same objections ruled out the other metal mirrors as well, together with the fear that they were at best highly experimental. It seemed wiser to stick to glass, modified in some way that would eliminate the usual drawbacks.

The first suggestions in this field came simultaneously from Ritchey, Sir Charles Parsons and the Bureau of Standards. With some variations they all proposed to *build up* a disk of the required size out of small pieces of glass cemented or welded together. Ritchey in particular believed that he had solved the problem of large mirrors entirely in a 60-inch disk he was then completing in Paris. It was built up of small plates of glass cemented to the top of a glass grid, and the whole was so thin and light that it seemed very promising. But there were serious optical complications introduced by the joints, as well as grave doubts of the mirror's keeping its shape.

The Observatory Council took all these proposals and weighed them carefully. In the end it seemed wiser to give them up as they had the suggestions for metal. It would be better, Hale thought, to avoid untried innovations as much as possible in this first major item of the project. If a mirror could be made by some more conventional means that would be satisfactory, then there would be time—and money—to "branch out."

Two less revolutionary proposals in the use of glass remained. The first came from Dr. Day in Washington; it was his belief that a special low-expansion glass could be developed that would be very nearly insensitive to temperature changes. Encouraging work along this line had already been done in America. Before the war only the Germans and Austrians had known the secret of such high-quality glass, but when hostilities stopped all exports, the War Industries Board had stimulated American concerns to take up the research. Day himself had assisted and the final result was a special heat resistant product manufactured under the trade mark "Pyrex." The Corning Glass Works was already making this kind of glass into dishes and kitchen ware which could be put directly on the stove without cracking. Day thought that further research would produce a glass even better, that is, even less responsive to heat. "Undoubtedly such a glass can be made and cast into a disk as large as 200 inches in diameter," he said. "And the resulting mirror will give you fine results."

The second and final suggestion came from Professor Elihu Thomson, an inventor of great genius and a founder of the electrical industry. His idea was to use fused quartz. It had, he pointed out, almost no temperature response at all.

Unlike low-expansion glass, fused quartz already had a long history. Day himself had worked on it at the time when the Snow telescope mirrors were suffering from distortion by the Sun's heat. Fifty years before that laboratory scientists had learned to draw it into infinitesimally fine fibers for use in suspending tiny galvanometer mirrors. The glassmakers of Jena had found a way to make almost perfect microscope lenses with it. Professor Thomson had always wanted to develop it and had been investigating its properties off and on for twenty years. He had even cast small astronomical mirrors of quartz which he said were practically ideal. "If you ever need a larger telescope," he had told Hale during the war, "use fused quartz. There is nothing in the world like it."

Hale had once been on a visit to Yellowstone Park where he had seen whole cliffs made of a natural glass called obsidian. He and Day had talked of its use for astronomical purposes. There were cubic miles of it available for the mere trouble of cutting it loose. If it worked, one would never have to worry again about glass for mirrors. But it was not abundant in large pieces, certainly not in seventeen-foot slabs.

Nevertheless, when the subject of quartz came up Hale remembered the old obsidian scheme and it spurred his interest in using nature's own glasses without the contamination of outside materials. Perhaps his friend Thomson could devise some means of fusing quartz rock into a large enough mass to make the big mirror. If he could, their fondest hopes would be achieved.

Dr. Noyes was even more enthusiastic for quartz than Hale. As a physical chemist he knew its extreme stability and it seemed to him the only possible material for the mirror. Everyone else agreed: quartz was well worth a trial. Everyone but Pease. Pease was an engineer as well as an astronomer. Forty tons of fused quartz looked to him like a big order. He feared that it might be more experimental than it appeared. And to the practical engineer experiment is an evil, necessary sometimes, but undesirable.

Pease's opinion, however, did not outweigh the others. The advantages of fused quartz would be very great, they said. Besides, a moderate amount of experiment would do no harm. Why not take a flyer in these optimistic days, with six million dollars to spend?

But in Hale's clear mind the risks of experiment were sharply defined. He did not decide upon quartz blindly, without full knowledge of the alternatives.

"We have," he said, "four lines of defense: quartz, 'Pyrex,' glass-on-metal, and finally metal alone. If our first does not hold we shall be able to fall back on the others."

With that clearly understood he and Noyes went East to confer with Professor Thomson in New York. The veteran of sixty years of scientific research met them with a smile of complete confidence.

"I will make your mirror," he said.

## CHAPTER XV

## FUSED QUARTZ

"Fused quartz," said Professor Thomson, "is nothing but sand and energy."

The next two years were to prove that even the titanic combined energies of the seasoned inventor and all his assistants were not enough to make a 200-inch fused quartz disk.

It was not a story of failure, but of honorable defeat. Though it was one of the great sagas of science, it has never been adequately told. In fact, it has been intentionally ignored. The American worship of commercial success is partly to blame for this. Here was a research carried on under ideal conditions, by men of skill and genius in the most up-to-date laboratory in the country. The public was told that there could not be failure; it was even led to believe that the quartz mirror was the White Hope of all astronomy.

Then the project failed; there was a sudden collapse of publicity and everybody became devoutly anxious to keep quiet.

The foolish over-optimism of the times was partly to blame. In the year 1929 reputable people were in the habit of mortgaging the future in every direction, assuming that all failure was of the past and that one need only to advertise a boast to make it come true. Gold lay in the streets; everybody had a job and was on the way to promotion.

The Professor had said that sand and energy would make a telescope disk; there was an abundance of both, so why not publish the fact to the world and cash in on the glory at once?

Thomson and his laboratory men were guilty of overconfidence themselves. Though the Professor was seventy-five years old, he was still incorrigibly optimistic about every research. It had been his lifelong habit to drive an invention forward till he

made it work. His whole philosophy was one of dogged persistence plus unlimited time and money. Repeated industrial success had long since clinched this attitude; nearly everything he
had done *had* worked. Fused quartz was now his laboratory
darling. It never entered his head that he could not make that
work, too.

If it was his fault that he was too sanguine at the start, it was
his misfortune that he became enmired in a depression he did
not anticipate or understand. He was a typical inventor and the
story of the quartz disk he tried to make is the old old tale of a
scientific battle that ended without victory.

When Elihu Thomson was eleven he made an electrical friction machine out of a wine bottle and some pieces of velvet. At
twenty-three he was appointed professor of chemistry and mechanics at a high school in Philadelphia; the title stuck to him
for the rest of his life. By the time he was twenty-eight he had
invented the electric arc lamp and formed a company to manufacture it. A few years later he merged this concern with one
that had been started by Edison, and the General Electric Company was the result. The laboratory which he had established
at Lynn, Massachusetts, was absorbed by the new organization
and remained his headquarters until his death.

Among other things, Thomson was an amateur astronomer
of sorts, and in his spare time built a good sized observatory on
his estate at Swampscott. Pursuing this interest about 1900, he
made an investigation of fused quartz for telescopes. He cast
two small mirrors: one of glass and the other of quartz. These
he set up side by side in the same Foucault test that Ritchey was
to use later for figuring the 100-inch mirror. Then he took a
small gas flame and deliberately applied it to the back of the glass
mirror, meanwhile watching the optical test carefully. The instant the flame struck the disk the mirror expanded and the image it was making was ruined. After a moment or two the
glass smashed. The Professor repeated the experiment with the
quartz mirror; not only did it remain whole, but the image it

formed kept its shape till the disk was too hot to touch.

It was a promising demonstration and Thomson tucked it away in the back of his mind for future reference. Further work was impossible for the moment as there was no way then of making quartz mirrors large enough to be of value. Twenty years later he took up the experiments again, this time seeking to apply quartz to a score of other uses where extreme insensitivity to heat was important.

All glass is sand melted down with soda and some other substance such as a metallic oxide for a "flux." Fused quartz is sand also, but very pure and without the flux. The absence of the chemicals raises the melting point to 3000 degrees Fahrenheit, the temperature at which silver turns to steam. Each grain of sand, as it is fused in the furnace, deposits a tiny bubble of air, so that the entire mass becomes like a red-hot sponge. No amount of rough handling will get these bubbles out, for quartz never becomes thoroughly liquid, but passes almost directly from solid to vapor as it is heated. After the "melt" is cooled again the quartz "glass" has a queer pearl-gray look, like a piece of solidified fog. The myriad bubbles are trapped in it forever.

But what Thomson really needed was *clear* fused quartz, and he finally discovered a way of making it in blocks and sheets a few inches square. Instead of using sand he obtained a supply of pure quartz crystals as clear as droplets of spring water and about the same size. When he melted these in a special furnace with utmost care, he found they would run together into a single mass without bubbles. He could then cast the material in small molds or draw it out into rods and tubes. The new quartz was most remarkable. It had a brilliancy and luster no glass possessed. Rods made of it conducted heat as readily as pipes carry water. Sheets of it were as transparent as air, not only to ordinary light but to ultra-violet as well. This alone was a property of high scientific value. Common glass is almost as impervious to ultra-violet as iron.

The only drawback to the stuff was the difficulty of making it into large pieces. No matter how much care was taken, a few of the offensive bubbles would begin to creep in.

Thomson and his laboratory men learned to make both opaque and clear fused quartz with great skill and many valuable applications were soon found for them. Tubes and rods and dishes for laboratory use; electrical insulators, high-temperature thermometers, special prisms for optical instruments, quartz threads and springs; mercury lamps for ultra-violet therapy and sterilization—and many more. All of these either created brand new uses or displaced expensive materials of inferior properties.

Sulphuric acid, for instance, had always been manufactured in platinum stills at high temperature, for only platinum could withstand both heat and acid action. But they cost as much as $100,000 apiece and sooner or later dissolved and blew up. It was a regular part of the acid-maker's work to risk his life as long as he dared, letting the valuable stills get as thin as possible before he threw them away. Now, all that was unnecessary. Quartz-lined stills could be made for a few thousand dollars and would last indefinitely.

So by the time Hale and Noyes met Thomson in New York the quartz work had become so well established and reliable that the Professor could say with pardonable confidence: "I will make your mirror."

President Gerard Swope of General Electric had been following the plans for the new telescope with great interest. While the Observatory Council was still debating its decision between Pyrex glass and quartz Dr. Max Mason, a well-known physicist and the President of Chicago University, resigned his position to become head of the Rockefeller Foundation. Mason was a great friend of Swope's and of Thomson's. In his new work he was very close to the astronomers in Pasadena. He was heartily in favor of the quartz attempt, and immediately pointed out to Swope the importance of the whole project and the prestige it would give to his company to become a contributor to it. The industrialist got the point exactly and hastened to join Hale's conferences in New York.

"I can offer you," he said, "the entire facilities of our Lynn Laboratory, together with the services of Dr. Thomson and his staff. Pay us for our time and materials; we will absorb the overhead and all other commercial expenses ourselves. For the sake of science we will do the job at less than cost."

A contract was signed without delay. And at this precise point boom-time psychology made some men talk too soon.

The entire resources of the largest industrial laboratory in the country were turned on at full blast. Thomson cleared his decks for action; it was the one situation that the old Professor loved best: a tough problem to solve, limitless equipment, plenty of money, and the great good of all science for a goal. His seventy-five years dropped from him like a winter overcoat. He was young again, stripped for the sprint of his life.

He summoned to his office the assistant director of the laboratory, A. L. Ellis.

"A. L.," he said in his quiet, comical way, "this morning we will commence to make the 200-inch mirror."

Ellis gulped, stared, and then left without a word, stumbling over the door sill as he went.

In the young days of the G.E., Ellis had been a jeweler in Lynn. When he joined the company to work under Thomson he brought with him an uncanny sense of touch with small objects and a genius for devising new instruments that worked. He was careful and minute. He could tinker for months at his bench with a tiny contraption of wheels and springs and in the end still love what he had accomplished. His painstaking accuracy had finally made him second in command, and with that office had come at last the ambition to do something large, something measured in feet instead of in thousandths of an inch. The seventeen-foot quartz mirror was the perfect answer to his longing.

Ellis had been lying awake at night praying for it. "I'm a religious man," he once confided to a friend, "but I never thought I could pray as well as that."

Before Hale had ever mentioned the 200-inch the Professor and Ellis had attempted to make a 12-inch quartz mirror by covering a cake of opaque material with clear quartz slabs and melting them down into an even surface with a blow-torch. It had been fairly satisfactory, too. The quartz slabs did not quite weld together on some of the edges, but the surface was smooth and could be ground concave without many bad spots.

"Do you think," Ellis said nervously, "that we can do that with a surface as big as a garage floor?"

It did seem doubtful. It would be like putting thirty thousand watch crystals together and making them blend into one.

"Let us solve the matter when we come to it," said the Professor. "At present we must demonstrate that we can make small disks that are perfect."

So they began—not just the two of them alone, but with a whole section of the Laboratory at their backs: glass experts, engineers, chemists, machinists, brick layers, electricians, scrub-women—everything. This was not Thomson the boy, making a wine bottle into an electric machine. This was Thomson the veteran, in command of organized science. Big business at work, doing things in a big 1929 way.

Quartz sand was ordered by the ton. A whole floor of the vast laboratory building was cleared; furnaces were built, electric power lines put in, testing rooms equipped, control devices of every description installed. The whole business was set in motion with the interlocking precision of one of Ellis's old watches gone Gargantuan. No stone anywhere was left unturned.

The problem of making the opaque quartz disks was a comparatively simple one. Dr. Day had developed the fundamental principle of it twenty years before. Inside a special high-temperature vacuum furnace (which first had to be designed and built) the workmen would lay down a circular firebrick mold or tray the size of the disk desired. Into this went a pile of the best selected quartz sand. Then the furnace was closed and sealed tight. On would go the electric heating elements; for hours or days the temperature would rise and the vacuum pumps would gurgle along, sucking as much of the air as possible out of the melting mass. When the fusing was complete the heavy heating current was reduced, so that the disk might cool gradually and evenly without cracking.

It was no easy matter to create and maintain a vacuum high enough to reduce the bubbles in the quartz. Even a child can suck the air out of an orange. But it takes an engine of considerable proportions to pump it out of a space the size of a wardrobe trunk. The big furnace had a thousand places for leaks to develop; every one had to be found and plugged up. Brick, ironwork and cement together trapped a lot more air, which had to be got out, too. By and large it was a pretty stiff problem. However, it was straight engineering development work and a dozen able hands were available to carry it on. Time and money were the only other ingredients necessary and both seemed inexhaustible.

So finally there would lie the rough quartz blank, solid and cold. Then the workmen would go into the furnace again and carefully smash up the mold and cart it away to the dump, while the technical men lifted the new disk gently out and took it away to be cleaned with a sand blast and the bumps and hollows ground off it to make it perfectly round. After all this, the disk would be ready for the much more critical process of melting on the clear quartz slabs.

Thomson discovered before long that this method wasn't going to work. The larger the surface the more difficult it became to get those little slabs welded on evenly. Some other way would have to be found. The Professor was certain that he could find it, given enough time and money and men. He brought his whole inventing organization to bear upon the problem at once.

A chap named Niedergesass eventually thought up the solution while watching one of the men trying to weld the quartz slabs together. It was winter in Lynn and there had just been

one of those chilly rainstorms that freeze as they fall and coat
everything with a crystal sheath of ice. It suddenly struck him
that clear quartz looked just like ice. Supposing you could rain
it down as a liquid on the surface of the disk and let it freeze
as it struck?

"How?" asked Thomson, realizing at once that here was
something worth looking into.

"By blowing quartz dust through the flame of the torch,"
ventured Niedergesass. "Anyway, we might try it and see."

"A high temperature sleet storm, eh?" the Professor chuckled. "It might work. Send Mr. Ellis in to me right away."

Ellis came, and *he* thought it might work, too. Bells rang and
messengers flew; there were conferences and requisitions and
memoranda galore. Niedergesass got taken off whatever he was
doing and told to go ahead and develop his idea—and let them
know as soon as he had something definite.

A week went by, and another. "Nieder" (as they all called
him) was having trouble. He couldn't get the quartz dust hot
enough to turn it into rain. So he went into that problem with a
battery of assistants to help him. Somebody thought of the oxy-
hydrogen torch—the hottest flame known in the laboratory.
It was tried, and it worked.

Now for "development." A special torch had to be designed
that would do the trick every time; special means of pulverizing
the quartz; a special way to control the temperature of the
disk's surface. And according to laboratory routine, all this; it
was not Edison, working by inspiration back in the early days of
invention; it was a high-powered organization going at a problem with the massive deliberation of a fleet of twentieth-century
battleships steaming toward a major engagement.

Not an idea came to light but a sketch of it went to headquarters. Not a part of the new mechanism was devised but
blueprints had to be made and whole chains of machinists, glassblowers, electricians and clerks had to go into action to bring the
thing through, standardized and perfect.

Nor were the company patent attorneys idle through all this. Though the quartz work was to be done without actual profit, it was part of the set-up to secure the rights to every invention and improvement that came along. As the months went by many a valuable patent was filed.

But the main point was that the quartz sleet-storm worked! That was all Thomson or Ellis or Niedergesass cared about: it *worked*. Beautiful, clear, transparent quartz icing was going onto the disks. They were making real mirrors at last. Not merely 8-inch or 12-inch ones, but disks two feet in diameter. If nothing more were ever accomplished by all this, astronomy had nevertheless gained an important new weapon for its attack upon the stars. Thomson and his men had moved in on the problem and begun to conquer!

# CHAPTER XVI

## "THE COEFFICIENT OF DIFFICULTY"

THERE is an unbeatable rule in this practical world, that the bigger you make a thing the more it costs. If you are lucky, an object twice as large costs twice as much; another, ten times as big, ten times as much. Occasionally a little less.

It is also the rule that the bigger the object the harder it is to make. Twice as big, twice as hard. Ten times as big . . . But there science departs from the simple relation. More often the rule reads: Ten times as big, a hundred times as hard, or a thousand. Perhaps even infinitely harder, which means that it is impossible.

This soaring relationship is what Harlan T. Stetson of the Perkins Observatory once ruefully named the "Coefficient of Difficulty." It cropped out at Lynn after they had been working a few months and cut a path up into the sky like the track of a runaway balloon in a gale. A two-foot telescope disk had been successfully coated with fused quartz as clear as crystal. But a five-foot disk, which Thomson and Ellis began on next, proved well nigh impossible.

"It has taken considerable effort and time, and some money, to arrive at this stage in the operation," said the Professor before the Franklin Institute just before Christmas in 1929. "But the results are justifying themselves right along. We cannot speak of taking only months to produce the large mirror. It may be two or three years. But every product of our work is itself an acquisition for astronomy, whether it be a two-foot, three-foot, five-foot, or six-foot mirror. We must go to our goal by steps."

It was a noble hope. Never for a moment did the Professor doubt that he could make a seventeen-foot disk when the time arrived. He did not realize what the Coefficient of Difficulty was doing in the background of the laboratory at Lynn.

Neither did the members of the Observatory Council, apparently. At the end of 1929 Hale published another article in *Harper's*, describing the plans for the 200-inch telescope and the work being done at Lynn. "The special methods required for producing large disks have been developed," he wrote confidently, "with every promise of success." The fact that the Stock Market and most of the rest of the country had climbed

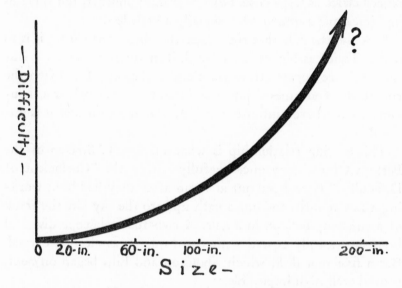

THE COEFFICIENT OF DIFFICULTY

onto a greased slide that led down into the dark, had not yet reached the astronomers. They were too busy with the sky.

The making of a 60-inch quartz disk gave Ellis and his staff plenty of prompt headaches. For years now they had been turning out little disks with ease, by hand, so to speak. But all that was over now. The very furnace for the 60-inch was so big the workmen had to get inside it to build the brick mold for casting the glass.

The old method of melting down a pile of quartz sand had been abandoned; instead, the disk was to be built up entirely of droplets sprayed from a nozzle slowly circling around inside the furnace under the control of an operator. This process was found to be successful but it made such a deafening roar that all work in the offices adjoining the laboratory had to be abandoned. To solve the problem Thomson ordered the removal of the entire set-up to a special building of its own. This was hustled together in the yard outside without much delay. But it cost, with its equipment, $75,000.

The adoption of the spraying process immediately injected a serious new problem. How were they to get sufficient supplies of hydrogen gas to feed the burners? Ellis had estimated that 7,000,000 cubic feet of the gas would be needed to complete the 200-inch disk—enough to fill a dirigible the size of the ill-fated *Hindenburg.*

Hydrogen could not be pulled out of the air for nothing as oxygen could. It had to be manufactured, either by electrolysis from water or as a by-product of some chemical process. In his earlier work Ellis had drawn on the Laboratory's regular supply, manufactured electrically within the plant for general research purposes. But a hasty computation showed that to make any such quantity as this would require more electric power than the whole works could supply. A special feed line would have to be run down from Boston to do it. The only alternative seemed to be to move the disk-making bodily to some chemical works where hydrogen was thrown away as waste.

Clearly some new source must be found. Ellis appealed to the chemists in the Laboratory, and for once an answer was forthcoming without delay. They suggested that butane, an oil well product, would probably furnish a cheap and abundant supply of hydrogen—provided that it could be "cracked" and purified without too many complications. A railroad tank car of butane was ordered and when it arrived the chemists set to work developing the paraphernalia to break it down. With vast relief Ellis soon learned that it could be done, and that the one carful of butane would probably see him through.

Many weeks were required to lay down the disk, for 4000 pounds of pulverized quartz had to go through the burners. During all this time the furnace, which had grown to a great circular oven twenty feet in diameter, had to be kept at an intense heat by huge electric grids, energized with heavy currents. That meant large banks of transformers and switches, special feed lines from the power house, special switchboards; all of them installed for the occasion by dozens of skilled workmen in a dozen trades.

But in time the work was done and a tolerably symmetrical quartz disk was turned out, sixty-three inches in diameter and fifteen inches thick. Thomson and Ellis both pronounced it highly satisfactory.

The disk was now put on a special grinding machine built for the purpose and a hollow ground in its upper face to about the depth needed to make the mirror's reflecting surface. This in itself was easy, for there was no such demand for care as Ritchey had used. It could be done with grindstones, or with chisels and hammers, for that matter, just so long as it came out approximately right. It did take time and money, of course. But these were considered to be inexhaustible. . . .

Then back into the oven the disk was hauled, with a dozen men straining on it and a problem or two in the handling to be solved. And here the real fight with the Coefficient of Difficulty began.

Ellis had been worrying for a long time about coating so large a surface with a sleet storm of clear quartz. The making of the underlying disk was easy, once Niedergesass had developed his oxy-hydrogen spraying device. One nozzle, supported over the disk, with a means for directing it to all parts of the surface, was enough. But for laying on the top layer this method would not do. A single nozzle could not coat the whole surface evenly.

So Ellis turned to with his lifelong genius for small things and began to develop a system of multiple nozzles, to be set in the roof of the oven in such a way that the rain of quartz would be uniform over an area five feet in diameter. He thought it was going to be easy, but it wasn't. In the first place, the enormous quantity of heat liberated by so many burners side by side instantly melted the nozzle tips. That meant a long search for a special material which could stand the heat—dozens of laboratory samples to be tested and reported upon; experimental burners designed, built and tested under much more severe conditions than would ever be expected of them in service; tools and machinery installed that would turn out these burners to an elaborately uniform standard.

But after a time these problems, like the others before them, were solved. A special battery of nozzles was built of nickel and found to give a fine uniform spray of quartz over the entire area of the oven. Time and money had triumphed again.

Next came the matter of the quartz dust to be blown through the nozzles. It was to be made by pulverizing the highest grade of quartz sand available. The sand used for the disk foundation was not nearly good enough for this because it was not pure. After canvassing all possible sources of high grade sand in this country it was decided to import a special Brazilian quartz; only there could it be found clear enough and abundant enough to meet the severe requirements. But even crystals brought four thousand miles to Lynn were not good enough when they arrived. They had to be burned in a furnace to rid them of impurities of iron and aluminum, then treated chemically to remove still more contamination, then washed and graded and pulverized down to the flour-like powder that could be blown through the flame jets without clogging the holes.

Plenty of work there was for everyone in all this—plenty of just that kind of fighting that Thomson and Ellis loved.

Not Ellis so much any more, though. He was gradually sinking under the mass of complications, expenses and delays. In his own mind he was becoming alarmed.

But it was a great day for Thomson when the big slab of spongy quartz was finally trundled into its spraying oven and carefully leveled in position under the nozzles. Months of continuous work were behind him and his men. In all his years of research he had never faced such a tough and intricate problem; nor in all that time had he seen so much ingenuity and downright inventive ability come to light. It had cost a small fortune, it is true, but there it was, the first of the large disks, ready for its coating of clear quartz, and not a reasonable doubt left that the trick could be done. Once accomplished, the road seemed clear through the other disks to the giant itself.

And for the moment it looked as if the Professor had not miscalculated.

On go the electric heating elements surrounding the disk. Gradually the great slab warms up: two hundred degrees, then five, then a thousand, two thousand, three. At last it is hot; the crucial operation can begin.

With Ellis and a dozen others at the controls the oxygen and hydrogen are turned on; they hiss through the nozzles and burst into white, blinding flame. Now the quartz dust is fed in, slowly at first, then at full speed as it becomes evident that there will be no trouble.

The men are anxiously watching through the peep holes to see that all is well. Not a hitch nor a slip can they find anywhere. Inside the rosy inferno the invisible shower of liquid quartz is descending upon the disk as smoothly as that glazing winter rain that begot the idea so long ago. The Professor puts an affectionate hand on Ellis's shoulder.

"A. L.," he says. "It works. We have nothing to fear now."

The process is soon over, for only an inch or so deep need the disk be coated. The nozzles are turned off and the oven heaters set to die out gradually, so that the disk may be properly annealed and not crack.

Nine days, Ellis had figured for the annealing time—almost nothing when compared to the months Saint Gobain had put on the plate glass slabs for the 100-inch. This extraordinary quartz! It would revolutionize astronomy—as soon as they made the disks. And nine days went by, while the Professor and all his assistants waited impatiently. Or almost nine. . . .

Someone, somehow—nobody quite knew who or how—some member of the big staff opened the oven just a few hours ahead of the dead line. Why not? The disk was of quartz—the stuff that defied the heat and the cold and did not expand.

The disk was cracked!

They were tight lipped men, all of them, and nobody was to blame, unless all had committed the fault of being too confident. Ellis was more shaken than he would admit, but Thomson's mind was clear. This was just what you must expect—the fortunes of war.

"Lay down another 60-inch disk," was all he said. "We have proved that we can do it."

He would have liked to go on to the next larger size but that was not in the agreement. A five-foot disk was needed for the telescope.

Months passed again; a second 60-inch was in the furnace, being fired to make the rough quartz blank. The men were more confident now and worked more swiftly and surely. And, so they thought, with less chance of failure. But in the midst of the run a piece of brick from the furnace lining fell with a thud into the molten mass, splintered under the heat and soon penetrated into the melt. Ellis stopped the electric heaters as soon as he could and looked in. The brick had contaminated the whole top layer. It was hopeless to go on. Another new disk must be begun!

Thomson kept his head, pointed out to Ellis that it was just one more fortune of war. They must keep on till they won, no matter how long it took. Ellis did not feel so hopeful. These disks cost money; you couldn't simply snap your fingers and order up a new one every time something went wrong. They would all be dead before they got to the end of it.

"Perhaps we can mend the first one, then," the Professor suggested. "That would certainly be quicker and less expensive if it could be done."

"I'm going to try," Ellis said, grimly. And try he did. With glass he never would have attempted it—patching up a crack in a five-foot slab. It would have smashed the minute the heat was turned on. But with quartz it ought to be easy. With a blowtorch and care new material might be melted into the break and welded in place, just as if it had been steel.

Ellis set himself to the task in person. He was thoroughly uneasy now about the whole thing—not only about this disk but about the one three times as big that was to follow. He was a worrying kind of man.

Everything went well. Up rose the temperature in the electric oven till the disk was hot. With a special torch he had devised for the purpose Ellis began filling in the crack in the quartz. The disk accepted the new material without a murmur. Ellis worked all day and into the night. He was nearing the end and a great load was slipping off his shoulders. If he could indeed weld up a cracked disk and make it like new, there would be one more thing that quartz could do and glass could not.

Then at midnight the electric current failed. Somebody had blown out a switch in the power house. The whole plant was dark. The heating units in the oven went out and the disk began to cool rapidly, without control. The quartz stopped welding. The crack, so nearly closed, split open again, widened, grew serious, sprang with a dull thud across the whole expanse of the glass. Involuntarily, like a skater on treacherous ice, Ellis leaped back, then stood, blowtorch in hand, staring at the disk. The crack was not serious now, it was fatal.

For the past eighteen months the astronomers had been avoiding the Laboratory, purposely leaving the quartz men alone to work out their problems in their own way. Weekly reports had been sent to Anderson, and the inference was that everything was all right. But among themselves the Californians had long ago begun to be uneasy.

More than twenty-five thousand dollars a month had been going into those furnaces; only a few disks less than two feet in diameter had come out. The precious fund which had been given to them to buy a telescope was dwindling at the rate of nearly a thousand dollars a day!

They had never seen quite eye to eye with the Laboratory. They were building a telescope. The quartz experiments were

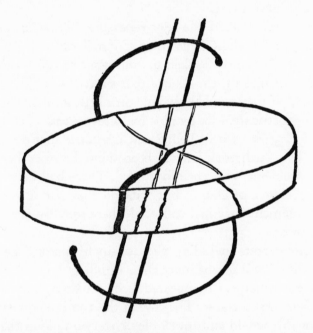

only a means to an end. They had dragged interminably. And now the Depression was settling down with all its weight. Even the courage of men with six million dollars to spend had reached a rock-bottom low.

All but Thomson's. He saw beyond all obstacles and all expenditures to the end of the road—the 200-inch quartz disk. Nothing in the foreground mattered. "Ultimately we cannot fail," he said over and over again.

During the summer of 1931 Russell Porter visited Lynn to

see just how things stood. He found Ellis pitifully anxious to please him. Ever since the failure to mend the cracked disk, Ellis had been desperately trying to resurface the one that had been spoiled by the falling brick. He had got a fairly smooth top layer on it at last and had given it a rough polish. Porter looked at it carefully and thought it would make a satisfactory mirror. He promised to carry a favorable report of it to Pasadena.

Ellis drove him back to Boston to his train, abjectly grateful for the encouragement.

"Pray for me, Porter," he kept repeating. "Pray for me!"

But in the fall the Observatory Council called for a showdown. Ellis reluctantly packed up and went to California himself. He must make them believe that success was "just around the corner," if they would only hold on a little longer. The meeting was unfortunate. Ellis by now had a severe case of the jitters, which he disguised with a belligerent insistence that success was certain. The hard work had all been done, he told them—the difficult problems were entirely solved. There had been unfortunate accidents, of course, but with all they had learned, and all the equipment they had collected, there should—there *could* —be no more.

"The total cost, including the 200-inch mirror," he stated with finality, "will not be more than a million dollars."

But the astronomers, it appeared, had been doing a little figuring on their own account. The cost of the 200-inch quartz disk, they thought, would run much closer to two million than one, and might be considerably more. "In the end," said Millikan, "we might have a mirror but no money left to make it into a telescope."

Ellis eyed them frightenedly, then made one more desperate attempt.

"The Rockefeller Foundation should supply more money," he said.

"No!" It was Hale talking now. The time had come to stop.

Ellis went home a beaten man.

There was a conference shortly afterward in New York. Hale and Mason went to lunch with Swope and his chief engineer, C. E. Eveleth. They faced the question squarely.

"There is no doubt," said Swope, "that a quartz disk will be very expensive. There is nothing we can do to prevent it."

Soon after that funds to the General Electric Company were stopped. Six hundred thousand dollars had been used up in the experiment.

## CHAPTER XVII

## FAITH, HOPE AND PYREX

AND so, in the Christmas season of 1931, the saga of the quartz disk came to an end. The last payment was made, the last furnace grew cold.

For Elihu Thomson it was the wreck of a voyage of discovery, half way to the goal. Only the resolute task of returning to earth remained. To A. L. Ellis it seemed like utter defeat. Never again would there be such an opportunity to pit his skill against something truly large. To the others who had helped, it was merely the end of one job and the beginning of the next. And to the company it was a sheaf of valuable patents and the knowledge that they had done all that could be done to make an important advance in the art, and had only been stopped by a depression which had engulfed the world.

The old inventor took it as only a great pioneer can—with courage and silence. No one was to blame. The effort and money had not been wasted. Though the 200-inch quartz mirror was a vanishing mirage, the Professor knew that he had broken the back of the problem of quartz in a dozen places, devising techniques which were destined to make fused silica of fundamental importance to science, industry and medicine.

A little while after that, when a successor had been found in the Corning Glass Works, two Corning men went to Lynn to select some of the furnace equipment which belonged to the astronomers. They waited upon Thomson in the outer room of his office; it was the most uncomfortable thing either of them had ever done. When they were at last shown in, the Professor sat at his desk with his head bent down, writing. For a full minute he paid them no attention at all, and they feared the worst.

Then he looked up. In his steady gray eyes there was not a

trace of the tragedy of defeat they had expected to see.

"Gentlemen," said Elihu Thomson softly, "I am humbly sorry to have kept you waiting. Please tell me what I can do to help you make the 200-inch Pyrex disk a success."

Thomson was too big a man to be defeated by his failures; there was important work ahead for him in many fields. He died, finally, in 1937, full of honors, and still believing in fused quartz for astronomical mirrors. "Some day they will use nothing else," he told his secretary near the last, "though I shall not live to see it."

Ellis followed his chief soon after, his health broken by a discouragement he could not overcome.

For Hale the moment was a crucial one also. He was growing old now, and his illness was profoundly influencing his life. Quartz had failed. The dream of an ideal mirror was gone now— a dream that for many years had seemed altogether attainable.

"With quartz," he told himself bitterly, "we could have pointed the mirror straight at the Sun without harm. We could have ground and polished it without the slightest fear that heat would delay the tests. We could have—

"But quartz is impossible," he interrupted himself sternly. " 'Pyrex' is not. It must be 'Pyrex.' . . . And if that doesn't work, what next?" Whatever material was eventually used, he knew now that the making of a 200-inch disk was bound to be a job for a big organization—long, expensive, uncertain. He was not exactly discouraged, but he had become somewhat grim. With a wrench he turned his back on useless speculation and without further delay called for a conference on Pyrex glass.

Under the skillful leadership of Max Mason a general meeting was held in New York. It included Dr. Day, Dr. Jewett of the Bell Telephone Laboratories, and Drs. Gage, Hostetter and Mc-Cauley of the Corning Glass Works. Dr. Day was the star performer. He had been a vice-president at Corning and an important contributor to their glass technology.

It was a lovely demonstration of the proverb that all things come to him who waits. Day might have said "I told you so!" with considerable justice, but he didn't. Crowing over other people's failures is a politician's trick, not a scientist's. Day quietly recalled to the gathering the very promising possibilities of making the 200-inch mirror out of Pyrex glass.

Hale brushed the argument aside. He had already made up his mind to "Pyrex." What he wanted to know was, were they facing further costly experimentation.

"There will be experiment, of course," he said. "But how elaborate must it be? Are we to expect another Lynn?"

"By no means," Day assured him. Twenty-five years of development work had already been done on low-expansion glasses. Corning was already making hundreds of kinds of Pyrex objects for the commercial market. The material could be drawn, blown or cast by the same general methods that artisans had been using for five thousand years on ordinary glass.

"But only in small sizes," Hale insisted. "There was no difficulty with quartz in small sizes, remember. Can you cast a slab of Pyrex glass seventeen feet across and guarantee it?"

Day looked at him steadily. "Yes, I believe we can," he said. "And furthermore, we will drive the coefficient of expansion even lower than it is at present. We'll make your mirror of 'super-Pyrex' with less than a third the heat response of the 100-inch plate-glass job."

But the Corning officials were not so sanguine. The disk, they pointed out, would have to be thirty inches thick to be rigid enough and would weigh something like forty tons. No glass-maker had ever attempted such a thing with *any* kind of glass.

"You mean—you will have to learn how, from the ground up?" Hale asked.

"We shall have to learn how from the ground up," the Corning men admitted.

It did not look too hopeful. It was the enormous bulk and

weight of the glass that worried them. And special glass at that: an untried product.

But Day was not to be downed so easily. There was another hope on the horizon. Why was it necessary to have a solid disk? Supposing it were hollow; then the weight would be cut down, the thickness of material reduced and the mirror would be less a prey to changing temperatures, both in the casting and in the telescope.

Someone suggested, with a twinkle in his eye, that they might contrive to introduce sheets of air bubbles in the mass. Like quartz.

"No!" Hale interposed instantly. "*That* I will not agree to."

Day cut the joke short.

"I have been wondering," he said, "why glass should not be treated just as steel is treated. Nobody makes large objects of *solid* steel. Foundrymen make them hollow and keep up their strength by proper structural design. Take an automobile body, for instance. It is just about as strong as if it were solid, yet it is so thin it weighs very little. Supposing we design the disk with a thin face supported on a ribbed back. The ribs can be arranged as stiffeners just like the girders in a building."

The conference tightened up immediately. The scientists drew closer around the table. Hale was skeptical but open minded. All along, the great obstacle had been the enormous mass of the glass. Not only had a 40-ton mirror seemed impossible to make, but the task of building a telescope strong enough to hold it looked well-nigh impossible, too. If the weight of the mirror could be reduced, say, by half, there might indeed be a chance. *Thin* enough glass might even compare closely in performance with solid quartz.

"It is going to be pretty expensive to cast," Hostetter said. "And highly experimental."

"Let's ask Corning to estimate what it would cost," Day urged. "I'll bet that the whole solution to the tangle lies right here."

The conference broke up. Hale was not convinced. It was not that he opposed experiment—his life had been dedicated to it. But there was a definite objective to be reached, and only so much money to reach it. He strongly opposed further innovations.

There was a considerable interval now while the "Pyrex" engineers sat down to figure the cost from every angle. And in this interval several things happened to improve the situation.

For some time back Dr. Pease had been working on a suggestion offered by Day's associate, Dr. F. E. Wright, in Washington, for improving the supporting system of the 100-inch mirror on Mount Wilson. Occasionally, in certain positions of the telescope its star images were bad and the astronomers were delayed by the uncertainty of its performance. The trouble had always been blamed on the thickness of the mirror itself, and its sensitivity to changes in temperature.

Dr. Wright thought otherwise. The mirror rested in the telescope on cast iron pads; he believed that these introduced friction when the instrument was turned from one position to another and so caused distortion. He proposed to replace the old supports with a ball-bearing arrangement to eliminate that friction.

So Pease, the engineer in the family, had been working for a year or more on a system of ball-bearing supports. His designs were now complete and the shop at Pasadena had just finished building the new "cell" to put in the bottom of the telescope tube and hold the mirror. When it was tried out the results were immediate and remarkable. All signs of distortion were gone. In every direction the instrument could be pointed it worked perfectly. For fourteen years they had been getting along with an uncertain support. Now it was fixed—for good.

Hale was delighted with this result and Day, who had followed him to California, made the most of the opportunity it offered. He got Pease to design a ribbed 200-inch disk and together they went to Hale with the drawings. Pease demonstrated that the pockets between the ribs would be the very things to catch and hold the new ball-bearing supports—even better than the arrangement on the 100-inch disk. Day pointed out that structurally the design would be better than a solid disk—stronger and less liable to distortion. They argued it every way they could think of and in the end fairly pleaded for the scheme.

Hale suddenly gave in, and as he always did, threw the whole weight of his enthusiasm behind the ribbed disk overnight. All

CROSS-SECTION OF THE PROPOSED DISK

his misgivings had vanished. Day and Pease breathed a sigh of relief. They were coming out of the woods at last.

It was a different Dr. Hale entirely who joined the others at the third conference in New York. His old fighting spirit had returned.

"Gentlemen," he briskly asked of the Corning representatives, "what have you found out about costs?"

The Corning Glass Works have never been willing to make public the figure they gave him then, but for a whole series of ribbed mirrors for the telescope, including a 200-inch, made to a special formula they guaranteed to develop, the total came to less than the amount Lynn had spent for nothing. They had made a supreme effort and their lack of confidence was gone.

When the 200-inch disk was finally shipped to California several years later, the total insurance it carried was one hundred thousand dollars. The ribbed back idea had broken the jam.

For the sake of accuracy it must be recorded here that there is some doubt as to who actually did think of the ribbing scheme first. Day proposed it at the New York meeting—there is no question of that. But Thomson's colleagues at Lynn insist that the Professor had sketched a similar idea in his notebook years before, and had actually communicated it to Anderson in Pasadena. And there are others who give Pease the credit. However, ribbing the back of an object for structural strength is an old engineering idea and not a patentable construction, so the only way to settle the matter is to divide the honors among them all.

The question of scientific credits is always a delicate one. Though scientists have a way of leaning over backward in their zeal to give the other fellow his due, the best of them are not without envy, and there are times when scientific modesty seems something less than genuine. When it is overdone it is apt to arise from the fear of criticism for theft.

But Hale was one man who put credits where they belonged, taking what was legitimately his and giving others their fair share, too. It was in this spirit that he wrote a letter to Elihu Thomson, three years later, expressing his sincere regret:

"It is hardly necessary to tell you that we turned very reluctantly indeed from your bold and very ingenious work with fused silica (quartz) to Pyrex glass. I had been extremely anxious to give your great ability and skill their fullest scope, but the circumstances were such that we could find no way that seemed financially possible.

"There seems to be no doubt about getting a good Pyrex mirror which will perform well in the 200-inch telescope. But I shall always regret that we felt compelled, decidedly against our will, to stop the work at Lynn."

One last bit of irony might be added to this phase of the story. Professor Thomson always blamed the Depression for his defeat. But it was the Depression itself which so slackened off the work at Corning that those in charge felt willing to undertake the Pyrex disk for the moderate figure they did.

# CHAPTER XVIII

## BRINGING UP THE REAR

WHILE the East was acting as the theatre of interest for the disk, Hale and his associates were getting into action on the home grounds too. There were many important questions to settle and many preliminaries to accomplish.

Plans for the three laboratory buildings on the California Institute's campus were soon finished and final designs turned out by the architectural firm of The Goodhue Associates in New York. The buildings themselves began to go up. By 1930 the administration headquarters was finished and a score of neat little offices and drafting rooms were ready for occupancy. Dr. Anderson, "loaned" by the Mount Wilson Observatory on a half time basis, was beginning to collect his staff of experts.

Actual engineering design of the telescope as a whole was to be postponed until it was certain that a satisfactory 200-inch mirror disk could be cast. But this did not prevent the Observatory Council from seeking a "general solution" to the telescope problem that could be relied upon to give the desired results in the future. First it was necessary to decide upon the optical design that would make the giant mirror most effective; then to determine how the telescope should actually be built to incorporate this design.

The astronomers wanted a very "fast" instrument—fast in the same sense that a good camera has a fast lens. Pease had computed that a focal ratio as low as F:3.3 would be possible if the star images outside of the central region of the photographic plate were sacrificed somewhat.* Dr. Frank Ross of Yerkes had corroborated this, but believed that he could improve these images with a correcting lens which he would attempt to design.

* This effect, a necessary evil in large mirrors, is called "off-axis distortion" or "coma."

This focal ratio, well understood by camera fans, merely means the relation between focal length and mirror diameter, and is a direct measure of the intensity of light concentrated at the focus by the mirror. The lower the F-ratio, therefore, the faster will the telescope be in taking pictures.

Using F:3.3 had another important advantage: it would bring the focal length down to 55 feet and permit a relatively short telescope tube. If the instrument were kept as "slow" as the 100-inch, for instance, with a ratio of F:5, the tube would be some 83 feet long, and very much more difficult to build. F:3.3, therefore, was decided upon. With this as a base of operations, the various auxiliary mirror systems were now worked out.

When the main mirror of a reflecting telescope is held in position to observe a particular star, the light reflected from its surface travels back in the direction from which it came, converging to a focal point in front of the mirror, directly between it and the star. Obviously the observer with his photographic plate or spectrograph will be in the way here and will prevent a lot of the starlight from reaching the mirror.

In small telescopes and even in the 100-inch itself, this is serious and must be avoided by using extra mirrors to reflect the light out to the observer at one side. Sir Isaac Newton first solved the difficulty by interposing a small mirror set diagonally at the upper end of his telescope to pass the light off at right angles where he could view it through an eyepiece well out of the way. This did not rob the big mirror of much light because the rays near the focus were closely bundled together and a very small diagonal mirror was enough. Newton held this little mirror in place with a small pedestal and the whole arrangement cut the light down less than ten per cent.

Guillaume Cassegrain in France in the same year (1672) suggested another way of removing the observer from the path of light. Instead of Newton's diagonal he placed a small *convex* mirror at the upper end of his telescope, facing directly back toward the main glass. The beam of light, reflected upward,

struck this small mirror, was reflected downward again and
passed out of the telescope through a hole in the center of the
main glass, reaching the observer at a point beneath it.

The advantage of Cassegrain's scheme was that by adjusting
the curve on the little mirror he could stretch out the focal
length of his telescope without actually elongating the instru-

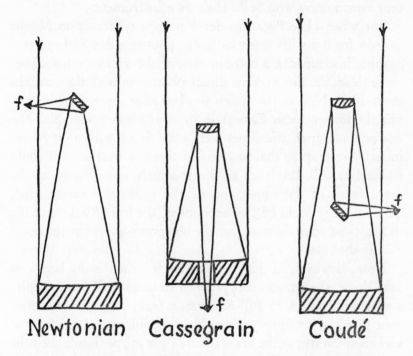

Newtonian     Cassegrain          Coudé

THREE COMMON ARRANGEMENTS OF THE REFLECTING TELESCOPE

ment itself. He could thus obtain much larger magnifications
than Newton could.

A third system, invented much later on by Director M. Loewy
of the Paris Observatory, was called the "coudé." This used both
Newtonian and Cassegrain principles and the light beam, after
being three times reflected inside the telescope, finally emerged
at right angles to the tube near its lower end and was delivered
to the observer at that point. The advantage here was an even

greater focal length, and the fact that no hole was necessary in the main miror.

Thus there were four ways to bring starlight to a focus with a train of mirrors: the direct focus method, the Newtonian, Cassegrain and coudé. For many years only the Newtonian was practicable; it is still preferred today by the thousands of amateur astronomers who build their own instruments.

But when Hale began to develop huge reflectors on Mount Wilson for use with many different photographic and spectrographic instruments, a combination of the various schemes became desirable. For making direct photographs of the stars the short-focus Newtonian design was best; for spectrograph analysis the longer focus Cassegrain or coudé was preferable. The 60- and 100-inch telescopes were each fitted with a set of removable mirrors so that any one of three or four set-ups could be used at will. But even in the 100-inch, observations at the main focus at the upper end of the tube were rarely made (though they could be) on account of the loss of light and the difficulty of compensating for the observer's weight at the outer end of the tube.

Now, however, as designs for the 200-inch giant began to take shape, the astronomers planned to include all possible mirror systems and reap full advantage from each. For the first time in telescopic history it would be possible to put an observer and his apparatus at the main focus of the mirror inside the tube without seriously reducing the incoming light or upsetting the balance. And so vast were the dimensions that at least four other set-ups could be used as well, with as many different observing stations and types of apparatus. Eight mirrors in all were planned.

The principal question now was: how to arrange all these different mirrors and observing positions so as not to interfere with the paths of light, nor to load the telescope down so much that it would bend out of shape. The answer lay in a design so rigid and well balanced that men, mirrors and instruments could be carried together on board the machine itself. If this could be done it would be a vast improvement on the 100-inch telescope in which the observer had to ride around on a movable platform fifty to seventy-five feet in the air, tagging along after the instrument as best he could.

Galileo held his little "optik glass" to his eye with both hands, or steadied it on the window sill. But modern telescopes are swung in massive bearings on concrete pedestals that no human hand can shake. In order to follow the stars for hours, and sometimes all night, the telescope tube is moved around by a clockwork drive more accurate than the finest watch. The bearings of the instrument are fixed on a slant that makes the axis parallel to the axis of the Earth. Thus the simple rotation of the clock keeps the telescope pointed at a single region of the heavens while the Earth rolls around underneath. This scheme is called the "equatorial mounting" and is used on all professional instruments where long-exposure photographs are taken.

In actual construction the equatorial mounting is a shaft or beam of steel rolling slowly around in heavy main bearings which are anchored solidly to the earth. This shaft is known as the "polar axis," because it is adjusted with great accuracy to be parallel to the Earth's own. Anywhere north of the equator it will slope upward from south to north and point almost exactly at the North Star.

The tube of the telescope with its system of mirrors is fastened to this main axis through a second set of bearings which allow it to swing up and down from horizon to zenith and beyond, so that it may be pointed at different stars. This second direction of swing is called the "motion in declination." When the telescope is to be set for the night's "run," the whole machine is rolled around on its polar axis to the position of the desired star, then the tube itself is swung up or down in declination till the star is picked up. After this the declination axis is locked tight and the telescope drive thrown into gear and the clock started. From now on everything is automatic, except for small adjustments which the astronomer makes by hand. All night long, if necessary, the mirror train will point at that same star. The whole mechanism complete is like a gigantic clock running on star time, the tube representing the hour hand which travels one revolution in 23 hours and 56 minutes. (The gain of four minutes a day, of course, represents the progress of the Earth in its annual trip around the Sun.)

The 200-inch mirror was to weigh twenty tons. If it were to have a focal length of 55 feet, the telescope tube would have to be about sixty feet long and at least seventeen feet in diameter. In its upper end there would be some kind of a capsule or cage in which the observer and his instruments could ride. Then the tube and its freight must be swung on a shaft that would form the polar axis and revolve with the stars; and the whole must be supported on massive bearings. As a machine it would rank beside the largest of locomotives, bridges and skyscrapers, but as a precision instrument it must be the equal of the best microscope.

The most fundamental requirement would be rigidity. In one of the mirror arrangements the light beam would travel back and forth for 150 feet, and come to a focus upon a spectrograph slit $\frac{1}{1000}$th of an inch wide. In all that distance no element of the telescope could be out of line more than a small fraction of an inch.

It was an entirely new kind of an engineering problem to support two or three hundred tons of mechanism high in the air so that it could move into any position without distortion. The secret of large structures is flexibility. A skyscraper sways many inches in the wind; it would crack at the foundations if it didn't. The Golden Gate Bridge rises and falls twenty feet with changes in the weather. The high-tension power line, the ocean steamship, even Boulder Dam, sway or weave or compress in resisting the forces put upon them. The 200-inch telescope could do none of these things. It must be so absolutely rigid that nothing short of an earthquake would jar it from its true path.

There were several general designs which could be followed, the two most promising of which were exemplified on Mount Wilson by the 60-inch and 100-inch instruments. The Sixty was of the "fork" type with the tube supported between the two prongs of a fork whose long handle sloped down through two large bearings, like a marshmallow being toasted. The 100-inch was of the "yoke" type, in which the tube was hung between two sloping beams joined at both ends and carried in bearings at the joints like a chicken on a spit.

From the first the astronomers favored the fork arrangement, because the telescope tube would hang out beyond the support-

THE TWO MAIN TYPES OF TELESCOPE MOUNT

ing piers and could be swung down parallel to the polar axis. The yoke mount of the 100-inch would not permit this, for the tube would strike the north bearing on its way down and so could not be pointed within several degrees of the North Star.

Dr. Pease in particular liked the fork mounting, as it seemed to him the most compact design. With the tube hung in the middle of the dome with both bearings to the south, half the circular floor was free for auxiliary apparatus and control equipment. The yoke type took up the whole floor space and unless the dome was made oversize, room to work was at a premium. Back in 1921 Pease had made a drawing for a 300-inch telescope on the fork principle, showing how, in theory at least, the instrument could be pointed down to the horizon at any point of the compass. It was a compact, if gigantic, machine, and had been one of the inspirations for Hale's article in *Harper's Magazine*.

Soon after the start of the project in 1928, Warner & Swasey sent E. P. Burrell, their chief engineer, to California to consult with the Council. He was given an office and for some months worked on preliminary designs for the telescope. He did not favor the fork mount—but studied it at Pease's insistence. Eventually he made a model from his plans, with a tiny human figure standing on the floor beneath the giant instrument to indicate the scale. For some reason he dressed his little man in full military uniform and gave him a gun, as if implying that the telescope should be likened to a great mortar to shoot earthly challenges across the Universe. The model was photographed and widely published as the final design, which of course it wasn't. One newspaper seized upon the warlike suggestion and ran a cartoon of an addled-headed astronomer called "Humanity," worriedly pointing a great columbiad about the night sky and saying in dismay: "All I seem to get is Mars, whichever way I turn!" The gun was labeled "Modern Civilization." The 200-inch telescope had already taken its place in the news.

The Observatory Council settled tentatively on the fork type of mounting as being both practicable and desirable; then the matter was left in abeyance with instructions to everybody to continue mulling it over and to bring forward any new ideas that came to them. There was a good deal of time to spare still; something might turn up that would change the whole design.

Another of the early questions that needed looking into was the choice of a site for the observatory. Mount Wilson had been eliminated, and it would not do, anyway. Los Angeles was sprawling farther and farther into the valley below and the night sky above it was getting brighter every year. The sensitivity of the new telescope would be so great that even with the blackest possible sky photographic plates would begin to fog after four hours from the effect of "permanent aurora." This time must not be cut down further by the interference of man-made light.

It was agreed that the new observatory should be in a moderate latitude, as in this region fully three-fourths of all the heavens is visible at some time in the year. A site in the southern hemisphere was considered but was given up because, as Hale pointed out, comparatively little preliminary work had been done on the southern stars. It would be unwise to use the 200-inch giant merely to explore virgin territory when so much important detail investigation had already been prepared for it in the north. So it was finally decided to locate the instrument as near Pasadena as possible at a site that was isolated but convenient.

Anderson himself took on the job of finding it. The requirements were more severe now than when Professor Hussey had made a survey of the region for establishing Mount Wilson Observatory, twenty-five years before. It must be isolated yet accessible; high enough to be untroubled by fog and clouds, and a record-breaker in the matter of fine "seeing,"—the astronomer's term for the optical condition of the atmosphere. When the seeing is good the atmosphere is optically homogeneous, without "heat waves," and the images of stars stand still in the telescope. Haziness, even thin clouds are less troublesome to the astronomer than a crackling, crystal-clear air made up of a thousand wavering layers of different densities. On such a night the stars twinkle and are very bright, but they may wobble around so much on the photographic plate that to take pictures of them is hopeless.

If the Earth were like the Moon, and had no atmosphere to speak of, we should not be able to live on it, but astronomers would find it ideal for their telescopes. There would be no dust, no moisture, no moving air masses to absorb and scatter the starlight. The presence of these elements in our atmosphere constitutes a limitation which science can never overcome. The partial remedy is bigger telescopes and more sensitive auxiliary instruments, located in out-of-the-way places that are often isolated and inconvenient.

Bad seeing comes from the fact that our atmosphere is not a homogeneous mass like optical glass, but a turbulent mixture of many layers of air at different temperatures, with sharp lines of separation between them. These drift hither and thither over

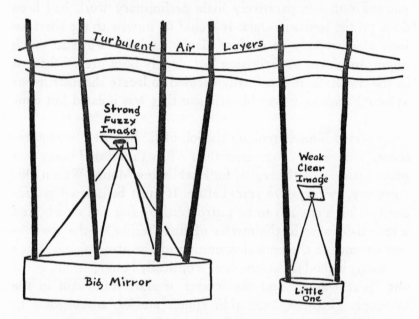

WITH BAD SEEING A SMALL MIRROR GIVES A SHARPER IMAGE

the Earth constantly and act, so far as incoming starlight is concerned, like a flight of windowpanes going helter skelter in a thousand directions at once. Light trying to penetrate this layer is pretty roughly handled, and a star image which would appear on the Moon as a fine bright point (in a good telescope), is kept dancing rapidly in all directions so fast that it appears like a disk. This is called the "tremor disk," and if it is at all large on any particular night the telescope may be unusable.

The larger and more sensitive the instrument, the more seriously does bad seeing affect it. For this reason: the greater the area of the mirror, the bigger the bundle of light rays that it collects. And a big bundle of rays is more broken up in passing through turbulent air than a small one. An example of the effect of bad seeing on Mount Wilson occurred recently. Observations were being made on the unusual behavior of a satellite of Jupiter. The 100-inch telescope was trained on the planet, but the image produced in the eyepiece was so confused that the satellite could scarcely be made out at all. In the 60-inch instrument the condition was a little better, but still too bad for useful observation. In the small six-inch refractor, however, every detail of Jupiter and his moons could be seen and studied clearly. Though the poor seeing made the images move in the little telescope, too, they moved as a unit and the eye could readily follow.

But Hale and Michelson and Pease had already satisfied themselves by tests with the interferometer that even a mirror of 200 inches aperture could be used to full advantage if the seeing were as good as the average on Mount Wilson. So it was now Anderson's task to find the spot in all that region where the seeing was the best.

Astronomical seeing has always been arbitrarily classified according to the numbers from 1 to 10, No. 1 being impossibly bad and No. 10 unattainably good. But this is based on personal estimates only and is not accurate enough for comparing observatory sites with precision. So Anderson invented a system of his own. He had discovered that the diameter of a star's tremor disk is a measure of the turbulence of the air and hence of the seeing. It was only necessary to measure this diameter with mathematical precision and reduce it to simple numbers.

He devised a small but powerful telescope with a scale incorporated in the eyepiece for measuring the size of a star image in seconds of arc. Then he had the astronomers at Mount Wilson test this instrument over a long period and calibrate it in terms of the old-style seeing numbers from one to ten. After this it was only necessary to fit a number of similar telescopes with identical eyepieces and make observations on a standard bright star such as Polaris, in order to measure the seeing at any locality with an accuracy entirely independent of the observer.

The 200-inch telescope was to be so powerful that it would "resolve" or separate two stars that were only $\frac{2}{100}$ths of a second apart under perfect seeing conditions. This resolving power would be of particular importance for separating the faint smudges of the nebulae into the billions of suns which compose them—a feat no other telescope could adequately perform. Seeing Five or better would be necessary to realize this ability to the full and thus justify the new instrument's huge size and cost. Therefore, sites where Seeing Five was a common occurrence must be found.

With a standard procedure settled Anderson gathered a group of young men, many from the student body of Cal Tech, armed them with standard four-inch telescopes which Porter designed for the purpose, and sent them scattering about the country to make prolonged studies of the seeing. He picked ten localities off the map more or less at random, being sure to get a fair sample of each kind of terrain for his tests. Starting as far north as Mono Lake in the Sierras, he dotted his men over the landscape southward as far as the Mexican border and over into Arizona as well. One fellow he packed off to the snow bound peak of 11,000-foot Mt. San Jacinto; another to the scorching flats of the Mojave Desert at Barstow; the others at levels and localities in between. One observer he even sent out to gaudy Catalina Island in the Pacific—not because there was any question of establishing the telescope there, but because Hale wanted to know how the air behaved over the wide expanse of the sea. The Catalina Chamber of Commerce misinterpreted the gesture and got so enthusiastic over the prospect of playing host to the world's largest telescope that the astronomers had some trouble extricating themselves from such an obviously impossible scheme.

When the results of the tests began to come in it was evident that average seeing conditions varied but little over the whole territory; they were excellent everywhere. The only thing to avoid, it seemed, was local configurations of land which favored rising currents of hot air. Such a situation existed at the edge of a mountain, where updrafts from the canyons below kept the seeing in trouble most of the night. The Mojave Desert at first looked very promising to the observer who camped there, for the temperature held steady all day and most of the night. But when a lady resident assured him that it was just the place for the telescope because the stars "twinkled so beautifully," he

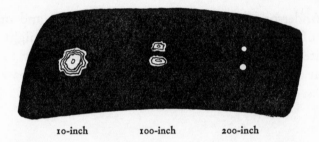

10-inch        100-inch        200-inch

THE LARGER THE TELESCOPE THE GREATER THE
"RESOLVING POWER"

got suspicious. A few nights of observation settled the matter; heat radiating upward from the sand kept the air turbulent till morning.

The effect of stored heat leaking off had been the bane of more than one astronomer in times past. Harlan Stetson had said disgustedly of the Perkins Observatory in Ohio: "If the thermometer drops faster than two degrees an hour I lock up and go home. The seeing is impossible and the mirror won't hold its figure anyway."

What Anderson had to find, therefore, was a small flat place high up—small enough to avoid storing much heat, large enough to be out of reach of the updrafts from canyon "chimneys," high enough to take advantage of the steady upper air.

Steadiness was really the crux of the problem. On just the right site the temperature would drop slightly as the sun went down and reach a dead level soon after dark, then stay there till dawn. There were only two locations where these ideal conditions existed: Table Mountain, north of Mount Wilson, and Palomar, a hundred miles to the south.

Table Mountain was extremely handy and could be made accessible enough by building a short road. But it had one troublesome defect. The great San Andreas fault passed straight through it—the forty-mile-deep cleft in the state of California that had been responsible for the San Francisco earthquake of 1906.

So Anderson turned his attention to Palomar and moved a group of observers down there to see whether it might be the ideal site he was hoping to find. It was not necessary to decide yet, but only to investigate. Eight or ten years must pass before the telescope would need a home.

# CHAPTER XIX

## "WE MUST NOT EXPERIMENT!" *

BACK East at the Corning Glass Works things were beginning
to hum. As soon as the delegation had returned from New York,
Dr. Hostetter had given Dr. McCauley full charge of making
the 200-inch disk and all its satellites. McCauley was already
hard at work developing a new casting technique and his colleagues a new "super-Pyrex" glass.

The term "Pyrex" is a trade mark and does not refer to any
one special glass. Instead it designates a whole family of glasses
whose chief characteristic is a remarkably low coefficient of
expansion—that is, slight response to heat. Actually the swelling
and shrinking of "Pyrex" objects upon heating or cooling may
be as little as one-third of the amount for ordinary glass, and this
property has opened up valuable applications hitherto impossible to glass products. The familiar "Pyrex" baking dishes and
laboratory ware are good examples.

The Pyrex composition is based on various proportions of
silica sand, soda and borax mixed together and fused, but its
very insensitivity to temperature makes it a tough customer to
handle in the factory, for even when thoroughly hot these low-
expansion glasses are viscous, hard to melt and harder still to
blow or cast.

"Worse than the traditional cold molasses in January,"
laughed McCauley, as he set to work. "And yet here we are deliberately increasing our troubles with a super-heat-resistant
glass!"

The silica sand, of course, was pure quartz, like the material
used at Lynn. To reduce the coefficient of expansion the pro-

---

* Experiment is second nature to the scientist. I have here abandoned his strict interpretation
of the word and use it in the popular sense, to denote extravagant excursions into the unknown.

portion of sand must be increased, the glass becoming more and more unmanageable meanwhile. If the coefficient for ordinary glass was taken as 100, then commercial Pyrex glass stood at 32 and pure quartz at 8. The problem was to see how much below 32 the coefficient could be driven and still avoid the costly difficulties encountered at Lynn. The final figure was 24, as usual a compromise between practicability and perfection.

McCauley's troubles were twofold. Pyrex glasses had never been cast in large pieces such as were necessary for telescope

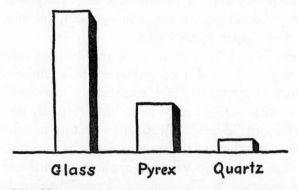

HOW THREE MIRROR MATERIALS EXPAND WITH HEAT

disks. First off, he had to learn how to do this. And secondly, he had to do the job without elaborate experiment.

Corning had taken up the challenge with this general promise: Only the absolute minimum of new research permitted. Everything possible to be done by standard methods and with standard materials; the work to be started by casting small disks first; when it was demonstrated that these could be made, then larger and larger disks were to follow until the 200-inch itself should be cast. The whole job was to be done on a cost-plus basis, as inexpensively as possible. If either the Observatory Council or the Corning Glass Works wished to withdraw at any time from the contract, it might do so, and work would be suspended. The job need not be hurried, but it must be done economically.

It was not by any snap judgment that Hostetter and the other officials at Corning chose George V. McCauley as engineer in charge of disk making. McCauley had been a physicist in their laboratory for thirteen years. He was not an exciting kind of man; he had no grandiloquent ideas, nor any great fame as a pioneer. He simply knew how to get things done with glass. He was a quiet, hard-plugging engineer who had worked with the Bureau of Standards during the war and had taken up the chemistry and physics of glass-making because it gave him the kind of clean-cut problems that an engineer likes—problems which can be solved by exact analysis, sound knowledge, and as Mary Heaton Vorse once said, the "application of the seat of the pants to the seat of the chair." A formidable set of qualifications for any human being; almost the attributes of a computing machine, perhaps. But George McCauley was saved by a sense of humor.

"All I have to do," he said, "is to melt the raw materials, transfer the molten glass to a mold of proper design, regulate the cooling to prevent breaking and limit internal stress, and remove the mold in preparation for inspection and shipment. It will be no different," he added, "from making a beanpot, except in the methods employed."

What he and his colleagues actually did was quite another matter. Their confidence was hardly more justified than Thomson's had been. As the work went on, unexpected problems crowded in from every direction. That same old ogre, the Co-efficient of Difficulty, soon rose to bedevil them at every step. Things that looked easy, proved to be hard. Things that seemed difficult had a way of remaining downright insoluble. And from the first day they were imprisoned in that straitjacket of no experiment.

"I don't know why we finally succeeded," McCauley admitted after it was all over. "Whether it was technical perfection or just plain ignorance of the dangers ahead. Probably a mixture of both." He knew very well why they had succeeded:

because they had had the humility to see each problem in its true size, and because they were pluggers.

McCauley began with a 26-inch disk—and struck trouble at once. It was a plain pancake of glass cast in a simple circular mold, and should have been easy. The Bureau of Standards had already cast a 69-inch plate glass disk and had succeeded fairly well. McCauley himself had made several little disks for the sun telescopes on Mount Wilson. But this was the first time that he or anybody else had come up against the new low-expansion glass in large quantities. It refused to behave.

He was confident that he could pour disks of fair size and get away with them. But he was not so sure of what to pour them into. The common practice at Corning was to blow small objects into metallic molds, remove them and cool them slowly. But big disks would have far too much heat for such simple methods. They must be cast in molds built up of insulating bricks, then set aside, mold and all, to cool slowly and steadily under careful control. "Standard brick," muttered McCauley. "We must not invent."

Common firebrick, he knew, could not be used. It was well enough for lining furnaces and melting-tanks, but in a mold the hot glass would instantly attack its surface and turn the brick material into gas. One could not bake beans in a pot which saturated the food with a vapor of clay.

So he turned to the same high quality brick that had seen the Bureau of Standards through the 69-inch job. It failed, miserably. There was so much more heat in the molten glass that the minute the fiery mass hit the mold the moisture in the brick boiled up into clouds of smoke and steam, which hissed and squirted out in every direction, filling the glass with bubbles and driving it out of contact with the walls altogether. He threw the brick away at once and looked around for another. Fortunately there were several other kinds of brick in the stock rooms of the plant and McCauley soon discovered one that was promising.

It was made of pure white silica and looked almost like a sponge. It was manufactured in a clever way. Ground-up cork and sand and water were mixed together and made into blocks. When these were fired in the kiln the cork burned out, leaving millions of tiny holes—almost the same structure as Thomson's opaque fused quartz and just as tough a resister of heat. The bricks were of rock, not clay, and absorbed no moisture. Neither did they break down under the onslaught of the glass and produce the troublesome gas. So when McCauley tried a few of them in a small experimental mold the hot glass filled it full and there was no difficulty about bubbles. Another advantage, he found, was the way the brick allowed the glass to "breathe." Whatever air or gas it brought with it from the furnace readily leaked out through the porous walls of the mold. But the glass itself could not follow for the holes were too small. This brick, then, was satisfactory. He ordered a carload at once.

McCauley next tackled the problem of how to get his "Pyrex" into the mold. Glassmakers for centuries had been tapping their melting furnaces and allowing the molten material to stream out along a trough into the molds they desired to fill. Large quantities of glass could be run in this way. But McCauley mistrusted it. Unmanageable enough at its hottest, this special glass was sure to chill and get so sluggish that it would never fill the mold. He decided to pour instead, by the equally ancient and honorable method of ladling by hand.

But who was to manage the ladle? The Corning glassworkers had little experience in pouring. They worked mostly by forming the glass with hand tools. The gatherers dipped small quantities of liquid glass out of the furnace on blow-irons and passed it over to the servers and gaffers, who twirled it by hand as they blew. Glass ladled out by the ton was a mystery to them. And mysteries were the very things McCauley was trying to avoid.

However, there was one glassblower in the plant named Wallace Woods, who was of an experimental turn of mind and who loved to work on something new. Ingenuity ran in the Woods family, and the rest of the workmen had a deep respect for them. There was a story in circulation in the plant that Woods's brother Will had actually blown the original bulb for Edison's incandescent lamp one day at lunch hour while the inventor was taking a nap. This was palpably a fiction because Will had been less than a year old at the time. Still, he had made important inventions in glassworking machinery and Wallace was known to be a chip from the same block. McCauley lost no time in sending for him now.

He took Woods out to the casting room and showed him the mold, the furnace of molten Pyrex glass and the ladle.

"Think you can do it?" he asked.

"I can try, chief," Woods smiled, and put on his gloves.

The 26-inch disk came out perfect.

McCauley wanted to feel jubilant, but he held himself down. It was much too soon to feel anything. He and Woods had merely graduated from kindergarten.

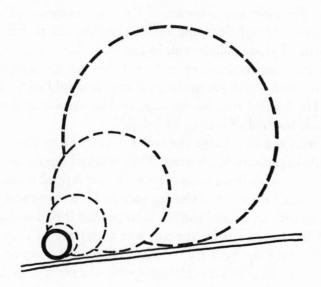

## CHAPTER XX

## GRIEF AND MORE GRIEF

THE 26-inch was only a practice job. Now it was up to Mc-Cauley to turn out the first mirror for the telescope—a mirror thirty inches in diameter, to be mounted halfway up the tube as a member of the coudé chain. It was not to be a flat pancake of glass, but a thin disk with its back cast in criss-crossed ribs to Pease's special design.

Here was the real demonstration which the Observatory Council awaited. If Corning could make a 30-inch ribbed disk, they could undoubtedly turn out the Two-Hundred.

Casting an intricate shape in glass is like casting it in metal: the mold, instead of being an empty circular basin, is studded with bumps or "cores," around which the molten material flows and hardens into a disk with hollows and ridges on the back. The spaces between the cores make channels and avenues which fill with glass and later become the ribs. The cores themselves leave pockets. If the glass is poured deep enough to cover all this, the final disk will be flat and smooth on top, with a lattice-work structure beneath. It is not very different from "casting" a bowl of jelly at home.

McCauley's 30-inch mold looked like the lower half of a waffle iron, made of gleaming white silica brick throughout. Nineteen cores were arranged around the bottom in a symmetrical figure like the petals of a flower. Some of these cores were round, others triangular, so that the spaces between them were all the same width. Each one was carefully fastened down with a standard furnace cement which McCauley judged sturdy enough to stand the heat.

The making of the cores gave him plenty of trouble. They were built up of pieces of brick cemented together, then cut down to exact size and shape with a carborundum saw and grinding wheel. Finally they were smoothed off so that no sharp corners were left, and then tapered a little toward the top to prevent the cold glass sticking when it was time to remove it. "It's an exercise in jig-saw puzzles in three dimensions," said McCauley, when the last one was safely cemented in place. "And we had to do it as if we'd known how all our lives."

Wallace Woods was waiting with his furnace of hot "Pyrex" when the mold was finally done, and the men in the shop gathered round with great curiosity and no little skepticism. The old Swedish gaffers and gatherers, whose fathers and grandfathers had twirled blow-irons before them, could not help regarding all this as an invasion of precious tradition. They would not be surprised if the whole thing failed.

But Woods was different. With the help of a couple of assistants McCauley had pressed into service, he began to draw the melt from the furnace in a big ladle and to pour it gingerly down between the cores in the mold. It gurgled and hissed as it went, but the bricks stood the strain and the glass flowed evenly through the narrow slots and slowly rose toward the top.

Suddenly, half way through, McCauley clutched his arm and shouted "Stop!"

"What's the matter?" Woods shouted back. "Don't you want to fill her up?"

"It's no use," McCauley returned. "It won't work."

Two or three of the cores had broken loose from the bottom and were bobbing merrily around on the heaving surface of the glass. The cement had given way and the cores, light as corks, had shot to the top. Woods put down the ladle and wiped the sweat from his eyes. The disk was ruined.

"Cement," said McCauley, quietly. "It can't stand the strain. We've got to begin again." He had known those cores were going to give trouble somehow, but he hadn't thought they would break loose. The only thing to do was to anchor them down better. How? The cement was the best he could get. . . .

Why not try dowels, and fasten them down as the cabinet-maker fastens the arms on a chair? Little pins sticking down from the cores to lock them to the bottom of the mold. Very well; but dowels of what? Of silica brick—of course—the only material that could possibly stand the heat. Here was a delicate operation indeed—to cut round pins out of porous stone and still keep them strong. But there were masons in the plant who managed it after some practice and in a few days a new mold was begun. This time McCauley was sure the cores would stay down.

Again Wallace Woods and his crew dipped the molten glass out of the melting tank, struggled across the concrete floor and carefully begun pouring. Again the blinding white liquid crawled into the valleys between the cores and rose inch by inch in the mold. But this time Woods kept stopping, following the boss's expression to be sure all was well.

"Keep on, keep on!" the physicist shouted, running around the mold from one side to the other. "Get the glass in as quick as you can!" The shop hands in the audience grinned at each other a little. Hot glass had Mac on the run!

There is always a faint little tinge of superiority among the men when a "white collar" invades the shop.

The cores were covered at last and Woods and his men threw the ladle down. McCauley was still walking around, scrutinizing the white pool. Would those cores stay on the bottom till the glass could set? That was a nervous half hour waiting for the disk to congeal. Then slowly it hardened and the danger was over. The first ribbed telescope disk in the world had been successfully made!

It was a short lived victory. A few days later, while the glass was cooling, it cracked.

Wearily McCauley began a third mold and when it was finished he wearily watched the men ladle the glass. What would happen now? More floating cores? More cracks? Or something entirely new?

Number Three slipped through the casting stage without fault; the cores all held their ground. And when, after long and careful cooling McCauley at last uncovered the disk, it was perfect. He examined the thing minutely, inch by inch, rather proud to be a pioneer. Then on the outer rim he came upon a flaw. His disk was not perfect at all. The glass had not quite filled the mold.

McCauley remembered ironically the confidence he and his colleagues had shown in the conferences in New York, and the promise they had given Hale to stick to standard methods. Here he was deep in experiment already—experiment that had so far failed. And there was more of it to come. Even if he had conquered the cores it was not much of a victory if the glass couldn't be counted upon to fill up the spaces between them. Besides, if things were as bad as this with a 30-inch disk, what chance had he of bringing off a great slab of glass seventeen feet in diameter?

McCauley sat down at his desk and looked out of the window across the yard at the ranks of gray buildings, where some of the finest glass work in the world was being done. The roar of a dozen distant furnaces came to his ears. For a moment he was very much alone.

Why had the "Pyrex" refused to fill the mold?

The answer was obvious. It had chilled and congealed before it could flow around the corners and fill in the pockets among the bricks. The mold had been too cold. There was only one thing to do; heat it. From now on the disks must be cast inside a furnace of their own. Work on the open floor was no longer possible.

It was a new experiment; considerable courage would be needed to keep it within bounds. But this was no time to lose one's nerve. McCauley made some drawings on his pad of a dome-shaped casting oven. It looked all right; he would try it. It would be a nuisance to make, of course, and would add to the expense and the complications of pouring successfully. It would have to be heated with special burners, and closely controlled as to temperature. It would have to be fitted with swinging doors to admit the ladles, and vents for the burned gases to escape. And it would have to be made of that same everlasting silica brick and cement. He smiled wistfully as he thought of the phrase he had used at the start: "It will be no different from making a beanpot, except in the methods employed." That little word "methods" was bulking large.

Back in the shop he gave orders to start the next size mold—the 60-inch to make the main Cassegrain mirror for the telescope. Fifty-five cores this time, every one fitted with its cemented dowel pin and fastened down in just the right place. Weeks of work went into the making of it, and a whole gang of men were needed for the job. Meanwhile McCauley superintended the work on the oven.

He designed and constructed a steel ring that fitted over the rim of the mold and was hung by a series of beams from overhead. Using this ring as a base, he reared a brickwork dome several feet high, closing in over the mold, dotted with holes for ventilation, and provided with a heavy brick-and-steel door in the side. The whole thing had the appearance of an Eskimo hut and within a day or two the shop was making affectionate fun of it and calling it the "igloo."

During all this preparation the glassblowers had been getting more and more interested and a little envious besides. This strange monster, suddenly springing to life in the midst of Factory A, had apparently come to stay. Evidently this man McCauley was headed for something big. Perhaps he would succeed after all. The shop foreman confided to him one day that he had overheard a couple of the workmen criticizing the way Wallace Woods handled glass. "They think he doesn't know how to manage a ladle," he said. "That's why you've been having so much trouble maybe."

It wasn't, of course. But McCauley understood the awakening spirit of co-operation that had prompted the remark.

"Do they think they can do any better?" he demanded.

"That's what they said. If you'd call for volunteers, Mr. Mc-Cauley, for instance—"

"All right, I will," McCauley told him.

It was at that point that the whole shop force of the Corning Glass Works began to get behind the 200-inch project. There was a rush of volunteers and McCauley had his hands full trying to pick the best of them without hurting anybody's feelings. It turned out there were two or three men who had had pouring experience, and to these he gave charge of the many important duties to come.

By and by all was ready for the 60-inch pouring. Mold and igloo, with its battery of gas burners thrusting long flames in through the walls of the dome; the annealing "can" with its system of electric heaters to keep the finished disk from cooling too fast; the pouring ladle with its long handle; the tank of melted Pyrex glass. McCauley was keeping his mouth tight shut. What new trick would the Coefficient of Difficulty spring on him now?

In went the hot glass through the doors of the igloo; up rose the level in the mold; back and forth went the crew, sweating, straining, grunting, pouring, going back for more; hardly stopping to breathe. And all the while McCauley stood silently as the hot disk grew. Could it all be as simple as this?

Then a shout rose among the spectators.

"There come those cores again!"

It wasn't so easy to see now, with the igloo in the way and the fiery blast inside. But there they were—bobbing to the top just as they had before. A long low groan ran through the crowd.

"Stop the ladling!" McCauley shouted. "Turn off the burners."

The room fell suddenly silent.

"I sat down and thought it all over," he said afterward. "Everything looked all right at the start, and we had been quite sure we had licked those cores. I decided to give it one more try."

So for the next weeks the whole thing was torn apart and begun again. McCauley spent every moment watching the mold as it grew under the hands of the most experienced masons he could find in the plant. Not a cemented joint anywhere but he personally inspected. Not a core but he set down himself and tested to be sure that it could not escape. When all was ready, he gathered the ladling crew around him and gave them special instructions for pouring the glass. Swiftly but gently it must be done; with an even flow, first into one part of the mold and then in another. The cores were the critical things; once submerged, they would steadily strain to set themselves loose; they must not be jarred till the glass had hardened.

"We'll do the best we can," the leading hand said. "And I bet we can pull it off!"

What happened next McCauley can best tell himself. "Again the ladles emptied their hot glass. In tense hope all eyes watched the liquid glass flow around and between the island cores and rise gradually over their tops as the fires in the igloo roared on. Success seemed near. Only a few ladles more were required. Then, as if to show the downright willfulness of inanimate objects, a single island rose to stick its head through that precious top layer of glass that was intended to form without blemish the convex Cassegrain mirror of the 200-inch telescope.

"I felt stunned. There was a hush in the shop and everyone quit and stood still. They were all looking at me to see what I would do next. Then a voice broke the silence. It was Dr. Littleton, the chief of our Physical Laboratory. 'Why don't you fish out that one floating core and finish the pouring? It will leave an extra lump of glass on the back of the disk, I know, but you could grind that off when the disk is cold.' "

" 'I guess I will,' I said."

The rest of the glass was put in, and the fires turned off while the casting set. Then, in more or less of a trance, McCauley superintended the removing of the igloo and the putting to bed of disk and mold in the annealer.

Sixty-nine days later the casting was cold and when the men broke the mold away and dug out the cores, there stood another Pyrex disk, complete in all but a single place where that one core had escaped. And as Dr. Littleton had predicted, this soon yielded to the grinding wheel and the disk for all practical purposes was perfect.

By the skin of his teeth McCauley was now two up on the job; the Thirty and Sixty were ready, neither one quite perfect but both in usable form. The igloo had been a success and the shop was behind him to a man.

But the cores were still untamed. One thing was certain: experiment or no experiment, he would have to find some other way to anchor them down. Cement and dowel pins were useless.

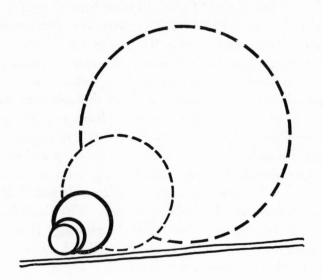

## CHAPTER XXI

## BIG GLASS

AGAIN he doubled his size, and prepared for a disk ten feet in diameter. Again he retired to his little office and pondered the problem that was still unsolved. And again the solution appeared on the little scratch pad as he glanced out of the window.

Metal rods to hold the cores down, that was it. If cement wouldn't stand the strain, then bolts of steel must. If little bolts weren't strong enough, then he would use big ones. "After all," he muttered, "I can't be stalled forever by a silly little mechanical problem like this."

The decision brought new complications. The bolts must be placed inside the cores and therefore the cores must be hollow. That meant they would be thinner than before, and not so easy to make. Much more care would be needed in building them up. And the bolt-heads must be firmly imbedded in the brick. Silica crumbled easily. It would be no good to fasten them down with iron and then have them crack and disintegrate like egg shells under foot. A special big-headed bolt would be needed; it must be hung in the core like a tongue in a bell, and the bricks built around it.

This much Mac settled in an afternoon; then went on to weightier problems. He was reasonably certain now that he could handle the glass for a 200-inch disk, even using the new "super-Pyrex" which the laboratory had worked out for him. It would therefore be the wisest course to build the casting and annealing machinery large enough to accommodate the 200-inch disk after it had finished the 120-inch. That would save much expense and also give the shop a chance to become thoroughly familiar with the apparatus before using it on the Big Glass.

Factory A was a little crowded for housing so large a

visitor, although it was the biggest building in the plant. Every sort of glassmaking was going on there: babies' bottles, laboratory glass and tableware, ovenware, dishes. Furnaces and melting tanks smoked and roared on every hand; a maze of machinery, overhead beams and girders and wires, wooden platforms at all sorts of different levels, obstructed the spaces; workmen were pushing wheelbarrows of sand and chemicals through to the furnace mouths; others were rolling flatcars loaded with hundreds of glass objects on their way to the finishing rooms, while great punch presses turned out thousands more; grinding wheels screeched, dousing tanks hissed and steamed, little knots of men shouted in each other's ears; gaffers and gatherers were plunging their blow-irons into the fiery melts, withdrawing them, twirling, shaping, cutting the limp glass with great pairs of shears before it could cool. Everywhere, a noisy, efficient jumble of men and machines and glass filled the murk and denied that depression had ever existed.

In the midst of this McCauley had to find room to bring forth a 20-ton slab of glass seventeen feet in diameter.

The making of the disk would be divided into three stages: the heating of the huge quantity of glass, the casting in the mold, and the long drawn out annealing. Fortunately there was a large melting tank in the shop which would comfortably hold the sixty-five tons of sand and chemicals needed. Ruthlessly taking precedence over everything, McCauley cleared the floor in the neighborhood of the tank and proceeded to lay out his machinery. He found that he had just room to squeeze in the casting oven and annealer and still leave space for the men to swing the great ladles of molten glass. His first job was to build a foundation for the whole affair.

Because the near-by Chemung River had a habit of flooding at frequent intervals, all the working equipment in the factory was on the second floor; underneath there was only a vast empty cellar of columns and beams on which the foundations of the furnaces rested. This would give McCauley a chance to move his newly made disk from the casting igloo to the annealer, merely by lowering it, moving it along on the ground below and hoisting it again into position. Down under the shop he installed a wide-gauge railroad capable of carrying fifty tons. On this he built a single heavy car fitted with small double-flanged wheels. A skeleton platform of girders rested on this car and could be raised and lowered by four powerful screw-jacks run by electric motors.

Next he constructed a heavy circular steel table to carry the mold for the disk. This he fitted with many rows of electric heating coils, so that the underside of the disk could be kept warm in the annealer. When the screw-jacks were raised to their top position the table came even with the upper floor of the shop and was ready to have the brick mold built upon it. McCauley turned now to the annealer itself.

This was an insulated steel tank just big enough to fit closely over the disk, and installed as near to the casting position as possible. Sides and roof were lined with electric heating elements and the wires from them led out to a special switchboard where a battery of thermostatic controls stood guard over the temperature day and night. Any degree of heat could be maintained in the annealer indefinitely, or the temperature could be lowered evenly by gradually reducing the current fed to the coils. A long row of electrically driven clocks and switches handled this operation automatically.

So far McCauley had been acting as an engineer, and in this he had had the able help of many other members of the staff and a large group of enthusiastic workmen besides. But the most important problem of all still remained to be solved. Just how long would it be necessary to anneal the big disks? For the moment he must become a physicist.

Annealing is the process of cooling an object so slowly that strains cannot build up in its interior. However slight they are, they make the texture of the glass uneven and, for telescopes, unusable. After a disk is cast the heat leaks away and the glass shrinks; the outer layers of the material, no longer big enough to contain what is inside, are forced to stretch; the inner layers, because of this stretching, are strongly compressed. If the cooling proceeds so fast that this condition cannot relieve itself, tremendous strains may be frozen permanently into the glass. If the cooling is exceedingly slow, even a very big disk can accommodate itself and come out free of any strains whatever. Even a little goblet weighing half a pound must be annealed for four hours to prevent it from breaking; a ten-ton disk 120 inches in diameter, McCauley was sure, would take months.

There was no precedent to follow, only a theory that had worked well enough with smaller disks at Corning and elsewhere. One of the strongest advantages claimed for disks of fused quartz had been that their annealing time was almost nil. In the early days at Lynn, A. L. Ellis had figured the comparative cooling periods for common glass and quartz. Using formulas and experience from the Bureau of Standards in Washington, he had computed that a 200-inch disk of plate glass could not be safely cooled in less than nine years!

McCauley took a less gloomy view. The special glass which had been developed for the job, he thought, should compare pretty favorably with quartz itself. But he did not dare to go ahead until he knew. So he detailed an assistant to study the annealing properties of the glass in the laboratory, and made doubly sure by asking a member of the Carnegie Institution staff to do the same. When their results were ready McCauley sat down and worked out an annealing theory of his own. He found that the cooling time for the 120-inch disk ought to be four months, for the 200-inch just under a year.

Once more the furnace was fired and glass was ready to pour. The new mold had been carefully built on the table of the jack hoist, its snow-white cores this time anchored down with solid steel. McCauley had installed a new system for handling the glass. Instead of expecting the men to lug the filled ladles from furnace to mold by main strength, he had built three overhead

monorail tracks for them, running from the mouth of the furnace to each of the three doors of the igloo. Three heavy ladles
were provided, each with a handle twenty feet long, and each
was suspended from one of the rails by a steel bar carried on
a free rolling trolley. The ladles could be kept in exact balance
whether filled or empty by adjusting the point of support while
in action. An entire pot of the molten liquid could be dipped
from the furnace, run across the floor and dumped in through
the igloo door with not a tenth the effort that had been needed
with the smaller ladles before.

The day for pouring the 120-inch disk came very quietly.
McCauley was hoping fervently that all this new apparatus
would work smoothly and in concert, but he was taking no
chances by crowing about it. As the crew assembled in front of
the furnace, the leading man armed with isin-glass helmet and
asbestos apron, McCauley stood quietly to one side, and when
no spectators were looking gave the order to pour.

Balancing the huge ladle with their own weight on the handle,
the men plunged it down into the sea of hot glass, righted it
quickly and drew it out, splashing and dripping with fiery "Pyrex." Then, with a jubilant shout they trolleyed it across the
floor, and rammed it home through the igloo door, dumping it
little by little, then swiftly removing it again and starting back
for more.

Ladle after ladle went in; and the mold filled up. McCauley,
hardly believing his eyes, watched silently. Finally he gave the
order to stop and closed the doors of the igloo himself. Not a core
had floated; not a hitch nor a pause in the proceedings had
marred the job from beginning to end. Long after the shop had
closed and the men had gone home, Mac was still there, opening the door for one more look, helping his official photographer
take pictures of the smooth broad surface that looked so much
like a neat bit of parquet floor.

"Well, Steve, I think we did it," he said.

When the 120-inch came out of the annealer in late October

it was perfect. Not a crack, not a missing rib, not a blemish. Mc-
Cauley tested it thoroughly, inch by inch, with a polariscope.
If there were the slightest strain anywhere in the glass, this instrument would show it up as a twisted band of light. There
were no strains. So far as he could see his pouring technique was
perfect and his home-made theory of cooling exact. It was the
evening of December 10, 1933. In just two years he had cast
three disks and all of them good. There was only one more to go.

Quietly the new disk, now the biggest in the world, was
packed in a wooden crate and loaded onto a flatcar; without
celebration it slipped out of Corning and traveled across the
country to Pasadena. Word soon came back to the Glass Works
that it had been received; the scientists were delighted. Their
fondest hopes had been exceeded.

McCauley may have smiled slightly as he sat at his desk making doodles on his scratch pad. But the smile was a fleeting one.
It was up to him now to make the 200-inch giant disk the world
had been waiting for.

First came the making of the new mold, with its nest of tall
cores—114 in all. The method of holding them had worked so
well with the 120-inch disk that McCauley ordered no change.
The brick masons cemented and shaped them up, ground them
smooth and fitted them onto the bottom of the mold, with bolts
which passed through holes drilled in the face of the table underneath and were held in place with springs.

When this was all done an igloo-shaped furnace was fitted in
place again—the same design as the 120-inch oven had been.
There were no changes here; nor was there any change needed
in the screw-hoist or annealer. Nothing except a series of exhaustive tests to be sure that every part of the intricate system
should come up to scratch. Things worked out so well that by
February of 1934 the whole outfit was ready and nothing remained but to melt the glass and produce the disk.

A month in advance of the pouring date the great melting
tank was cleaned out and put in order. Inside the oblong brick

furnace the nozzles of a dozen gas burners were arranged, the heat of their combined flames sufficient to melt sixty-five tons of glass. Ten days before charging, these furnaces were lighted to heat the walls and floor to the temperature of 2700 degrees Fahrenheit which the "super-Pyrex" required. Then three crews of men, working day and night around the clock, began ramming in the sand and chemicals through a door at one end. So slowly did the ingredients melt that only four tons a day could be added. Little by little the fiery pool spread over the bottom of the furnace and rose gradually to an incandescent lake fifty feet long and fifteen wide. When at last the whole charge was hot, six days more were needed for "fining" the glass, removing the bubbles and making sure that the whole mass was perfectly uniform in heat and texture. Then word was passed to McCauley that the melt was ready.

A trifling delay came in here, for one of the iron-bound doors at the delivery end of the tank could not stand the heat and the metal began to burn and chip and drop scales into the melt. McCauley ordered the temperature lowered a little and a new door installed with no iron exposed to the flames. A few metal scales would do no harm in the enormous lake of glass, but he had his pride. He wanted to have his disk that same beautiful opal-green color the others had been. The iron would tinge it slightly blue.

McCauley was sorry that this should have happened just now, for he fervently wished he could slip this disk into the annealer without fanfare, and let the praise and glory come later, when success was assured. But the rest of the world thought otherwise. Every man at Corning by now had joined in the great undertaking, either in fact or in spirit; word had long since spread abroad that the Glass Works was up to something big and newsmen and science editors all over the country were on the trail of the story.

President Amory Houghton of the Glass company would have preferred to have the big fellow cast quietly in the comfortable murk of Factory A, but his public relations man in New York persuaded him that this was impossible. So he finally decided to let the boys in on the show, together with such of the public as were sincere enough in their interest to request and obtain permits. In addition, he invited all the scientists and engineers who wished to come. After consultation with Mc-Cauley and his colleagues, he made an official announcement to the press late in February, and set March 25th as the day for the pouring. Before the month was up more than ten thousand people had written for permits.

A Saturday evening in March at last. Sixty-five tons of liquid glass lay ready in the furnace. Ladles were hanging in place, every foot of the monorail tracks to the igloo was working smooth and sure. The crew of five ladle men and twenty assistants were thoroughly rehearsed and ready to go. At noon a big area around the pouring space had been cleared of the usual factory clutter: machines moved out of the way, piles of cullet and sand, wheelbarrows, lines of water hose, tanks and platforms pushed aside. Sunday was to be the great day, because it would interfere less with the regular routine of the plant.

The town of Corning was already bulging with strangers—thousands of them—coming in by train and car from every corner of the country and from Europe and the Orient as well. High up on a wall inside the factory, carpenters were knocking together a narrow wooden "catwalk," from which the ticket-holding spectators, in a steadily moving stream, could catch a fleeting glimpse of the pouring as they were herded through by company guides. Down on the floor next the working space, more carpenters were fencing off a special enclosure for newsmen and photographers, and in front of that a sort of grandstand section for the scientists and other celebrities who had promised to attend.

They, too, were pouring into town in large numbers, many a world-renowned name among them. Headed by Dr. Adams and

Dr. Pease from California, the group included such notables as Sir William Bragg from England, Dr. Mees of the Kodak Company, Dr. Jewett of the Telephone Laboratories, Director Briggs of the Bureau of Standards, Dr. Mason of the Rockefeller Foundation, Dr. Day of the Carnegie Institution, and the directors of a score of important observatories throughout the country, as well as many a famous amateur astronomer besides.

Dr. Hale alone was absent. His tragic illness had kept him at home in California.

At ten o'clock the Floor Superintendent turned the gas into the torches of the igloo; the flames roared, and the temperature of the mold began its slow rise to 1200 degrees, to be ready for morning. One enthralled reporter, gazing at the great nest of cores in the flamelight, saw in them the towers and minarets of a miniature Moslem city. But not McCauley.

"Anything may happen tomorrow," was all he would say.

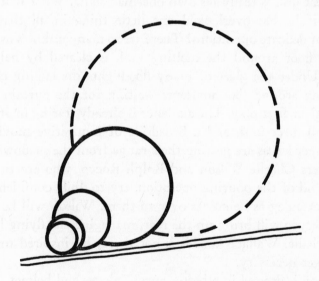

# CHAPTER XXII

## "ANYTHING MAY HAPPEN"

SUNDAY, March 25th, 1934. A preacher in Wellsboro, Pennsylvania, has angrily predicted that the casting will fail. God will not approve such a use of the Sabbath. McCauley is undismayed, but takes his own precautions and goes to a special Episcopal service his minister has arranged for him at seven in the morning. The six others in the church stare at him admiringly. How easily this mild little engineer seems to be taking his great responsibility!

Promptly at 8 A. M., the pouring is to begin. McCauley would like not to feel nervous, as the last minute approaches, but he does. Even though the whole plant is behind him the making of the great disk is really his own one-man show. What if it fails? What if he has overlooked one little thing in all that long chain of delicate operations? There are so many unknowns. . . .

The floor around the melting tank is cleared by half-past seven. Under the glare of many floodlights the ladling crew is fidgeting around like amateurs waiting for the curtain to go up on their first play. The audience is already staring in at them from all directions, and a broadside of inquisitive movie and newspaper lenses are getting their range from the shadows.

Gaffers Charlie Wilson and Ralph Rocco, who are to be in command of the pouring operation, try to smile confidently at Dr. McCauley as he comes over to them. Wilson will be front man; Rocco will bring up the rear, managing the flying handle of the ladle. Wallace Woods is not there; his inspired touch is no longer necessary.

Wilson is dressed in asbestos apron, gloves and helmet. There is a story about that helmet. Immemorial custom required him to hold it in his teeth. But recently he was seriously ill with an infection and the doctors insisted on taking his teeth all out. Charlie was determined to wait till the 200-inch was poured. They said he wouldn't live to pour it. So his colleagues got together and invented a face shield held on with a baseball mask, and Charlie agreed to part with his teeth.

At the doors of the igloo other members of the cast are stationed, ready to open and close, open and close as the pots of glass arrive. McCauley is silently checking everything, the pockets of his slightly rumpled brown suit stuffed with yellow pencils and a scratch pad or two. The furnace doors are all right; the one that failed last week has been replaced and works smoothly and fast. The overhead trolley system is clear and the switches operate every time. The temperature indicators on the igloo show exactly the right conditions inside.

McCauley takes his watch out of his pocket and looks at it a moment, puts it back, then nods silently to Wilson. There is nothing to do now except keep his fingers crossed. The only excited people are the newsreel men, jockeying one another for position.

With a little cry of relief at the ending of the suspense the five men leap to the haft of the great ladle; slowly the furnace door swings open. With a shout of "Over she goes now, boys!" the five strain on the handle and the ladle goes bottom up. Then they ram it forward into the bright inferno and with a deft concerted motion plunge it down into the molten glass. There is a moment of struggle; then the ladle is drawn out, filled to the brim with 750 pounds of "melt." For a brief second the men are silhouetted against the blue-white rim of molten glass that slops over the edge and tumbles to the floor; then a workman with a long bar runs up and slashes the excess away. Then with a shout the crew starts the heavy burden across the floor to the mold, another workman running alongside with a tank of water on his back and a spray nozzle to douse the outside of the ladle and keep it from melting.

The door of the igloo has swung aside; in goes the ladle neatly through the opening; again Wilson barks a quick order and the others twist with all their might on the handle. Over she goes and out flows the first 400-pound charge of "Pyrex" into the mold. The Glass Giant of Palomar is being born at last.

McCauley is staring through a peep hole anxiously. There is a slight hissing as liquid glass strikes brick, and through the audience goes a murmur of admiration at this handful of men who can so confidently enter upon so vast a project. Then out comes the ladle, empty.

Not quite empty, though, for more than three hundred pounds of the original dipping has frozen to its sides. Men run in now with bars and the ladle is bottomed up while they knock the hardened "ladle skin" into a metal wheelbarrow for return to the furnace. Little flames dart up here and there as bits of red hot glass scatter brightly and land on wooden platform boards; but the crew pays them no attention. Ladle No. 1 has finished its turn of duty and they have dumped it bodily into a big round tank at one side, where it sizzles and cools in a great cloud of steam.

Instantly Wilson and his men seize the handle of No. 2 ladle, which is sitting waiting in another tank of water, and thrust it in through a second door of the furnace, dip out more glass and trolley it across the room on another overhead monorail line to another door in the igloo. Again the glass flows evenly down over the white cores and McCauley watches it closely through his peep hole. Again the ladle is withdrawn, knocked clear of its frozen skin of "Pyrex" and set aside to chill. Then ladle No. 3 is hustled into service and the cycle of dipping and pouring, now well established, begins to repeat itself smoothly. Wilson and his men can scoop seven hundred pounds of glass from the tank, transfer it, discharge 400 of it into the mold, put aside the ladle and be ready to repeat the operation in just six minutes' time.

The crew falls into a rhythm, there under the floodlights, their sweaty faces lit alternately by the orange glare from the furnaces and by an occasional pipsqueak flash of a photographer's photo lamp. The scientists stand fascinated, humbled. In the dim loft of the place the guides lead in group after group of the ten thousand ticket holders. McCauley takes a long breath, relaxes a little, and steps back to watch.

Hour after hour the pouring goes on. Every six minutes by the clock a ladleful is dumped into the mold. The cores are beginning to submerge now; not a hitch so far anywhere. The scientists have begun to chat among themselves, joking learnedly, relieved of the first painful tension. McCauley and Hostetter are off somewhere, checking over the annealer. There is a bit of a flurry in the grandstand; one of the spectators has tripped and fallen and has broken a rib. His colleagues push a path through the crowd and carry him out. But the pouring goes steadily on.

A little later one of the ladlemen stumbles in the brilliant heat and falls against the plunging handle of the ladle, drops unconscious. A relief swiftly takes his place and he is removed. But the pouring goes on.

At noon the men knock off for an hour and the roaring burners in the igloo keep the disk hot. Then work is resumed and routine settles down once more. McCauley has gone to his office to answer some trivial question a London newspaper is asking over the transatlantic telephone. No, it is not a lens they are making, but a mirror. Please get that straight! . . . As he hangs up, Dr. Littleton is at his elbow, seizes his arm.

"Mac—!"

"What is it?"

"One of those cores has broken loose!"

McCauley stares at him incredulously, then leaps up and starts for the door, Littleton after him.

"But it's only one, old man," he cries, trying to reassure him.

"They're all stuck down the same way," Mac mutters. "If one has gone more will follow."

He runs across the great factory, leaping over the protruding ends of machines in his path, then takes the steps up the platform to the igloo in a single jump.

"Stop those ladles, Charlie!" he yells and jams his face against the black glass of the peep hole. Yes, there it is—a dark chunk floating high on the smooth surface of the disk, drifting about in the fiery blast from the burners. The open end of the core seems to leer at him, but he hasn't time to curse it, for as he stares in there is a boiling in the glass and another core bobs up and then another. He was right. They are all alike. Heaven knows how many more may fail. Instantly he makes his decision, leaps down from the platform and gives short, sharp orders to the shop men who cluster around.

A hush falls over the great space, and through it runs the one word, "Cores!" whispered from mouth to mouth. Scientists and spectators strain forward. The guards forget to move them on.

Three or four men with long slice-bars run up; the igloo doors are swung open. Braving the blinding glare inside, they shove in their bars and try desperately to fish the derelicts out. It is no use. The heat is so intense they cannot see what they are doing; in a few seconds they are driven back gasping.

"Never mind getting them out," shouts McCauley at their elbow. "See if you can break them up. Smash them into small pieces."

The men dash forward again—poke and slash madly at the cores.

"Watch out!" McCauley yells again. "Don't get those bars too hot. They'll melt off."

One by one the men withdraw, their faces tense and livid with the exertion. Perhaps they have helped, perhaps not. If the runaway cores are in little pieces they won't float so deep on the precious surface of the disk. Once before Mac saved a disk when the cores broke away. . . .

But McCauley's mind is leaping ahead. Same old trouble back again, is it? Well, there's only one thing to do. "I'll make another 200-inch disk," he says to himself grimly.

But he doesn't say that out loud. Quietly he gives the order to continue the pouring. Wilson stares at him momentarily, then gives him an approving cuff on the shoulder with his gloved hand, turns, and marshals his men around the ladle. The watchers nod among themselves. Good man, Mac! The gallery of newsmen chatters excitedly. What happened? What has McCauley done? "Nothing, nothing," says Adams briefly. His reassurance is effective, for the papers next day refer to the incident as "a trifling accident which temporarily suspended the work."

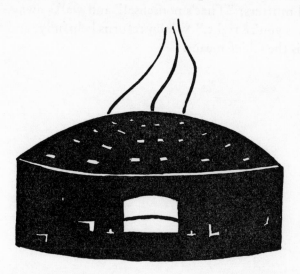

Time goes on; at six o'clock, exactly ten hours after the start, one hundred and five ladles full of glass have been dumped in —42,000 pounds. The mold is full and the disk is finished. No more cores have broken loose. Dr. Adams is smiling but silent. Quietly he slips away and takes a train for the West. He would rather not complicate matters with advice at this critical time. For once he is thankful that Hale is too ill to be on hand.

The rest of the crowd has thinned away and gone. Among the Corning men little is said. Undoubtedly, the disk can be cleared of the core pieces and saved. But no one knows whether it will be or not. Mac is left alone in the great space. It is hard to know what is in his mind as he stands there gazing in through the igloo door at his beloved disk. Charlie Wilson comes softly up behind him.

"Chief, it was a swell try, anyway," he falters. He doesn't quite know what a chap ought to say to a white collar man in trouble. "Anyway, better luck next time."

"Thanks, Charlie," Mac says, a trifle absently. "Thanks."

Maybe he is thinking of that Pennsylvania preacher and his prediction. If he is, it is only for a second. He squares his shoulders and mutters: "That's nonsense!" and walks away.

"I guess you're right," Wilson returns helpfully, and wonders what it is the Chief means.

# CHAPTER XXIII

## PYREX BEHAVES

AT midnight the disk was moved to the annealer and hoisted in. Some kind of a jam developed in one of the screw-jack controls and the disk could not be sealed tight in its oven for three days. But there was no feverish attempt to overcome this new trouble. Tacitly Hostetter and McCauley had agreed that there must be another 200-inch casting.

In the meanwhile, there were some interesting possibilities to be explored with this glass. For instance, how nearly correct was McCauley's home-made annealing theory? It would be easy to find out. Simply by setting the thermostatic controls on the switchboard he could cool the disk at any speed he wished. He would set it for ten times the safe rate and find out if the theory still held, by measuring the strains in the cold glass.

So for the next thirty days the great disk was subjected to a "breakneck" test, being allowed to cool at the rate of ten degrees a day instead of one, which was the proper figure. At the end of the month everyone gathered round eagerly. The disk was lowered out of the annealer and rolled on its car to an outer room in the factory. There before them was the whole story told in solid glass—the beautiful regular patternwork of all but a few of the cores showing through from the back.

McCauley ran his hand over the vast surface. If only—

Then resolutely he turned his back on regret.

Workmen with chisels and crowbars quickly pried the edge of the brick mold away from the glass and wiped it clean, and McCauley was soon on his knees beside it, testing the strains with his polariscope. This was a simple little device that could be held in one hand. A small electric bulb, a lens and a polarizing prism were mounted at one end of its frame; another prism and an eyepiece at the other. The instrument fitted down snugly over a rib so that the glass came between the two prisms. Light polarized into one plane of vibration by the first prism passed through the "Pyrex" and into the second prism, then on to the eyepiece.

If the glass were strained, the polarized light passing through it would be twisted a little and the second prism would have to be rotated by just that same angle to let the light through to the eye. The amount of this rotation gave a direct measure of the intensity of strain in the glass.

McCauley repeated the test over and over again, always finding the same condition: strains of exactly ten times the amount desired for a perfect disk. He was delighted, for it proved that his annealing theory had been correct. When the tests were finished he had the derelict core material drilled out of the front surface and the disk reheated till the surface was melted smooth. Then he gave it a second quick annealing run and tested it again. The glass, except for the damaged rib structure at the back, was perfect. Even with the ten-times normal strains it could easily be used for the telescope if the astronomers so desired.

But during the summer the Observatory Council made its decision: Corning was invited to cast another disk. The astronomers were quite satisfied with everything that had happened so far. The 120-inch disk was fully up to specifications; already it was being ground to an accurate flat surface to be used in testing the big mirror later on. The failure of the cores was only a detail. Disk No. 1 should be a spare. They were entirely confident that next time the casting would not fail.

McCauley went to work at once to improve the methods of anchoring his cores. The reason for their failure had been obvious: the steel bars that held them down had burned off under the prolonged high temperature. A new kind of bolt must be found. He devoted several weeks to a search for a metal that would neither burn nor "creep" (or stretch); after several tries he adopted a bolt made of chrome nickel steel two inches wide and half an inch thick. These he tested continuously for two weeks in a laboratory furnace at a temperature as high as any they would be required to stand.

Then, to make extra certain, he designed a special cooling system so that the interior of every core could be kept below the dangerous temperature. To do this he installed an air suction fan beneath the new mold and connected it by a series of tubes to each of the hollows in the cores above. A second set of tubes

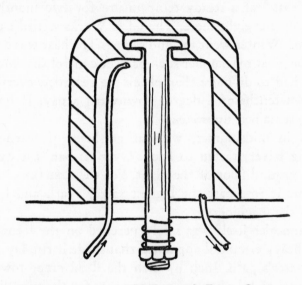

CROSS-SECTION OF McCAULEY'S FINAL CORE

led cool air in from outside so that when the system was running during the pouring operation, complete ventilation could be maintained.

Satisfied at last, McCauley prepared to pour again.

On December 2nd, 1934, Disk Number 2 was cast. There were few visitors this time; most of them were scientists. There were no warnings from irate preachers; no early morning devotions in church. McCauley held up the pouring till he had attended the regular service.

From the splendid experience on the first disk he had learned a great deal. Two crews of ladlers were on the job now, the second imported from another plant. The hot glass flowed almost twice as fast as it had before and in just six hours was complete in the mold. Not a core appeared to mar the surface, not a wheel of all the machinery jammed, not a person was hurt. For the first time since the beginning three years before McCauley felt that he could relax. He even began planning a trip to California.

The new giant slipped smoothly into the annealer, where it was to "soak" at a steady temperature for two months, then cool evenly for eight more. The Glass Works settled back into its routine. Winter went by, and spring. The heat was dribbling out of the great mass under such perfect control that McCauley scarcely had to do more than check the recorders every morning. Seven-tenths of a degree downward a day. If only that schedule remained unbroken!

Then, in midsummer, without an hour of warning, the Chemung River started to flood. Over its banks it came and into the ground floor of the plant. For the first time in seventeen years it rose past the highest safety mark and began to threaten the machinery.

The annealer itself was safely perched on the second floor, but the heavy electrical apparatus that made it run lay directly in the water's path. Inch by inch the flood crept toward the transformer and the bank of reactors that fed the annealing unit above. If the current failed, even for an hour, the whole cooling schedule might be ruined. Hostetter and McCauley dashed through the plant, gathering every available man, throwing them into the work of building a sandbag barrier around the pit where the apparatus hummed away unprotected. Sand, sod, dirt —everything that could be shoveled was used to fill the bags. Carpenters were pulled off their jobs and hustled in to build forms for a concrete dyke. Masons were pressed into service laying a brick wall. Gaffers, gatherers, helpers, even men from the office were drafted to stave off the flood. For a day and a night all hands worked desperately, up to their waists in the muddy slime under the disk. But the water kept on gaining.

It was up to the level of the main electric conductors now. In a few hours more deadly sparks would flash, short-circuiting the lines, and charging the flood. Dams and sandbags were abandoned, thrown out of the way; the apparatus itself must be lifted out. Wading back and forth up to their armpits now, the men worked bravely to get block and tackle around the big transformer that was the heart of the equipment.

"We've got to shut off that current," Hostetter decided grimly.

"You'll ruin the disk," shouted McCauley. "You can't shut it off."

"Can't help that. We're not going to kill our men even for the world's greatest telescope!"

The current went off. For seventy-two hours the annealer was out and the disk lay there, bleeding its heat away unhindered. For seventy-two hours McCauley floundered in the mud with his men, rescuing the equipment and getting it back into service on higher ground. And all the time he struggled he was figuring what to do with his wrecked annealer schedule—wondering if it were any use to do anything. Then at last the transformer and wiring were hauled high above the water and the life-sustaining current could go on.

Three months remained to the end of the cooling run. It was a hard three months for Mac—a long dismal wait with nothing to do but hope. The only break in the monotony was an earthquake which visited Corning on Hallowe'en night. It shook a few people out of bed but left the twenty tons of hot "Pyrex" untouched. McCauley said nothing. He was beginning to believe in fate.

Then at last the disk was brought out, cool and apparently sound. With his own hands McCauley knocked the core material out of the ribbing at the back, too intent to notice the blisters it cost him. Finally the beautiful yellow-green glass was clear. Methodically he began going over every inch of the vast surface with his testing set. If there were a strained place anywhere he would find it. If the whole job had to be done again, he would do it.

Eventually Mac turned to Hostetter and sighed.

"I can't find a thing," he said. "I guess you can telegraph the Coast. Dr. Hale can have his mirror now."

# PART III

# THE GIANT IS REARED

## CHAPTER XXIV

## PAPER TELESCOPES

FOR six years now the 200-inch telescope project had gradually been gathering momentum. An organization had been created, buildings had gone up and a successful Pyrex disk was at last under way. But the telescope itself was on paper only. Hale was becoming impatient to see his dream expressed in steel.

Those six years were fortunate ones for the project, for in that time no avenue or alley of possible design had been left unexplored. It is even likely that the expensive digression at Lynn had its value, for it gave more time for discussion and debate on the mechanical problems. This was to be no conventional instrument; every feature of its design was a pioneering job.

While all sorts of outside advice was solicited and considered, the main attack upon the problem of the telescope mounting was launched by the Cal Tech men themselves. Under Hale's personal guidance an informal but efficient engineering organization was slowly knitting itself together from the membership of the Institute faculty. Besides Anderson, Millikan and Adams there were, among others, Ira Bowen of the Physics Department, R. R. Martel of Civil Engineering, Theodore von Karman from Aviation, W. H. Clapp of Mechanical Engineering, Paul Epstein from Mathematics, R. C. Tolman of Chemistry and J. P. Buwalda from Geology. Wherever these men met—at lunch, on the golf course, in the laboratory—they would fall to discussing the new telescope and the air would soon be thick with proposals and counter proposals, sketches, arguments, even wrangles over the Giant's design. Six years of this had not brought a final decision, but it had unearthed innumerable brilliant ideas and dragged the problem out into the open where no contribution could be missed.

Hale had a deep faith in young men. He felt that many of the youngsters in the sciences had great talent and that their ideas were often of great value. And so, as he built up the ground-work of his organization, he included in it as many fledglings as he could find. The sagacity of this view was demonstrated from the start; today the Giant of Palomar stands as a monument to youth's potentialities. With the wisdom and experience of the older men behind them the young technicians have done much to establish a new record for science and engineering.

The Council unanimously supported Hale's desire that whenever possible graduates of Cal Tech should be used. They decided to pick these men from a group that had been out in the world a few years and so had had a chance to try their wings. Notable already among these were Dr. Sinclair Smith, who had been working in the Cavendish Laboratory in England and more recently at Mount Wilson; Mark Serrurier, a young civil engineer returning to his alma mater from work on the San Francisco Bay Bridge; Michael Karelitz, who had been with the Westinghouse company for several years; and Byron Hill, who came straight from graduation to a good berth on the project. Another outstanding youngster was John Strong, not a Cal Tech graduate but a scholarship student from Michigan, who had an idea he could improve the reflecting surfaces of mirrors by substituting aluminum for silver.

For the manual departments older and more experienced hands were needed. The big job of running the Instrument Shop went to Gardiner Sherburne, who had long since left Mount Wilson to establish a machine shop of his own. He had kept up a close contact with Hale however, and when the astronomer had invented the spectrohelioscope and had wanted it distributed by the score around the world for continuous solar study, Sherburne had been the man to build it. So now, he was the logical man to take charge at the Shop, for he knew telescopes from the ground up and understood the high precision of their workmanship.

Sherburne and Porter, the "idea man," made a number of trips into Los Angeles to pick out machinery for the shop and if they had been given free rein would have made it a pretty grand affair. Porter had in mind a remark Hale had once made to him: "You have no idea what a horse-laugh went up from the other observatories when I insisted on building a machine shop for Mount Wilson. But I think we have pretty well proved its value. Every observatory has one now."

But Hale was getting older and more cautious; moreover, he was deeply concerned over the heavy financial drain at Lynn.

"Whatever plan Sherburne and I brought him," said the Yankee architect, "he kept saying, 'Cut it down! Cut it down!' Well, we did the best we could, and bought only the bare necessities. We finally cut the bill down to a hundred thousand dollars."

A hundred thousand dollars would have bought five whole telescopes of the kind that Harlow Shapley was still finding most useful at Harvard.

Jerry Dowd also came upon the scene again as head electrician. Jerry had put in twenty good years of his life on Mount Wilson, building every switch and contact and cable of the control equipment for the big telescopes up there and keeping them all running day and night. Most of the time he and his wife had lived on the summit, but the lonely life had finally "got" Mrs. Dowd and Jerry had come down and gone to grape-fruit farming. Then the Depression had got him, and here he was, back in the shop, ready to tackle such a job of control wiring as fairly made him dizzy.

"If ever this stuff gets out of whack," he said, looking at the maze of lines on Sinclair Smith's early drawings, "it'll take a better man than me to get it going again." But he was game to try, anyway.

As for the Optical Shop, this was the most remarkable department of the lot. It was presided over by a young man of thirty-five named Brown, hand picked and trained for the job, with some twenty workers under him whom he in turn had trained himself. Not one of them was more than thirty-five years old. But it is necessary to withhold that story till its proper time.

From the first the question of the telescope mounting absorbed them all: How shall we support the tremendous weight of the mirror and its auxiliaries and still be sure that we can hold them steadily upon any star we wish? The crux of the problem lay in the choice between the fork- and the yoke-type mounting.

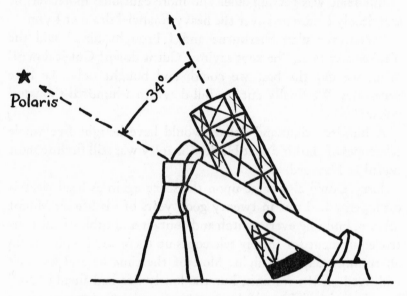

WHY THE 100-INCH CAN'T REACH THE POLE

Two somewhat unreconcilable requirements were involved. Good engineering demanded a design that could be made structurally rigid; good astronomy required a telescope that would reach all parts of the heavens.

On this latter point the 100-inch at Mount Wilson was an annoying offender. Its yoke-type mounting would not allow it to come within 34 degrees of the Pole Star. Hale did not want the new telescope to have any such limitation as this, even though it was not a paramount issue. He wanted it to do everything that any telescope could do.

It was true that many of the astronomers would not be hampered if the 200-inch failed to reach Polaris. The nebula men were concerned with other parts of the sky. So were the spectroscopists and the direct photographers. Nevertheless the region around the pole was important to some and Hale was determined not to rob anybody of the full advantages of the new instrument. Thus the earliest plan was for a fork type of mounting, since this alone would make the telescope universal.

But the great mass of machinery overhanging its bearings in the grip of a steel fork was structurally a poor arrangement. The tube of the telescope was to be nearly 60 feet long and must be swung near its middle to give the best balance. This meant that the prongs of the fork would have to be very long so that the tube could fold down to the polar axis without striking in the crotch. Several hundred tons of glass and steel held so far out in space without bending meant a gigantic structure with enormous bearings to support it.

Pease advocated the fork type from the start. He had been turning out 200-inch telescope designs for fifteen years and nothing would budge him from the belief that a fork could be made rigid enough for the job. No one else was as sanguine. Burrell from Warner & Swasey was very gloomy about it. So were Martel and von Karman. Hale and the others were on the fence. A tentative contract which gave the building of the whole instrument to Burrell's firm was broken after a few months because he would not guarantee the rigidity of any fork that could be built.

Meanwhile, like an impudent gargoyle, the yoke design sat comfortably leering at them, offering perfect rigidity at the price of that annoying blind spot. The dilemma seemed insoluble.

But it did not remain so for long. Argument soon pointed the way to a compromise. If one picked up a pencil and sketched his way through successive stages from the extreme fork toward

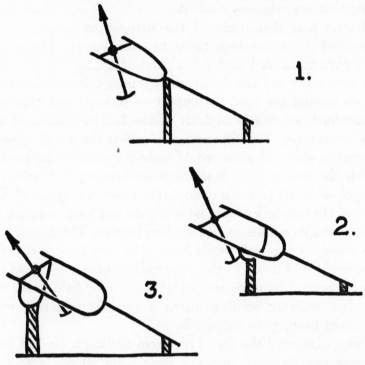

EVOLUTION OF

the extreme yoke, he passed through a neutral point where the shank of the fork became an upstanding U-shaped affair with the telescope tube nestling inside it. If he then moved the tube on down into the arms of the yoke but kept the U-shaped piece in the picture, the result would be a telescope which could fold down neatly onto its polar axis and look straight at the North Star. The drawings above will help to trace the course of this evolutionary process. Hundreds of sketches were made and Porter busied himself constructing model after model of wood or metal to demonstrate just how the machine could be built.

The U-idea appeared, as most good ideas do, from several sources at once. Pease thought of it and so did Porter; Martel discussed it and it had been vaguely in the minds of the others from the first. It was not news anyway, for the very same

the horns of this ring and reach the whole northern heavens."

He was so very eager and so sure that he had hit on something of value that Anderson talked it over with him for a long time.

Edgar went off a happy old man. From that day on he was timid no longer; time and again he came back with suggestions, many of them ingenious. Soon he was a familiar figure in the Laboratory; the freshness of his ideas delighted everyone, though his lack of scientific knowledge prevented him from actually joining the project. He is still an occasional visitor; at last accounts he was happily designing an 800-inch telescope which he hoped the astronomers would take up when they had "got tired of their 200-inch."

A short time later a dentist named Page Bailey burst into Anderson's office with a brand new idea for a horseshoe-type telescope.

"What, again?" Anderson laughed.

"I've actually built one in my back yard," said Bailey, "and I'd like to show it to you if you'd care to come over. I have a 15-inch mirror and it works swell!" Anderson thanked him gently and pointed out that the scheme was no longer new. It was already on the designing board.

Subsequently it turned out that Governor Hartness had obtained a patent in Russell Porter's name for a "ring type" of telescope mounting in 1922. It came to the same thing as the horseshoe reinvented by Messrs. Pease, Edgar and Bailey, and joined them in innocent plagiarism of Repsold's scheme of fifty years before. When the difficulties of designing the huge U-shape bearing were finally overcome and it was adopted for the Giant of Palomar, Hale in his usual kindly fashion gave published credit to everyone concerned.

# CHAPTER XXV

## CAPTAIN "SANDY"

"WE must begin to build our telescope!"

After six years of paper work and innumerable models by Porter, this was the cry in everyone's mind. Some of the theorists, perhaps, would have liked the discussion to go on still further, but the consensus was for action.

From paper telescopes to steel—it was a big jump. The Cal Tech men were scientists and engineers of the best, but largely theoretical. What they needed now was an actual construction executive—somebody who knew how to turn paper into steel.

In the days of the short-lived Warner & Swasey contract that firm had admitted that the telescope was too big for them to build in their own shops; they would have to farm out the large structural pieces to firms that were used to handling giants. Max Mason, who had been taking an increasing interest in the proceedings from the New York end, pointed out to Hale that there was no advantage in introducing a "middle man" in an undertaking of this magnitude. There would be two profits instead of one and it would be difficult to get important engineering advice from rival firms. Better, said Mason, for the Council to administer the construction work itself and thus maintain a free hand.

"Very well," said Hale. "Where can we find the man to superintend the job? None of us can do it."

It was a fall day in 1934. Hale was with Mason in his office at the top of Radio City. Mason reached for the telephone. "I think I know the man we want," he said.

Half an hour before that Captain Clyde S. McDowell of the United States Navy had locked up his office in the New York Shipbuilding Company's plant in Camden, N.J., and started for home in the suburbs. For the past thirty years he had been in every part of the world on important seafaring and engineering assignments and was just now engaged in the inspection of warships building for the government. When he reached home the telephone was ringing. It was his old friend and colleague of war days, Max Mason.

"Sandy," came Mason's voice, "we've got a problem over here that's right up your alley. We're going to build a 200-inch telescope and we need somebody to take charge of construction. We think maybe you're the man."

McDowell stammered over it a minute and then answered: "I've done about everything there is in the engineering field but build a telescope, but I suppose I could do that too, in a pinch—"

"Fine! Come over to my office in the morning," Mason told him.

McDowell went. The three men spent the entire day together. They went over the problem of the telescope from beginning to end. The Captain listened to the story eagerly, interrupting them constantly in a nervous little way he had, getting himself familiar with every detail. By noon his eyes were gleaming; by midafternoon he was walking excitedly up and down the office; by evening he was sitting down again, and with a pad and pencil was showing them exactly how they could organize their undertaking and make it a success. Hale's decision, as usual, was immediate.

"Will you come to California and co-ordinate the job?" he demanded.

McDowell hesitated.

"I shall have to get a leave of absence," he said.

"We'll arrange that," said Hale. "We need you more than the Navy does right now."

McDowell thought it over. He was soon to be in line for promotion to an admiral. No Navy man wants to miss that, with its high retirement pay and its honor. He couldn't be promoted on leave. Other officers would supersede him. But this was the

200-inch telescope. His experience in mounting big guns for the Navy would be ideal. His acquaintance with every large manufacturing firm in the country would certainly be invaluable.

"I'll come," he decided. "But I'll have to get hold of the Chief of Naval Operations first and arrange it. Admiral Standley. He's in London."

That night Hale cabled to Millikan, who was in London, too, and asked him to see Standley and settle the matter. Millikan did so at once, and the Admiral said he would be glad to let the Captain go. But there were complications. McDowell would have to get direct permission from the Secretary of the Navy and a release from the President himself. That might take time.

Ten days later Millikan returned and went to Washington, assuring McDowell that everything could be arranged. But by this time Sandy was so anxious for the job that he was afraid something would prevent his taking it. The Secretary was an ill man and might well frown upon so unprecedented a matter as loaning a high-ranking officer to a private group for several years. So he hurried to Washington himself and called at the Secretary's office. He was informed that Mr. Swanson had gone home and that he would have to see the Acting Secretary instead. McDowell turned on his courage and went in. Hardly inside the door he opened fire with his best arguments. He would clinch the matter at once.

"Sir," he began, "can you think of anything that would bring more credit to the Navy than to make possible a voyage of a billion light years into space?"

The Acting Secretary looked up. It was Admiral Standley himself.

"What's that? A *billion* light years, you say? Er—how long will you be gone?"

"Oh, it's you, Admiral!"

"Yes, it is," said the Admiral with a twinkle in his eye. "How long—?"

"Three or four years, probably. But—"

"I should think so," said the Admiral. "That's a very long leave."

McDowell moved up close to the desk and his voice was tight with emotion. "It's the biggest thing engineering has ever attempted," he hurried on. "For one-third of the price of a battleship we'll find out whether Einstein is right or wrong. We'll discover five billion new stars. Hang it, Admiral, we'll take the Universe apart!" He walked up and down rapidly. "Besides, all you fellows are going to be doing is take guns *out* of battleships!"

Standley grinned at him—this short, gray-haired man who never stood still a minute.

"Darn it, McDowell," he said. "You don't have to persuade *me*. Millikan's done that already. We want you to go. The President's delighted!"

McDowell gulped. "Well—but—but—. He *is?*"

"Of course he is! It's the best thing the Navy could ask— having a hand in that telescope." Standley got up and shook Sandy's hand. "Go to it," he smiled. "Let's see what you can do."

McDowell paused a minute, then rushed out. The Admiral looked after him with a grin, then sat down at his desk and whistled.

"A billion light years! That's as big as the budget!"


At Thanksgiving Sandy arrived in California and with his customary energy went about mastering the condition of the telescope project. It was an entirely new field for a naval officer and things seemed to him to be in rather a muddle. Several young engineering graduates were at work on detail designs for the telescope but no final plans were ready. Russell Porter was running up and down from office to carpenter shop making models of all the ideas that were being produced and alternating that with skillful architect's drawings which made it all look unbelievably simple. But the big scheme of things didn't seem to be ready.

McDowell's first job was to present himself to the Observatory Council and to be made officially a member of its two sub-groups—the Policy Committee and the Construction Committee. He lost no time in outlining to the Council his general plan of strategy. If they would give him full power to co-ordinate the whole undertaking he could make the thing a going concern in a few months. What he needed first, he said, was a watertight organization, with the work clearly divided into engineering departments. The set-up as it stood didn't seem to him watertight enough.

"I propose to build not only the best telescope I can," he told them, "but to make it the best one that can be built in the world today. You are astronomers and I am a Navy man. You will think of a lot of things you would like to have that can't be had. I expect to give you them all! And perhaps add one or two myself."

The Observatory Council was a trifle stunned with his vehemence. There was a little eyebrow-lifting and some doubt, and when the Captain had gone they discussed whether it was going to be wise to put so scientific an undertaking into the hands of a military slave-driver like this. He had a little the wrong idea, they thought. After all, the telescope problem had been largely solved. They did not have to be told what to do next. They wanted an executive, not a dreadnaught.

But the Captain hadn't waited to find out what they thought. He had gone back to his office and was putting up a progress chart along the whole length of one wall. Inside of a day he had a plan of organization all made out, dividing the work neatly into departments. Mechanical, electrical, structural, optical and architectural engineering groups should function clearly and independently, and he would correlate and direct them all. Sandy was back on the quarter deck of a battleship and things were going to move or he'd know the reason why.

He called all the young engineers together and gave them just such a fight talk as though they were all going into a battle together. The youngsters were a trifle stunned, too. They knew what they were doing and had known all along. Where was the fire? But they listened quietly enough.

"Go back to your drawing boards and simplify!" Sandy ordered. "I'm starting for New York now and when I get back I'd like to have the general scheme of the telescope waiting for me, or better still, two or three different schemes. Line up all the arguments for each one. Then I can decide what to do."

After they had gone he packed up his bag and took a train for the East to look into the business of making contacts. The organization settled back to its old tempo with a sigh.

McDowell seemed to know every person of importance in the world. The Council found that it was impossible to mention anybody, in or out of science, without having the Captain burst out immediately: "Oh, yes, he's an old friend of mine." It was a trifle irritating at first, but it was invaluable, too. McDowell did know everybody and had worked for or with most of them at some time or other in his career. And it had been quite a career, at that.

He had begun by going around the world with "Fighting Bob" Evans and the fleet in 1908. Although he was a regular deck officer out of Annapolis, he had shown such a talent for organization that he had been put in charge of the naval engineering laboratories in New York and San Francisco and Captain of the Yard in the Samoan Islands. He had done sea duty in the submarine force; when war came he was put in command of the experiment station at New London, and later sent to England to get the anti-submarine defense into action for Admiral Sims. That got him a Navy Cross and afterward an honorary degree of doctor of science from Wisconsin University.

After that Sandy's Scotch luck changed; two battleships he was building in the New York Navy Yard were scrapped by Harding's Washington Conference. Depression found him in San Francisco again and things were so slack that the Mayor got him to run a civilian committee for creating new work—"in command of the Boondoggling Force," as Sandy scathingly described it. And when Max Mason finally caught up with him in 1934 he was busy building 10,000-tonners and destroyers in New Jersey, devoutly wishing that something different would turn up.

With the 200-inch telescope he knew that it had, and now all the energy and self-confidence that had been clamoring for release were turned loose in organizing this voyage to the stars.

Sandy McDowell had had four wives but only one standard of action. So when he started his rounds among the big industrial concerns in the East, the dust began to rise at once.

His approach to them all was the same. "Do you want to have a hand in building the biggest engine science has ever produced? Very well. Let us have your proposals when we ask for them, without delay. Cut your red tape and don't expect to make any money. This is for your good as well as ours."

This eliminated the laggards and skimmed off the cream of the crop. Sandy went back to the Coast, leaving behind him a trail of wonder and irritation. But a willingness to jump fast and far when the starting gun boomed.

Settling down at Cal Tech he soon began to realize that Navy methods were better left on the outside as much as possible. It was a different world, this meticulous, pondering world of science. It had its own pace and it was not the pace of the high seas.

Sandy became a very valuable man indeed. There was constantly in the back of his mind the knowledge that he could never be promoted to an admiral while on leave, and this may have contributed to the staccato rhythm of his attack. He wanted to get through and get back to the Navy. But the job was longer than he thought and he would not leave it half done. Whether Washington was considering him for promotion or not he would stick till he was not needed any more. So he finally gave up his chance for an admiralcy and retired, in order to contribute his full share to the raising of the Giant of Palomar.

He did not find out till afterward that he was not on the list for promotion at all.

# CHAPTER XXVI

## A MILLION POUNDS OF GLASS AND STEEL

BACK on the Coast early in 1935, Sandy McDowell found the first large piece of the telescope was ready for manufacture. This was the steel supporting "cell" for the mirror—that is, the bottom of the telescope tube, with its machinery for holding the glass in place. As soon as the shape of the disk itself had been determined Pease and Clifford A. Mattson, the chief draftsman, had begun work on this cell. Not only was it to carry the mirror in the telescope but in the meantime it would be used as the turntable of the 200-inch grinding machine. Mattson had already designed a smaller grinder for the 120-inch disk and both this and the big one were being built by Sherburne in the shop.

The cell, however, was an outside job. It was to be a sort of circular pill box of welded steel, hollow and strongly braced, and nearly twenty feet in diameter. Symmetrically arranged about its smooth upper surface were to be thirty-six foundation plates to support the ball-bearing mechanisms for holding the mirror. The design was due mainly to Pease and its huge mass fairly staggered the aging engineer. It was to weigh nineteen tons.

McDowell picked out three of the largest firms in the East and sent them plans and specifications, asking for prompt bids. He soon got them, and a contract was about to be signed with General Electric, the low bidder, when that company sent word that it would have to raise the price considerably and put off the delivery date. It had neither machines nor facilities equal to the job. The Captain did not waste time arguing, but turned to the next lowest bidder and completed a contract. The Babcock and Wilcox Company who got the job, though the largest boiler makers in the world, were unable to do it alone but had to call in the Baldwin Locomotive Works in order to be sure of large enough machines to finish the work. Even the first minor piece of the Giant was straining the country's manufacturing equipment to the utmost.

With the cell started McDowell and the engineers began to concentrate their attention on the main design of the telescope itself. Working drawings of the tube and mount were now in order.

The question of adequate bearings to support the huge weight had to be settled first and this immediately involved the horseshoe design. This piece, standing at the north end of the instrument, was in reality to be a bearing itself—a great wheel turning in frictionless supports and holding the upper end of the yoke. How was this smoothness of operation to be attained?

The simplest type of bearing is the one that supports the wheels on a child's tricycle: a round hole in a piece of metal with a shaft which fits into it snugly. The shaft is free to rotate but it can't get away. If the tricycle is expensive the hole will be lined with balls or rollers but the principle is still the same: a cylindrical spindle rolling around with the minimum of friction in a hole. Actually there are two bearings for each shaft, to keep it in line.

In a large telescope the bearings do not have to restrain the shaft so completely because it turns very slowly and its great weight keeps it in place. Hence the lower halves of the bearings are the most important. On Mount Wilson the weight of the big telescopes is supported principally on hollow drums which float in tanks of mercury. This reduces the friction almost to zero and permits smooth turning without jerks. The rotating part of the 100-inch weighs 100 tons but it turns so easily that the visitor (if he is permitted) can push it around by hand.

For the 200-inch the question was whether the horseshoe— some 50 feet in diameter—could be floated in tanks of mercury at all. If it could, the difficulty from friction would be all but eliminated. A careful investigation was begun, in which young

Mark Serrurier took a leading part.

The result was less encouraging than he had expected. These bearings had given a good deal of trouble, especially in the 100-inch. During war time when mercury was very expensive, the quantity of the liquid metal had been cut to the minimum by reducing the spaces (or clearances) between stationary and moving parts of the bearing to less than an eighth of an inch with a "liner." Consequently, dirt and lint would gradually collect and combine with the natural scum on the mercury till the spaces would fill up and the telescope would "run aground." Then a very delicate cleaning operation would be needed, during which the telescope was out of service. When the price of mercury came down after the war, the liner was taken out again and the trouble eliminated.

It was evident that a bearing of this type on the 200-inch would be gigantic. Serrurier made computations and found that several tons of mercury would be required. What had looked promising at first proved unnecessarily cumbersome on careful study. And the expense would be enormous. The idea was reluctantly abandoned.

Pease and various other engineers had suggested supporting the horseshoe on rollers. These were widely used on shafting in heavy machinery and could support enormous weights with little friction. But for the telescope they did not seem ideal. It would be too heavy even for them. The same was true of ball bearings. Both types are made of steel and derive their low friction from the fact that the surfaces do not slide on one another, but roll. There would be no friction at all if the roller and the thing it rolls on kept their shape. But they do not. The roller flattens just a trifle under heavy load and the surface it rolls on is correspondingly dented. Thus it is always having to climb up hill to get out of the dents (but never succeeds). This is called "rolling friction" and it may take a heavy toll of power. For instance, on a railroad, where every wheel under every car amounts to a roller bearing, the whole train is perpetually denting the rails as it passes over them and is actually traveling up-hill even on level track. This uses up more power even than the friction in the axles.

The moving parts of a telescope must turn with the least possible friction, in order to avoid jerks. And in the 200-inch the reduction of friction would be more important than ever before, for if a bearing offered resistance at one end, the power put in at the other to overcome it would twist the whole instrument

EVEN A BALL BEARING IS NOT PERFECT

slightly and play havoc with the delicate optical alignment. McDowell was forced to admit that roller and similar bearings were out.

One thing was left—some kind of a modification of the ancient and honorable babbitted bearing fed with a film of oil.

As soon as the horseshoe idea had been settled upon, McDowell had communicated with a number of prominent engineers throughout the country, asking them for suggestions on bearings. He told them that an oil bearing would be ideal because it was the lightest and simplest to build. He asked them if they thought it would work. Many of the engineers said no. The huge weight of the telescope could not be supported on any known sliding bearing without causing great friction and requiring enormous power to drive it.

Dr. Hodgkinson of the Westinghouse Company in Philadelphia did not agree. Instead of having the horseshoe and its cradle rubbing against each other and simply made slippery with oil as is conventional, he suggested pumping oil in between the surfaces so as to force them apart, actually floating the telescope clear of its bearings.

Hodgkinson's suggestion was considered very promising in Pasadena and McDowell sought many engineering opinions on it. The answers were discouragingly noncommittal. At the Mare Island Navy Yard, where he went into the matter in detail, the naval engineers pointed out that it would be difficult if not impossible to keep the oil from leaking out under the horseshoe and leaving it high and dry. They did not think the scheme reliable enough to trust.

Loath to give up and go back to something more experimental, the Captain finally called on Lessels and Karelitz, an outside consulting firm, to make an independent study of the problem. The study was made and the report was entirely favorable to the oil flotation method. George Karelitz (who was Michael's brother) analyzed the flotation principle in terms of the physical theory behind it.

The amount of oil leaking out of the bearing, he said, would be negligible, for the action would come under the head of "viscous flow." "Oil is not like water; it is sticky and sluggish. All you need to float your telescope is a film just thick enough to separate the metallic surfaces. Pump it in at the center of the surfaces and let it spread toward the edges and leak out as it will. There will be so little of it anyway that you can simply catch the drip and use it over again."

Karelitz came to California with his report and the Council had Sherburne build a model flotation bearing in the Instrument Shop at once—two flat plates pressed together with a heavy weight, with a pump to force oil in between them. When it was tested they found that Karelitz was right. A film of oil 3/1000ths of an inch thick (about the thickness of the lightest tissue paper) could be forced by moderate pressure in between the plates, prying them apart and rendering them practically frictionless. From this model the Cal Tech engineers set to work to compute the full sized bearings for the telescope. The results were most encouraging. A few gallons of oil pumped in under 250 pounds pressure, would float the entire telescope with only 1/600th part

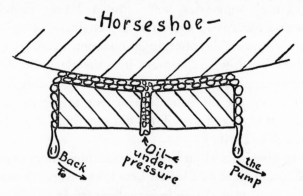

SCHEME OF THE OIL-PAD BEARING

of the friction that would have been caused by the best roller or ball bearings made.

The actual design when finally worked out called for two "oil pads" at the north pedestal under the horseshoe, each 28 inches square, faced with babbitt metal and provided with central holes to admit the oil. The south bearing was designed on the same principle, but was of the ball-and-cup type to take the downward thrust caused by the slope of the telescope's axis. It was a spherical shell seven feet in diameter resting on three pads. The solution was as simple as it was new, but it had taken the best brains in America to push it through.

With the elimination of the friction in the bearings, one of the worst difficulties of the telescope design was left behind. The astronomers had been worrying about what would happen to their delicate optical alignments if bearing friction required considerable power to turn the yoke and thus put a twist in it. Oil flotation set their minds at rest. The twist would be immeasurably small.

The engineering staff could now set to work at last upon the exact dimensions of the telescope: its tube, yoke and horseshoe, its pier supports and dome. Porter built a wooden model of the whole instrument complete except for the dome, and many of the proportions were readjusted from this. Then drawings were made for an actual steel model one-tenth the size of the Giant itself. This "tenth-scale" model should be an exact miniature of the real telescope in every possible detail—mirror and all—an actual instrument for use on the stars. It was to serve as a guinea pig so that every refinement of design might be tested and approved before anything full-sized was actually built.

In the fall of 1935 the model was completed and set up for tests. With a very few exceptions it demonstrated that the proportions had been correctly designed, and that the full-sized telescope would perform even better than the astronomers required. From it came the first realization of just how gigantic the Giant was to be. When the staff had finished their preliminary computations, this is the way they came out:

The telescope tube, carrying the 200-inch mirror, the string of auxiliaries and the observer's cage would be sixty feet long and twenty-two feet in diameter. It would weigh one hundred and twenty-five tons.

The yoke holding the tube, with the horseshoe at one end and a cross beam and bearing at the other, would be sixty feet long and about fifty feet wide. Its weight would reach three hundred tons.

These two together, with their driving machinery and controls, would constitute the moving part of the telescope. Though they weighed together four hundred and twenty-five tons they would run so smoothly in their bearings that $\frac{1}{165,000}$th of a horsepower would be enough, theoretically, to turn the telescope around the heavens. That is to say, if a workman rested a bottle of milk on one of the arms of the yoke at lunch hour, the telescope would begin to turn.

The two pedestals at the north and south ends of the instrument, made of heavy steel beams and plates, would weigh another seventy-five tons.

The whole instrument assembled would come close to five hundred tons—a million pounds of glass and steel, working with a precision that the most expensive watch could not hope to imitate.

# CHAPTER XXVII

# PALOMAR

THE mounting for the telescope was decided upon and Mc-Dowell had gone East to consult with various manufacturers about building it. The successful 200-inch Pyrex disk had survived earthquake and flood in Corning and was in process of being packed for shipment.

A final choice of a site for the observatory must be made. It would soon be time to break ground.

Anderson had just called in his field scouts, after four years of search for the ideal location, with the choice narrowed down to Table Mountain and Palomar. But Table Mountain was too dangerous because the San Andreas earthquake fault bisected it. Therefore Anderson provisionally accepted Palomar Mountain and began an intensive study of its suitability.

Palomar was not a peak at all but a long hog-back which rose some 6000 feet in the scattered range of the San Jacinto Mountains. It had been considered a promising spot for a telescope ever since Hussey had investigated it for the Carnegie Institution at the turn of the century. But Hussey had thought it too isolated. It was in the midst of a wilderness of broken hills and canyons; San Diego was fifty miles away to the south. The settled area around Los Angeles was a hundred miles to the northwest. Only the Imperial Valley was near by, to the east, and this was hardly an asset, being one of the hottest places in the world.

Anderson had always been impressed with Palomar and for five years had been conducting tests there. Several of the Mount Wilson astronomers made studies of the seeing for him, among them Ferdinand Ellerman, who decided that the "air" was even better than at Pasadena. Director Marvin of the U. S. Weather Bureau had lent Dr. Hale three complete sets of recording instruments and with these Anderson's scouts made a long and comprehensive record of the Palomar climate. It proved to be about the same as on other mountains in California. In the winter there were short but frequent storms and several feet of snow; in the summer it was cool and windless. All the year round the air was beautifully clear. It appeared ideal for an observatory.

"About the same kind of a climate," grinned Russell Porter, "as we have in New England. Only we don't have to climb any mountains to get it."

The question of accessibility was not so simple. When Hussey tried to climb Palomar from the Imperial Valley side in 1903 there were no roads at all and he had to leave his testing telescope behind. Many years later a road was built from the Valley up along the shoulder and down again on the west side. This latter end of it came to be known as the "Nigger Grade," in honor of an escaped slave who had come up here to hide fifty years before. It was a terrible stretch of sandy, boulder-strewn trail hacked like a whiplash out of the side of the mountain.

In the early part of the investigation Anderson and Sinclair Smith went to Palomar on a reconnoitering trip in Smith's old 3-ton Locomobile, taking with them a telescope of very high magnifying power. They managed to get up the eastern grade to a tiny inn called Bailey's, where they were told that the road along the summit was impassable. They decided to try it anyway.

They had been all day getting this far and now struck off in the dark over a road that not even a carriage could negotiate. The Locomobile's electric system soon broke down and the lights went out. Smith said he thought he could fix them on the spot and got underneath to try. Anderson, with nothing to do and a skyful of stars over his head, decided to set up the telescope and do a little observing. He trained the instrument on Polaris. The seeing was poor and the star's tremor disk large. Suddenly, as he stared at it, the whole principle of measuring the seeing by the size of the disk burst upon him. He yelled at Smith, who came running through the bushes to see what was the matter.

Anderson showed him the image in the eyepiece and explained his idea.

"By George!" Smith cried. "You've got it! That's the principle we've been looking for all this time!"

The two walked back to the inn, leaving the car and the telescope where they stood.

Next day they hired a couple of donkeys and rode across the hog-back to the west end, which was the highest point. It was here if anywhere that the observatory would be built. There was a small homestead up here occupied by a very friendly farmer named Beach, and the astronomers were soon being entertained in style. Beach, it seemed, owned several hundred acres along the top of the mountain and was interested to learn that the land might be desirable for scientific purposes.

"How many acres would you need, about?" he inquired.

"How many do you own?" countered Anderson.

"Three hundred and twenty."

"That would give us a start, anyway."

"A start! My gosh!"

Then Mr. Beach became very friendly indeed. He is friendly still, after ten years of juggling land titles and persuading the neighboring ranchers to part with their holdings for a reasonable sum. The astronomers owe him quite a debt, part of which he collected in the price of his own farm.

Anderson realized at once that if the observatory was to be built on Palomar a new road would have to be constructed. As the Observatory Council did not intend to buy the whole mountain and put in its own road, it was necessary to approach the County authorities to see if they were willing to donate one. Anderson visited them in San Diego. The idea of a big observatory out there in the wilderness appealed to them immediately. They saw visions of great droves of tourists flowing in from the north, taking a peek through the telescope and then dropping over to San Diego to spend their money. Certainly, they would be delighted to build a road, and a very fine road, too—hard surfaced from end to end, with low grades and wide turns so that the astronomers could get that million pounds of steel and glass up there without the slightest difficulty.

Anderson did not tell them that astronomers abhor visitors; he simply accepted the promised road and left. One of the most vexing problems of all seemed to be settled.

On the tenth of March, 1933, the city of Long Beach, near Los Angeles, was partially shaken into ruins by a severe earthquake. A hundred and twenty people were killed, either by falling debris or fright. Hundreds more were injured. By a miracle the quake occurred late in the afternoon, when children and grown-ups had all returned home for the evening. It was an act of Providence, for not a single one of the city's schools, which had been crowded an hour before, escaped damage, and many were totally destroyed.

A wave of horror swept Southern California and for the first time in the history of Los Angeles the citizens faced the earthquake danger and did something about it. A joint committee of technical men and chambers of commerce representatives was organized under Dr. Millikan, and a study of the earthquake hazard was begun. In less than two months a complete scientific report was ready. It was a succinct, almost brutal document. The whole southern part of the state, it said, was in constant danger, and earthquakes of deadly intensity were not only likely but sure to occur from time to time. The only safety lay in preparedness.

Even Mount Wilson had felt the Long Beach quake severely and the seismographs at the Observatory had been thrown clean off the scale by it. The telescopes were not damaged but many people were asking how Cal Tech could be so sure of itself on Palomar. Was it not folly to erect a six-million-dollar telescope in earthquake country if there were any risk at all that it might be knocked to pieces in a shake? Professor Buwalda of Cal Tech's geology department explained calmly that there was no danger at all. A telescope anchored to a mountain is about the most unassailable combination known.

In California, earthquake trouble comes as a result of the process of gradual mountain building which is going on continuously along the coast. The ranges here are geological infants only a few million years old; slowly they are being thrust up from below, while the continental shelf under the Pacific is going down. This mighty laboring of the earth has cut the land into long strips, running nearly north and south. The fissures which separate them run down into the ground twenty, thirty or even forty miles and are known as "faults." These do not show on the surface like knife-cuts in a pan of home made candy. They are filled in with soil and pulverized rock and debris, and often only a geologist can recognize them.

The strips of land between faults are rising at geological speeds so slow that compared to them the movement of a glacier is like the dash of a streamlined train. So from that source there is little danger. Quite independently, however, the strips are moving horizontally also, at considerable "speed," and it is this which gives rise to earthquakes. Forty miles down the pressure of the overlying rock is so enormous that the lower layers become plastic and the strips of land drift along on them, crunching and grinding like the pieces of a huge iceberg.

The friction of two neighboring strips along a fault is very large and as they try to slide past each other they stick fast and cannot actually move. Instead, gigantic pressures build up and the loose top layers of sand and boulders along the fault are actually compressed and sprung out of shape as if they were made of rubber. A fence or road built across a fault often shows this condition by being noticeably bent into the form of an "S." Eventually, even friction cannot withstand the pressure any longer and the situation is relieved in a sudden awful jumping of one strip past another. With a roar and a shudder whole cubic miles of rock spring into action and the territory near by is shaken as a dog shakes a rat. This is an earthquake, California style. For years the inhabitants have insistently turned their backs on the danger, and even today would have you think it mostly a myth.

In Southern California quakes are apt to be especially bad because the whole region is a plain made of loose alluvial material washed down from the mountains. It acts like a jelly, and even a small slip on a fault is apt to cause vibrations which build up to devastating proportions. A quake lasts no more than fifteen seconds, as a rule, but that is long enough to do plenty of harm.

Most of the damage is confined to the lowlands; the mountains, being heavy and solid, vibrate very little. Hale had known this when he established the Carnegie Observatory in 1904, and thirty years of experience had proved that he was right. Only once had an earthquake made trouble on tranquil Mount Wilson—the same quake that threw Long Beach down.

It was customary to resilver the 100-inch mirror every six months. To do this the disk was lowered from the telescope into a room underneath, the old silver dissolved and scrubbed off and a new coat put on with a chemical solution. On this occasion the astronomers had spent all day recoating the great mirror and at five o'clock it was standing there ready to be burnished and then hoisted into the telescope again. The men had knocked off and were on their way to the Monastery for supper.

One of the group held back; he had a feeling something was going to happen. Hadn't somebody better stay behind and watch the new silvered surface? His companions laughed at him.

Not fifteen minutes later Mount Wilson shuddered suddenly —more violently than she had for half a century. The dishes rattled on the table and the soup slopped over. The astronomers leaped up and rushed to the observatory to see what had happened. They found that plenty had. The mercury in the big north bearing of the telescope had got to slopping in the shake, had spilled over the edge of the tank and dropped down on the helpless mirror underneath. As the astronomers rushed in it was just devouring the last of the new silver coating by amalgamation.

The accident cost them another day's work resilvering the mirror, but it did no harm to the telescope itself. The 100-ton instrument did not even need to be readjusted.

Palomar, Professor Buwalda pointed out, has a geological set-up all its own. It is a lone block of granite about 30 miles long and ten wide, which for the past few million years has been gradually rising from the surrounding flat plain. It used to be a part of the plain itself and so the top, even today, is more or less flat. The edges have been worn away by the weather and the

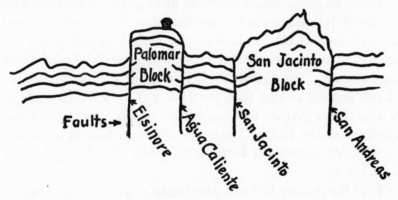

THE GEOLOGICAL FORMATION AT PALOMAR

sharp cleavages covered up by sweeping banks of gravel and boulders. The east and west faces of the mountain are bounded by two well defined cracks known as the Elsinore and the Agua Caliente faults, both of which are active. Thus the whole mountain is a typical strip of land isolated between two faults, rising as well as traveling horizontally.

Earthquakes are sure to occur in the Palomar region. But, since it is a solid granite block some twenty-five miles deep, the chances of a serious shake are nil. Granite, unlike loose pebbles and sand, transmits shock as a single train of vibrations of very high frequency but infinitesimal size. No better place in all California could probably be found for the observatory than on the top of this island of rock.

All that would be necessary, said Buwalda, was to make the telescope structure heavy and rigid and anchor it firmly to the virgin granite of the mountain top. If they wished, he added, they could install some kind of a device on the horseshoe bearing to prevent the telescope jumping off its pedestal altogether. But this would be merely a matter of choice. The worst that could happen was that Palomar, in the next few million years, might move north as a unit and perhaps bring the observatory to the outskirts of Pasadena itself.

With this all the major questions of Palomar's suitability were answered. It remained to buy up the top of the mountain. About a square mile of the flat land on the summit would be needed, most of it to prevent encroachment by settlers who might raise smoke or dust and disturb the holy calm of the air. To acquire all this was not an easy task, for while a good deal of it could be bought from private owners, a considerable tract to the east belonged to the United States Government. Part of Palomar's summit lay within the boundaries of the Cleveland National Park Forest.

The Observatory Council now began a long series of negotiations with the Departments of the Interior and Agriculture, and with the influence of such men as Hale and Henry M. Robinson, a spirit of co-operation was soon established.

The Government was prevented by law from selling national park lands to private parties, and for a time the only solution seemed to be to obtain an act of Congress to break the jam. Then a way to circumvent the difficulty was found. Public lands could not be sold, but they could be *swapped*. The Park Service was anxious to increase the recreational area in another part of the territory. The astronomers agreed to buy up private land there and give it to the Government, taking in exchange the summit of Palomar which they needed.

This process was sure but it was slow. With 120 acres at the actual site of the observatory as a start, the Council by 1939 had collected seven hundred. Cal Tech's lawyers are still at work on the problem, and will not stop till they have insulated the Giant with the enormous tract of 2000 acres.

With all this done or under way, Palomar looked promising indeed. It had ideal weather and exceptionally good seeing. It was blessed with abundant water. It was within three hours' ride of headquarters at Pasadena, yet so deeply buried in the wilderness that there would never be the danger that towns or cities with their belching smoke or their blaze of lights would interfere with the telescope's performance. And the local politicians had promised to build a boulevard to the summit free.

What the astronomers would do with the inevitable horde of visitors the road would bring, they didn't stop to bother about then. That worry was postponed for a later chapter in the story.

# CHAPTER XXVIII

## WESTWARD HO!

CORNING was well pleased with the work McCauley and his men had done on the second 200-inch disk. So well pleased that on a Sunday in January 1936, they invited the public in to take a look. There was a blizzard that day and only 2000 people showed up. During the week so many requests came in that the disk was again thrown open to visitors the next Sunday. Five thousand people attended.

The great disk stood upright in its tin shed at the back of the plant and filled the spectators with awe and puzzlement. McCauley stood around in the shadows and tried not to look too pleased. Two old ladies walked around and around it for some time and then asked him where was the big lens they had come to see.

"It's a mirror, not a lens," McCauley gently set them straight. "You know—a looking glass." The two walked around it again, examining the great ribs and the rough, hubbly front surface. Then they returned to Mac and stared him up and down.

"Looking glass, is it!" said one old lady positively. "If that's a looking glass, young man, you ought to be ashamed!"

After the curious were gone, McCauley set about packing the Pyrex giant for shipment. First, a complete layer of rubber sheeting half an inch thick was fastened around it, then a circular box made of half-inch steel plates was built and the disk fitted snugly into it. Disk and box together weighed thirty-five tons.

The disk was to be shipped by railroad, standing up. This was the only way it could be done. Lying flat on a car would have been impossible. Most railroads cannot take shipments wider than thirteen feet. The disk was over seventeen. Even standing up it was going to be a problem on account of low bridges and tunnels. And this problem a group of railroad men now set out to solve.

The steel crate was of vital importance, not only for protection but for handling, too. Along the circumference were several heavy steel eyes. At exactly the height of the center of gravity spindles stuck out from either side so that the disk could be picked up by a rope sling and balanced. Near the bottom, heavy side-girders were welded on to form the legs on which it would stand in its car.

The car itself was something rather special—known to railroad men as a "well-car." It looked more or less like an ordinary flatcar, but the flooring at the middle was omitted, leaving a hole down through to the rails. The whole construction of it was exceptionally heavy and low. The car had been ordered from the New York Central some time before and was now on a siding near the plant. The railroad had not delivered it until a thoroughgoing inspection had been made of it from end to end. And now, while waiting, they were going over it again.

To receive the disk the car could not be backed into the shop or anywhere near it. The tin house where the glass was waiting in its crate stood within a few feet of the bank of the river and there was only a narrow dirt lane running along the water's edge to offer an exit to the street and thence to the nearest railroad crossing. This part of the journey would have to be made on a motor trailer.

When the disk was snugly packed into its steel casing and bolted fast, early in February, it was trundled out into the open air on rollers, and there made ready to be loaded on the trailer. It was just at this time that six weeks of torrential rains culminated in serious floods throughout the East. The Chemung, like every other river, rose and inundated the countryside. It crept steadily toward the back of the plant and presently began to threaten the road which the truck must follow. Hour after hour it gained on the disk, reached the wooden blocking under it, rose a little more, slopped over into the shed whence the Giant had just come. Then, as if understanding the worry it was causing, it began to go down again.

"I hope," said McCauley very quietly, "that we don't have to repeat what happened last summer."

The riggers who were doing the loading laughed. "It's all over now," they assured him. But it wasn't. The water began to rise again. The men began working like mad to get the disk onto the trailer and out of the way. But that sort of a job can't be hurried. There was no room for a crane to lift the 35-ton burden. It had to be jacked up a fraction of an inch at a time by hand, then slid along on heavy beams onto the platform of the trailer. It took a week.

The men worked doggedly in the rain, sloshing about in rubber boots in the muddy river water. They had to lay down a corduroy road of planks for the trailer to keep it from miring down. Then the disk, lying flat on its side, had to be carefully balanced so that it would not slip off. And all the while the river crept up, an inch at a time. "Hurry up, boys," it seemed to be saying. "I can't hold on much longer."

It was a lively week, insofar as one can be lively with forty tons of glass and steel. But finally the loading was done and the procession could move. The water was still waiting patiently. A truck was now backed hastily in and hitched to the trailer. Without a minute's ceremony the driver began to pull and the disk creaked off across the corduroy road a foot at a time. Out of danger at last!

But down at the end of the road a corner of the factory was in the way. In the narrow path still left by the flood the disk couldn't squeeze by. There was no time for red tape; the water was coming. Something must be done. Inside of ten minutes a gang of wreckers arrived and with pickaxes and crowbars attacked the obstructing walls. For another day the disk lay at the mercy of the elements. Then a passage was cleared and with a roar the trailer was yanked through it to safety. Forty-eight hours afterward the scene of operations disappeared under the wild Chemung River.

The only point suitable for loading the disk on its well-car was at an intersection of a railroad siding and one of the main streets of Corning. The company got the city authorities to close the street at both ends of the block, and the trailer was drawn onto the tracks. A steam wrecking crane lent by the New York Central was waiting for it—a crane capable of lifting a locomotive. Nothing smaller was considered safe.

It was miserably cold and rainy that day, yet hundreds of spectators lined the street. They even stood on the roofs of near-by buildings and crowded doors and windows as the crane with a mighty show of steam and noise let down its main hook to catch the load. A double cross-beam of steel girders had been attached to the hook and a massive steel bar hung down from each end. Holes had been provided in the lower end of each bar to fit over the studs in the disk casing.

When everything was ready the crane ponderously swung into position and the engineer lowered the cross-beam directly over the trailer. A bar was slipped over each stud and locked in place. The boss rigger shouted and waved his hand and with a roar the engineer "took a strain" on the hoisting cable. For a moment things stood still, while the crane pitched and groaned under the load. Then the disk rose deliberately into the air an inch—two inches—six—a foot. Then, burning his bridges behind him, the rigger shouted a word to the truck driver, and the trailer was pulled out of the way and the disk hung alone in mid-air.

McCauley and his fellow executives paced nervously up and down as their world's record Pyrex casting swung gently under the crane four feet from the ground. If anything gave way at that moment and it dropped—

"I wonder if they'd let us make a third disk," thought McCauley, pulling his coat collar up a little.

Then the riggers hurried in from the sides; gingerly pushing and lifting, they gradually turned it into an upright position and eased it down on boards laid in the street. Another critical moment was passed.

The well-car had been standing in readiness on another track and was now pushed up alongside by a switching locomotive. Again the crane picked the disk up—high, this time—and swung it over the car and eased it down on its final resting place on heavy rubber pads at each end of the well. Down it went into place, the feet welded to the casing fitting exactly on the heavy cross-girders bolted to the car. The bottom of the disk passed down through the hole and when the car bore its whole weight, the steel casing was just five inches above the rails. The loading was complete. It had taken one day.

The car with its precious burden was backed into the factory siding and left there for the night. Next morning, the men re-assembled to bolt the disk in place for its long journey. A flying battalion of movie cameramen got the good-natured glass people and railroad officials to hitch the car up into the special train which would soon accompany the disk to the Coast. A day or two later newsreels all over the country informed millions of theatergoers that the "great eye" for the world's largest telescope was on its way to Palomar Mountain.

But it wasn't. When the riggers came to fit the steel guys in place to keep the disk firmly fastened to the well-car, they found that the rubber pads had been crushed down almost to nothing; the disk had sunk practically to the level of the rails. McCauley scratched his head. Was bad luck going to dog him indefinitely?

Silently he sent for the lifting jacks again, and the disk was boosted up off the pads. Then he set about finding some other material besides rubber to cushion the shocks between disk and beams. The delay cost him a month's time.

It was not a month wasted, however, for it gave the railroad people a chance to check once more the route the disk train was to take to California.

When any large object is to be shipped by freight the railroad company puts an expert called a "clearance engineer" on the problem. This fellow has before him a book in which are listed all the bridges, tunnels, rock cuts and "narrow squeezes" in the United States, Canada, and Mexico—over a million entries in all. It is up to him to route the shipment to its destination as expeditiously as possible without hitting anything or interfering unduly with regular rail traffic. He supplements the data in the clearance book with many charts, maps, tables and formulas which apply to his own railroad, and rounds it out with experience and sometimes with the ingenuity of a Houdini for getting out of tight places. Occasionally the problem becomes very complicated, for shippers of heavy machinery, tanks, girders and even yachts are apt to expect the impossible. The clearance man must find some way to accommodate his clients or else lose their business and elaborate preparations are often necessary, even to removing roadside obstructions or shifting the tracks themselves.

Some big shipments can be taken apart and loaded on separate cars, but the giant Pyrex disk could not. It stood seventeen feet seven inches over the rails and nothing could be done to lower it. Seventeen ten was the actual clearance under at least two bridges between Corning and California.

Everyone remotely connected with the telescope had a hand in routing the disk west, and there had been innumerable conferences among officials for months. Even railroad presidents were involved. The actual routing was finally worked out by two New York Central clearance engineers—Buckley and Molloy—at their desks in New York. The disk would go by New York Central to St. Louis, by Burlington to Kansas City and then make the long hop to Pasadena over the Sante Fe. Every inch of the journey was planned and checked and then verified by other engineers along the line. Special precautions were discussed and agreed upon; special inspections of the right-of-way arranged for. This was almost unheard of in railroad freight handling, but then, the 200-inch disk was already famous and no one wanted to be responsible for smashing it up. Moreover, it was to be the most valuable single object ever shipped on an American railroad. It would be insured by Lloyd's of London for one hundred thousand dollars.

The special precautions included a detailed survey of every foot of the track on the 3000 mile journey. Orders were sent out to the division superintendents all along the line and engineers were dispatched to check the bridge heights wherever the clearance was known to be close. The track itself was also inspected with minute care. As the shipment was to be made in March, there was considerable chance that frost in the ground would "heave" the rails, cutting down clearances or putting unevennesses in the roadbed that might tip the disk dangerously.

McCauley found the solution of the rubber pad difficulty easier than he had anticipated. He substituted gum rubber and hardwood blocks counterbalanced with heavy springs. The disk casing was then set down solidly on the wood and bolted there, with springs under the bolt heads. Thus any sudden jar from the roadbed would cause the disk to jump slightly against the compression of the springs. Rods of steel two inches thick were run from the top of the crate to the four corners of the car and pulled tight with turnbuckles. As a final precaution heavy steel plates were leaned up at an angle on each side of the disk so that if any crank along the route took a pot-shot at the Giant with a rifle he would be disappointed. Then, all night long before the final date of departure in March workmen gave everything a coat of aluminum paint and printed the words: "Pyrex 200-Inch Telescope Disk" across both sides in letters two feet high.

The morning of March 26th, 1936, came quietly, and the disk train was made up with as little excitement as possible. It consisted of a box car loaded with lifting tackle, the well-car with the disk, and a caboose. It was to be hauled by a heavy freight locomotive in charge of an experienced engineer with a Road Foreman of Engines beside him all the way. One of the best conductors on the line was to ride behind.

McCauley would have been delighted to go along with the

Giant on its triumphal march west, but he was too wise. Many others at Corning coveted the same privilege; the only solution was for them all to stay behind.

For the same reason none of the astronomers was present. But the caboose nevertheless was well filled with railroad executives, delighted to take this little holiday. Among them was Frank Murphy, Burlington's safety engineer, who intended to ride as far as Kansas City. Murphy was so eager for the trip that he had been hanging around in Corning for a month, expecting every few days to make a start. One day his headquarters in Chicago had telegraphed him in great alarm. Where was the disk train? They had seen it start off several weeks before in the newsreels and nothing had been heard from it since. Murphy wired back that the pictures had been premature and sat down to swing his feet and wait. When the train finally was ready to start, he was nowhere to be found. Eventually McCauley located him in a one-arm lunch and he had to skip off without his breakfast.

When the train and its passengers were finally ready to start Trainmaster Phil Barrow of the Central performed the last rites by setting in motion the clockwork of two sensitive vibration recorders attached to the disk. For the whole two weeks of the trip these would keep a continuous record on a sheet of paper of every jiggle and jar the Giant would suffer from Corning to Pasadena. If anything got loose, watchers on the train would know about it before any harm could be done. If the disk arrived cracked the exact spot where it happened could be told and responsibility placed.

When the recorders were set, Barrow waved his hand. The engineer gave a single toot and "cracked" his throttle ever so gently, and the largest telescope mirror in the world was off on its 3000-mile journey, while a little group of Glass Works people stood in silence in the chill March air. Everyone was saddened and subdued at this final departure of an old, old friend.

No prince or potentate—not even a President—ever crossed the country under more tender care than this disk. The train proceeded at a steady speed of twenty-five miles an hour all day. It was given the right of way all along the line, and all ordinary train movements were subordinated to it. Many a crack flyer played second fiddle to the "Telescope Special" as it rolled deliberately westward. Even the limiteds got out of its way. When night came the disk train was hauled carefully onto a well-inspected side track and the switches were securely spiked so that no careless engineer could back another train in on top of it. And all night long under the glare of a battery of floodlights four uniformed railroad policemen patrolled the siding with loaded rifles, allowing nobody whatever to come within five hundred yards of the train.

During the whole period while the disk was in transit, railroad officials all along the line eagerly awaited the daily telegrams from each stopping point, saying that all was well. No one was more concerned than Buckley and Molloy in New York, upon whom the success of the routing mainly depended. It was a happy day for them when, just at lunch time on April 10th, the final wire came: "Optical disk arrived destination 8:25 A. M. today."

From one end of the route to the other requests poured in from civic organizations and schools to stop over and let the Giant become the center of an ovation. All were refused; the train never once stopped at a station or anywhere else unless absolutely necessary. In Geneva, N.Y., and in a score of towns along the way, schools were let out for the day and the children lined the tracks and yelled a brief welcome and good-by as the disk sped west. An alarmed lady in Missouri wrote to the Glass Works by air mail to ask what this so-called 200-inch disk might be. She said she had seen the 120-inch go by two years before and supposed that there were only eighty inches of glass left to come.

When the train was eased under the Buffalo bridge at dead slow speed half a dozen top-flight officials watched the civil engineers take the clearance. It was a close thing, but the disk made it with ease. Between the top of the steel casing and the bridge girders above they could slip in a pocket Bible, nothing more. But at Kansas City, several days later, something had gone wrong with the plans. The Bible wouldn't go in. Neither would a sheet of paper. Frost had heaved the tracks just enough to destroy the tiny margin of clearance. The disk and its fellow celebrities were stalled until local routing experts devised a detour around the city over the tracks of a rival railroad.

Into the west went the train and with every mile the interest and excitement increased. Murphy and the other eastern officials were gone now, but at every division point some local railway potentate hopped on, to bask in the reflected glory of Palomar. Hundreds of school children lined the tracks; little towns turned out en masse to watch the "telescope" go by. Such a deal of excitement and interest in a scientific undertaking had not been stirred up since Lindbergh flew his triumphant circuit around the country in 1927.

Across Kansas and the tip of Colorado and down into New Mexico sailed the Giant. The Santa Fe Railroad had determined to outdo itself. Not since Queen Marie of Rumania had passed this way had the road felt so honored. A gasoline "scooter car" loaded with inspectors sprinted on ahead of the train, scrutinizing every inch of the track. Every time the procession halted armed guards would dive in underneath to make sure no hoboes had stowed away under the Giant's flank.

At Albuquerque a coaling spout hung down over the track, blocking the way. "We dodged that one by detouring to a side track," said proud Freightmaster R. A. Podlech, who had elected himself as inspection committee to ride the caboose to California.

Before the train had left Corning six tons of old rails had been piled on the well-car to lower its center of gravity. With the disk standing so high it was feared that it might get to swaying dangerously on some sharp curve and even topple over. And now that the narrow clearances and tortuous bends of the Rockies were ahead, the danger was critical. Podlech and his men were worried, and at every curve the engineer proceeded on a "slow order" at five miles an hour while all hands ran along beside, fairly feeling of the track with their hands.

So small was the clearance in a tunnel at Johnson Canyon, Arizona, that the train had to be shunted onto the eastgoing tracks, which had a foot more to spare. Word was sent on ahead to stop all traffic; flagmen ran through the tunnel and stood guard. Then the disk was pulled into the dark cavern and eased through at dead slow speed, while the inspectors choked from the smoke and bit their nails.

And so on through Arizona went the Giant and into California, the state of his adoption; across the Mojave Desert past Barstow and Victorville and down through long, winding Cajon Pass to the coastal plain at San Bernardino. Here the train crew rolled their precious charge into the freight yards, "as nervous as a little boy with his first watch," one newsman thought, and put the disk up for the night. And that evening word went off to the Observatory Council sixty miles away, that their "lens" would be brought into Pasadena in the morning.

With the able help of Los Angeles and Pasadena papers, excitement was whipped to a high pitch by the morning of April 10th. The disk was scheduled to arrive at the little Lamanda Park station at nine, but hours before that the streets were so crowded that a dozen policemen were detailed to rope off the area and keep the peace.

Platoons of news photographers and movie men got inside the lines by special dispensation. In a few minutes the rest of the spectators caught onto the trick and, waving cameras of every description, surged forward into preferred positions—on the tops of cars, up telephone poles, on the roof of the station. Five thousand people, it was said, were there; if in reality there had been anywhere near that number, half of them would have been forced to swing like monkeys from the palm trees about the tiny station. But there was a crowd.

"There has been no such excitement," said the *Pasadena Star-News*, "since Ambler's feed mill burned."

Right on the dot the procession began to arrive. First was "Big Tom," the Barstow wrecker, Santa Fe's mightiest steam crane; then a special train full of officials of every description —divisional and mechanical superintendents, trainmasters and every other railroad employee on or off duty who could invent an excuse to be present. Then W. R. Flynn, the official receptionist for the Santa Fe in Pasadena. Then Bob Belyea from Los Angeles, with his enormous twenty-two-wheel trailer and his crew of strong-arm men. Then Gardiner Sherburne and Marcus Brown and *their* assistants. Then the Chamber of Commerce and the Mayor and the city Fathers.

Everybody in the state seemed to be there except the people who owned the disk. So little did the astronomers relish the crowd and the publicity that they carefully stayed at home.

And then, three minutes ahead of schedule Special No. 3157 roared majestically around the bend and came to a shrieking stop that was quickly drowned by the shouts of the crowd. On the back platform of the caboose stood Pease; he alone of all the astronomers had gone to San Bernardino to ride in with the train.

Then for five hours Big Tom impatiently blew off steam and frightened the good Californians half to death while Sherburne and Brown and Belyea cut the rods that held the Giant down, unscrewed a hundred bolts (which the crowd instantly appropriated for souvenirs) and cast off the last bonds that held him. In mid-afternoon came the crucial moment, when, according to the papers, "the progress of astronomy during the next decade literally hung in the balance." Or, according to the simple truth, the disk was lifted gently out of the well-car and deposited without a jar on Belyea's trailer. The crowd "breathed easier" then, of course, and had to be forcibly restrained from rushing forward and adding their initials to the many already scratched on the Giant's crate by a score of railroaders from Corning to the Pacific. For the first time all day patient Russell Porter and his wife managed to get close enough to see what was going on, and

Pease, imprisoned by the crowd since morning, was able to escape.

At the speed of an impressive funeral, now, with a full complement of motorcycle police yowling on ahead of it, the 200-inch disk rolled through the streets of Pasadena, following the sanctified route of the Rose Bowl Parade, jamming traffic and stopping all normal life in the California city. And at five o'clock precisely Belyea and his men jockeyed the trailer in through the arch of the Optical Shop, and the Giant was at last among its own.

It was a quiet reception. Hale was at home in bed; the others stood around and gazed mutely at this enormous thing the railroad had brought them; walked up and touched it tentatively like Lilliputians exploring a Gulliver; then, realizing the crowd was watching, embarrassedly turned away.

They wanted people to know that it was not a sentimental occasion. It was just the routine arrival of an astronomical mirror in a laboratory where public excitement and noise was as unimportant as the Earth itself is among the stars.

Only quiet Dr. Anderson did anything in the least emotional —and he didn't mention it to anybody till three years afterward.

In the course of his usual early morning drive that day he "happened" to guide his car to a lonely railroad crossing in the country. And there he sat and watched the Giant and its train go by.

## CHAPTER XXIX

## FIRE AND STEEL

THE next morning the 200-inch disk disappeared within the surgically clean, air-conditioned atmosphere of the Optical Shop and for four years became the personal responsibility of Marcus H. Brown, whose job it was to remove some four tons of glass in just the right place.

In the meantime Captain McDowell was in the East, stirring up action on the steelwork. Over nine hundred thousand pounds of beams, plates and tubes were needed, made up in sizes never before attempted by any foundry or machine shop. It was not going to be possible to ship much of this to California by rail; therefore a manufacturer must be found who had a plant on tidewater and wharf facilities for loading a seagoing ship.

After a thorough canvass by McDowell, the Council settled upon the Westinghouse Company, and awarded the contract for the tube, yoke and horseshoe to their South Philadelphia plant on the Delaware River. If anyone could make the huge telescope, these men could, for they were regularly turning out the world's largest steam turbines and electric generators.

Inspired as everyone else had been by the magnitude and importance of the job, the Westinghouse technicians threw themselves into the game at once. Four skillful mechanical engineers took the brunt of the work: Hodgkinson, Ormondroyd, Froebel and a young Dutchman named Kroon.

To translate blueprints and models into the actual Giant it was necessary to do a lot of preliminary work on paper in what is called stress analysis. This meant computing the actual mechanical forces that would act in the metal at every point in the whole telescope—forces of tension, compression and bending caused by suspending so great a weight in mid-air. The controlling factor was to be rigidity. The instrument must not sag under its own weight. In a bridge, a building or a steamship a certain amount of elasticity, or "give," is indispensable. But for the telescope it was taboo. The problem before the Westinghouse engineers, therefore, was to obtain the utmost in stiffness without unduly increasing the weight. To do this they adopted a design for the structural parts quite similar to Pease's latticework back for the mirror: a thin shell with carefully proportioned bracing in the right places. They took advantage of the well known civil engineering axiom that massiveness does not always add strength, and planned their telescope as far as possible like a skeleton.

Kroon went to California for three months to learn every detail of the telescope's design. He and Serrurier and Karelitz spent weeks discussing the structural requirements and making cardboard models to test their ideas. Serrurier had just made a brilliant solution of the problem of the rigid tube, along lines suggested by Professor Martel. In small telescopes the tube is the whole instrument. Even in large refractors like the 40-inch Yerkes it remains a big steel cylinder weighing several tons. Serrurier's tube for the 200-inch, however, departed from all that and cut away every pound of metal that was not essential to rigidity. It was a mere spider's web by comparison, yet stronger than the best of its predecessors.

"When I gave him the problem to solve," said Martel, "I honestly thought it was impossible. I'm proud to say Mark's old professor was wrong."

Serrurier's difficulty was to hold a 40-ton mirror assembly in any desired position in mid-air and then, sixty feet away, at its focal point, float a six-foot house full of mirrors and instruments and carrying an observer—several tons in all—and at no time let the two elements slip out of line with each other by more than $\frac{3}{100}$ths of an inch. In between must be a pair of bearings so that mirror and observer together could be swung up and down and back and forth in search of the stars.

Most engineers would have called any such rigidity impossible. And Serrurier solved the problem by agreeing with them: it *was* impossible. However strong he made the tube those great weights suspended at either end of it were bound to bend it. Very well, then, let them bend it. Simply design the tube, he said, so that the mirror and the observer's cage will move to-

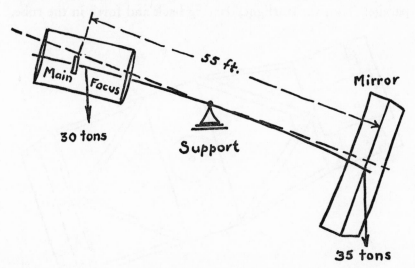

SERRURIER'S PROBLEM IN RIGIDITY. ONLY $\frac{8}{100}$THS INCH BENDING AT MAIN FOCUS WAS ALLOWED

gether, by the same amount and in the same direction, and thus in relation to each other stand still.

Serrurier's design was this: a very rigid hollow square for the center section of the tube, and two equally rigid rings for the two ends. The three to be tied together by stiff diagonal beams forming triangles whose bases were on the sides of the square and whose apexes held the rings at four points around their circumferences. The bearings on which the tube would swing in the telescope would be held in two opposite sides of the square center section and the diagonals were to be so proportioned that the mirror, held in one ring, would just balance the observer and his equipment, held in the other.

When the tube lay on its side (the position for worst bending), the two rings would sag downward slightly at the ends of their triangular supports. But by designing these supports carefully, Serrurier proved by his computations that he could cause mirror and observer to sag just the same amount. And because of a simple geometrical law they would remain always parallel. Thus the starlight, darting back and forth in the tube,

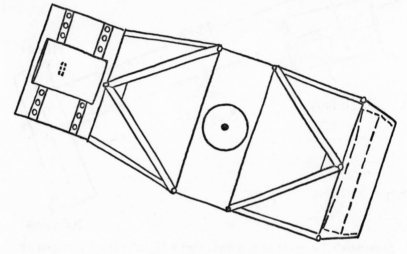

How He Solved It

would arrive at the desired point, within the allowable error of 8/100ths of an inch.

When Kroon and the others admired the idea, Serrurier modestly played down its importance. "That 8/100ths business," he told them, "is just a 'limit of convenience.' It's nice the computations show we can come so close, but if they didn't we'd put up with a much greater error and correct it some other way."

There was a great deal of dramatic interest when Serrurier's design was actually built into the tenth-scale model and tried out. That interest turned to downright delight when the deflections proved to be only *one-third* of the amount he had promised.

Back in Philadelphia with the finished designs, Kroon and his colleagues set about expressing them in hundreds of tons of steel. First they ordered a scale model of their own, ⅓₂ full size, made entirely of celluloid. There was a man in the plant who did nothing else but make miniatures of large and intricate machines, using thin strips of celluloid "welded" together by hypodermic injections of acetone at the joints. The model took him several months to build, for it was a perfect replica of the coming Giant in every detail. It cost $2000.

The new model was by no means for show only; when it was finished Kroon and Froebel set it up in their laboratory and loaded it with weights to represent the actual forces that would act in the finished machine. Then, with delicate micrometers and electric meters they measured the exact amount of sag and distortion at every point. Celluloid is just eighty-five times as flexible as steel, and the model, though only a toy, gave them a strongly exaggerated picture of the conditions that would exist in the real telescope.

From these tests it was possible to adjust the number, size and strength of every steel part in order to attain the rigidity required, before cutting a single piece of actual metal.

To save the utmost in weight and gain the greatest stiffness, the whole telescope was to be built by welding: there would not be a single rivet in it. When metal plates are fastened with rivets they must be overlapped considerably and thus doubled in thickness. In welded construction the plates are butted together and steel is melted into the joints with the electric arc. The result is a smooth continuous surface that is light and strong.

The tube was built first, and it was indeed a skeleton. Constructed mostly of half-inch-thick plates welded together, it was so enormously bulky that the Westinghouse plant's largest shop was needed to set it up. The men climbed around on it like pygmies; a workman could stand upright in one of the bearing holes and jump up and down without bumping his head. The two end-rings and the box center were fabricated first: then the cross-beams were bolted in place, and the whole gigantic affair assembled—twenty-two feet square and forty-four feet long. It weighed 143,000 pounds.

Kroon described it afterward with unassuming pride. "That it was large," he said, "I will not deny. But yet only a case of good engineering—of which I did a small part—and careful shop practice. Our men are very proud, of course. Why not? They built the tube in a year. They made no mistakes and wasted no materials. And their greatest error in 44 feet did not exceed one thirty-second of an inch."

That was getting 71 tons of steel together with an error less than the thickness of a toothpick. The day the first ring was done and laid out on the assembly floor one hundred and twenty-eight men stood inside it and had their picture taken.

The Westinghouse management was quite proud, too, and when the tube was completed they invited a number of celebrities in for a dedication party. A platform was built in the shadow of the Gargantuan star-ship and an imposing array of two hundred first-string scientists, editors, engineers and educators listened while Mr. Ormondroyd gave a short lecture through a microphone and loud speakers. The celluloid model stood on a table beside the orator, surrounded by a select little gathering of honored guests. Fluffy headed Albert Einstein sat behind it and kept peeking through its shimmering flanks at the audience with hardly suppressed excitement.

He made a little speech of his own by and by, and said with charming humility: "When I make a mistake in a calculation it is on a piece of paper; I throw it away—zo! But when you make a mistake in steel—" And he ended with a little shrug and a smile. The audience applauded loudly at the compliment and Westinghouse clinched it by reminding them that not a pound of metal had been thrown away. After the dedication was over, many a science editor rushed home with a pocketful of photographs and handouts which the Publicity Department had taken good care to provide. Next day the country was well aware of the progress Westinghouse had made.

Referring in particular to the welding process, the official statement said:

"No essential difficulties existed, since most of the plates and shapes were less than an inch thick. After the fabrication of each section, stresses had to be relieved by annealing at 1150° Fahrenheit. Without this, the sections would warp during the machining process and might even continue to warp after the telescope was assembled.

"The largest element in the whole telescope is the diaphragm cage which forms the top of the tube. This piece is twenty-two feet in diameter and twelve feet high. No furnace at Westinghouse or neighboring plants was big enough to handle it. Even if a furnace of proper dimensions had existed near by, the piece could not have been transported by rail or truck, since clearances on railroad or street would not let the cage pass. A special furnace, therefore, had to be constructed, and in it all the pieces of the telescope will be annealed."

But fortunately not for ten months as in the case of the Pyrex disk. Only a few days is necessary to relieve the strains in steel.

The second piece of the telescope to be built was the horseshoe—the most gigantic of all: the largest bearing ever fashioned by the hand of man. It, too, was to be welded entirely. But because it was 46 feet in diameter and four feet thick—and would weigh 340,000 pounds—it would have to be made in three pieces and then bolted together. Kroon and the others spent many long hours with the company's shipping experts determining just where the joints should come. For this piece of the Giant would have to make a preliminary excursion by rail and all three parts of it must be small enough for shipment. Only one milling machine in the world was big enough to cut the smooth outer surface—the one that had made the giant parts for Boulder Dam. It was in the Westinghouse plant at Pittsburgh. Once made in Philadelphia, the huge bearing would have to be taken apart and shipped through the Allegheny Mountain tunnels to the Smoky City, then returned to Philadelphia for loading on the boat for California.

The actual diameter of the horseshoe was so chosen that each of the three parts could just be squeezed through the tunnels. For a while Westinghouse considered the idea of shipping the pieces by boat to New Orleans and up the Mississippi and Ohio Rivers to Pittsburgh. But they gave it up as too elaborate just for the sake of a few inches more of diameter—one of the largest scale engineering compromises ever made.

Obtaining the necessary stiffness in the horseshoe presented many difficult problems of design. In addition to the knockdown feature, which must not weaken the structure, the great ring must be able to hold the telescope in any position without deformation. A complete circle is structurally one of the strongest mechanisms there is, but a broken circle is one of the weakest, especially when the load comes far out on the horns. Consequently the body of the horseshoe had to be made like the shank of a hook, twelve feet wide at the throat, and tapering to nothing at the ends.

The outer rim especially gave trouble because it would have to be so strong that the enormous weight bearing on it would not flatten it out of round. Pieces of special boiler plate four and a half inches thick were furnished for this by the Bethlehem Steel Company and rolled into sections of a circle in a 10,000-ton armor plate press. Three pieces were needed—one for each section of the outer rim; and three more a trifle thinner for the inside rim.

The men stood a pair of these great rinds on edge on the steel erecting floor of the shop, then proceeded to box them in by welding on top and bottom plates and ends. Before the plates could be put on, however, the inside had to be filled up with complicated bracing in a special pattern which Kroon and the others had worked out. A series of vanes protruded inward from the rim; straight and circular plates were fitted into the interior and cross braces were supplied, running in a dozen different directions. When it was done the interior looked exactly like the bizarre geometric patterns of a surrealist picture.

"Such a picture is nothing in comparison," Kroon admitted, "for when the top cover was put in place, men had to get inside and weld it down. Our problem was to arrange the bracing in such fashion that the welders could get out again when they were finished. To do this we were obliged to cut holes in the plates big enough for a man to squeeze through—yet not so big as to weaken the structure. A surrealist picture, it was nothing beside this."

Nearly a mile of welded seams were needed to put the three pieces together, yet when the horseshoe was finally assembled in Philadelphia it was as accurate as the tube had been. It was now pulled apart and sent to Pittsburgh, and assembled there on the giant milling machine. Here, machine-shop conventions were broken all over again. It was bad enough to have to turn a true circular surface forty-six feet in diameter, but the problem now was to turn one that was *not* circular, but elliptical. The reason for this new complication was this:

When the telescope turned over on its side, the entire weight would rest on one horn of the horseshoe alone. In spite of all the internal stiffeners and braces, the upper horn would sag, throwing the circular rim out of true, and acting like a flat wheel on a railroad train. This was not permissible because it would introduce a twist into the telescope tube itself and throw the mirrors out of line. The only way to remedy it was to make the horseshoe rim a little more open than a true circle, so that when it sagged it would become truly round.

The machinists in charge of the job did not have to be surrealists, but the engineers did, and it took the combined skill of them all, including Serrurier, to determine what to do. A lathe can only cut a perfect circle, they said; therefore, when the horseshoe goes under the knife it must be distorted by just the same amount as it will eventually be in actual practice. This amount turned out to be very small—only one-twentieth of an inch at the outermost tips of the horns. But in order to warp this piece of Gargantua, which they had built so rigidly, even by that little fraction, the horns had to be pulled together with a turnbuckle exerting a tension of one hundred and thirty tons, while a spreader in the throat of the horseshoe pushed outward with two hundred and twenty-five tons more.

The machinists in Pittsburgh looked on with mild curiosity while the engineers puzzled and figured; but when they were finally told to go ahead with the cutting they were not without their troubles, too. Three thousand hours of intensely concentrated work were necessary before the horseshoe was finally smoothed and polished to just the shape required. And they, too, were accurate; nowhere did the surface err by more than three thousandths of an inch.

But in Philadelphia meanwhile the engineers were going at it again with the third and last piece of the Giant—the yoke. In some ways this was less complicated; in others it was worse. The two side arms were to be made as simple cylinders, ten feet in diameter and some forty-seven feet long, welded up out of common steel plates an inch thick. The cross-piece at the end of the yoke was to be a bent box-girder forty-six feet long and nearly eleven deep. It was to be in one piece made up of steel plates all welded together (with appropriate holes for the men to wriggle in and out), and all provided with criss-cross stiffeners wherever needed. And when it was all done and cemented together with molten steel, it would weigh—

But we are in danger of getting crushed under the burden of all these figures. Let us escape from the computing room for a moment and make an imaginary visit to the Westinghouse plant during the last days of assembly, when the telescope parts were nearly complete. McDowell's resident engineer, Frank Fredericks, will be our guide.

We are in the big turbine shop, following the engineer in and out among somber black machines whose cavernous interiors yawn at us on every hand. It is the noon hour. A deep and hollow

silence presides in this vast space that is nearly a quarter of a
mile long. Workmen, singly and in groups, are perched like
elephant boys on the protruding shapes, eating pieces of pie and
sucking coffee out of their dinner pails. Fredericks nods here
and there as he passes; they are all his friends. He turns to say
something to us, but it is lost, for a man with a power-driven
chisel just then attacks the flank of a casting as big as a bungalow. You can almost see the air jump with the noise that echoes
up and down the long hall. The chiseler stops; silence drops down
gradually, chasing the weakening echoes away.

Then, emerging from a tangle of towering machines, we stand
face to face with the California Giant. He has been painted
white; he stands there gleaming and alone in a great open court
under the high skylights, as aloof from these other grimy mon-
sters as if he were in reality some visiting machine from another
world. For an instant we forget that Fredericks is not Verne's
J. T. Maston and we his fellow travelers in the *Journey to the
Moon*. As he swings his arm up in a proud, wide gesture, we
think we hear him say: "Gentlemen, the Columbiad is ready!
When I give the word, fire!"

In the center of the floor high above us, the yoke-piece is
stretched out on tall pedestals, complete. Beyond, at the side,
the horseshoe raises up its massive horns into the roof; opposite,
the tube, with its mighty rings and square laced together with
spidery beams, seems to stare at us with complacent eyes. All
three have the peculiar air of being alive—waiting for their turn
to go somewhere, do something new. Unlike the other Brobding-
nagian tenants of the place they have the power to whip the imagination into preposterous adventures in a future century. It is
as if one were standing in the midst of New York's mad World's
Fair, and had suddenly discovered that its fantastic modernism
made sense.

Fredericks is touching our elbows; he would like to take us
up a long ladder into the interior of the yoke. Carefully, one by
one, we climb and swing inside the great hole into a metal

cylinder as big as a subway. It is a spectroscopic laboratory, explains our guide, enclosed in the moving arm of the telescope in a plan so bold that Verne himself could hardly have thought of it. Here, on future nights, the astronomers will cling to a revolving platform and keep their balance as the Giant rolls among the stars. The sense of fantasy becomes all at once overpowering. This chamber is indeed the inside of a projectile, headed for the boundaries of the Universe. It is hard not to believe that we are already hurtling out across the Galaxy, with nothing but star-studded space around us.

Instinctively we step to a great round opening in the side to look out upon the void; just in time our engineer seizes us by the arm and pulls us in again. "Look out," he admonishes, "you're up in the air in a telescope, don't forget!" This great hole, he tells us, will be occupied by one of Kroon's specially designed flexible supports, so large that a whole train of optical mirrors will shoot the starlight through it without touching anywhere—so original in design that hundreds of stretched steel rods, ranged around it like the spokes in a bicycle wheel, will bear the weight of the telescope tube in a cradle that defies distortion.

Presently we are down in the shop again, our imaginary journey over, and Fredericks has led us in beneath the skeleton tube, lying on its side near by. Like the framework of a great gun it soars above us, aiming its huge bore down the length of the shop. It is as if we had crawled inside an engine built to turn the earth itself (and we remember that Jules Verne did once describe such an engine, to shift the Earth and change the seasons to perpetual summer). Its lofty rings seem to sweep around silently and take us with them. Its thin straight beams are the living expression of vast energy under perfect control.

And then, beyond them, as through a frame, we see the horseshoe towering upward past the doors and windows of the shop, past the crane beams forty feet above the floor, past the roof girders themselves and into the sky almost. So high that a single man, clinging to the upper end of one of the horns wielding a paintbrush, looks like a fly on the tip end of a section of water-melon—

But here imagination (aided by press photographs from West-inghouse) outruns the facts. But who can blame it? During the long months of construction in Philadelphia the company press department was assiduously circulating a picture of the mighty horseshoe standing upright against the background of the shop, with men climbing up it on ladders leaned against its flank. Newspapers published the picture everywhere; even the Sunday readers of the *New York Times* were given it in good faith. Ac-cording to the engineers the photograph was a fake. It was both unnecessary and impossible to stand the horseshoe on edge in the plant. But it seemed a good thing to boast of anyway, so, as the great piece lay flat on the shop floor, ladders were ar-ranged, men carefully disposed upon their stomachs on them, and cameras were snapped. The rest was the old familiar game of retouching, and if newspaper editors were suspicious they never said a word.

But the story of the Giant itself needs no retouching. Half a million dollars worth of steel was put together in Philadelphia presently, then dragged to the waterfront and shipped on freighters through the Panama Canal to San Diego. One more real record had fallen: these were the largest pieces of machinery ever shipped on the high seas.

# CHAPTER XXX

## ON THE MOUNTAIN

IN the summer of 1935, Captain McDowell was ready to break ground on top of Palomar Mountain. It had taken eight years to settle even the preliminaries for the 200-inch telescope. But work on the steel was at last begun and a definite start must be made on the observatory itself.

At this point county politics reared its tousled head. The San Diego County Supervisors had promised two years ago to build a wonderful new road up the mountain, but so far not a shovelful of earth had been turned.

Without the road McDowell could do nothing about moving the huge pieces to the summit. Until transportation facilities were assured it was not safe to start the observatory. So he took Cal Tech's attorney and drove down to San Diego in a fiery mood to issue an ultimatum.

The Supervisors received them almost abjectly. They hoped to start the new road "soon."

"When?" demanded McDowell.

"When we can get our people to agree where the road's to go."

It was a typical case of local finagling. No sooner had the proposal for the "Highway to the Stars" come through than every little crossroads demagogue in the district rose to insist that it must pass through his bailiwick, or else—

The Supervisors were in a quandary. A million and a half of the County's money had been voted for the job. How could they go against the County's wishes? They wanted nothing more than to get the road done, they protested. Couldn't the Pasadena people lend a hand? McDowell and the lawyer realized that it was no use to threaten, though they did say that unless something was accomplished soon they'd have to move the whole project onto Table Mountain in Los Angeles County. For the moment the deadlock was complete. The politicians wrangled on.

Anderson took a hand, with various others, but the Supervisors remained helpless. The situation began to look serious. Then, finally, a picturesque old character named Cave Couts broke the jam. Couts was born a fighter, half Spanish—the last of the Dons, and the model from which Helen Hunt Jackson drew Señor Felipe for her novel *Ramona*. He was by long experience a clever politician. One night when the County fathers were cat-fighting as usual over the location of the road, Couts broke in on them and issued an ultimatum.

"You know," he said, "how many people go to Boulder Dam every year? Six hundred thousand! That's how many will visit us, maybe, *if*—"

He stared at them owlishly.

"It would be a pity if all those people and their money had to go up to Los Angeles County to see that telescope, now wouldn't it? . . . I'll give you boys just ten minutes to decide about that road."

Ten minutes was enough. The County started the road the next day, in a stampede to keep the observatory from running away. They had a bad time finding labor on short notice and finally had to turn loose a gang of "convicts" to break the ground. It was a strange crew, for the convicts had come from an alimony jail. Some of them had never seen a shovel. But the road was begun and Cal Tech judged that it was safe to go ahead with their plans.

First to arrive on Palomar was Russell Porter, with a surveying transit and plane table. He brought with him a tent and camped all alone on the summit for several weeks, making a preliminary survey. The lay of the land was ideal. For some thousands of feet a level ridge ran along on the west side, flanked by a broad sloping meadow. Beyond this a second ridge receded to the south and disappeared in the distance as a chain of lesser peaks. This one small glen between the two was the only flat spot in all the highlands of San Diego County. It was a little astronomical paradise lifted bodily above the tumbled canyons and forests of the wilderness.

In a few days Porter had in mind a layout for the whole settlement: the main dome would stand at the center of the

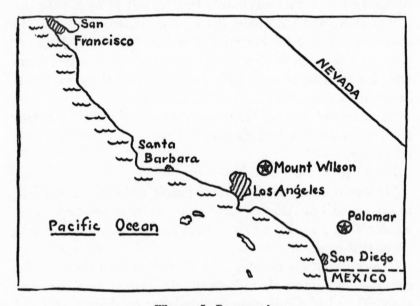

WHERE IS PALOMAR?

lesser ridge, 5700 feet above the sea, flanked by two smaller domes housing auxiliary telescopes. The meadow would be left intact as "insulation." Then on the other ridge opposite, would be the water tanks, machine shops, garages and service buildings. Over the slopes among the pines he would put the living quarters for the permanent staff, the "Residence" and the "Monastery." The whole thing would be landscaped as a unit, with the main observatory as the centerpiece.

When Porter got back to Pasadena he reduced his survey to a contour map and from that to a landscape drawing of the whole thing. Then he made himself a scale model of the mountain top, with the observatory and all the future buildings in place. One thing struck him at once: that meadow in the center of the summit would make a wonderful aviation field. Here was a natural airport. For the first time in history astronomers would fly to their work. Instead of several wearying hours' drive from Pasadena over winding roads and heavy grades, a forty-minute spin through the air would set them down in front of the observatory.

When he broached the idea to the others he found it had been in consideration for some time, but was generally frowned upon. They had discussed it and decided it was too expensive. "We've got to stop somewhere," they said.

"We're going to have everything else under the stars, so why not include aviation?" Porter persisted.

"If you don't look out," Max Mason remarked, "the astronomers will get so lazy they won't do anything at all."

H. M. Robinson, when he heard about it, agreed with Porter. "Flying is inevitable in the end," he said. "You're making a mistake."

Anderson determined to find out. He never let anything go by guesswork that could be proved. He got hold of an experienced aviator and took him to the top of Palomar and showed him the future layout. The aviator was not impressed. There was only one direction in which a runway could be built, hence only two winds that would let you land or take off. Even then, it would require a special low-speed plane to do the trick safely. "Unless, of course, you use a helicopter or an Autogiro," he said.

Anderson was satisfied. "We'll wait for one of those," he said.

The first thing to be done on the mountain top was to provide the services—water, sanitation, light, power and living quarters. McDowell got hold of a retired army officer named Colonel Brett and set him to work. Water was the first requisite. It was planned to have a huge storage tank holding a million gallons and in addition an elevated 50,000-gallon tank to provide a steady pressure. The purpose of so much water was adequate fire protection. Hundreds of square miles of heavy pine forest surrounded Palomar and the menace during the long dry season was serious. Fire hazard is an important problem all over the California mountain regions and rarely a summer goes by without huge conflagrations. It would not do to have the observatory buried in a wilderness of tinder without the best defenses known.

Hussey had found abundant water on Palomar thirty years before. All that was necessary now was to go half a mile down the mountain side to "Horse Thief Spring" and tap in on the "granite sponge" which stored the water of the melting winter snows.

Four shafts were driven in horizontally and fitted with pipes discharging into a large open sump. From here the main pipe line was run to the summit. Temporary gasoline-driven pumps were installed at the sump to lift the water—later to be replaced by electric units. Ground-water measurements had been taken consistently for several years already and the flow of water even at the height of the dry season was found to average better than 20 gallons a minute—ample for all the observatory's needs. In any emergency the supply would come from the storage tanks.

Fire mains were run below frost level out along the ridges surrounding the observatory site and hydrants were installed at frequent intervals. Forest Ranger stations were built so as to command the slopes of the mountain in every direction. Anderson and the Observatory Council conferred with Supervisor Brenneis of the Cleveland National Park, and got him to promise to take charge of all the fire-fighting work on the mountain.

A reservation of an acre and a half was set aside within a short distance of the observatory and here the government agreed to build a special fire protection office, garage and barracks for ten men. This would be equipped with a motor fire truck, hose and chemical apparatus and permanently manned as soon as possible. The top of Palomar would soon be as thoroughly protected from fire as the middle of a big city.

Colonel Brett quartered the first crew of workmen in a tent colony on the edge of the meadow, army fashion. But as soon as the water supply system was well along, McDowell had him build more permanent wooden quarters instead. The Observatory Council had decided to be its own boss in developing the site, instead of relying on outside contractors, and a large resident crew must be provided for. The little settlement that soon rose was complete with barracks for a hundred men, dining hall, recreation center and first-aid station. Brett put it in charge of another retired army officer, Captain Blythe, as steward. There were also a number of private cabins to which several of the skilled workers and foremen brought their wives and families. Still others lived in trailers and Brett arranged parking space for them over the edge of the hill.

For a time the workingmen's children were taken by bus to a district school twelve miles away. But as the Palomar colony increased and filled the school up with its own children, permission was obtained from the County authorities to move the school bodily onto the mountain. Later on, as many as eighteen observatory children attended it, while the two or three from outside were brought up the mountain by bus.

The problem of power supply was one of the first to require solution. The main observatory was to be completely electrified, with hundreds of motors, ranging from the small ones of ½ horsepower for driving the telescope to the four heavy 5-h.p. machines to drive the dome around, and the still larger ones to operate the 60-ton crane. There were also the drives for the water, fuel and fire pumps, and a complete system of electric lighting, cooking and refrigeration for the permanent settlement to be supplied.

The Construction Committee investigated the matter of bringing electric current to the mountain by a power line run up from the valley twenty miles away. This had been done successfully on Mount Wilson and the power supply had been thoroughly reliable. But out here in the wilderness there was a much greater risk of failure. If everything on the summit depended on one little line coming in from outside, the colony would be constantly at the mercy of cloudbursts, blizzards and rock slides. There was also a technical difficulty. A lengthy "stub-end" power line like this is apt to magnify electrical disturbances on the main power system and build up voltage "surges" just the way a small motion in a bath tub sets up waves that eventually slop over onto the floor. Such surges would throw the delicate timing devices of the telescope out of synchronism and make it erratic. Furthermore, the astronomers wanted more than anything else to be independent and self-sufficient. So they decided to build a whole power plant of their own.

Three Diesel-driven generating units were ordered, and the plant was soon under construction. The building was also designed to include a machine shop and an office, and a large garage and service station were laid out next to it to take care of the five trucks and the tractor that had been bought to do the grading work.

The electric generating units aggregated about 400 horsepower, and their installation was interesting on account of the special provisions included for serving the observatory. Instead of being bolted to the solid floor of the power house, the machines were fastened to great blocks of concrete weighing several tons. These blocks in turn were supported in pits on big springs at the four corners. The object was to kill all vibration. Although the observatory was to be 1000 feet away, the delicate mirror systems would respond even to minute shaking transmitted through the solid rock of the mountain top.

A Telechron master clock system controlled the speed of the Diesel engines through a delicate governor mechanism—the same outfit exactly as is used at Boulder Dam to control half a million horsepower. Thus the current from the three little units would be generated at a frequency within one per cent of sixty cycles at all times, and form a steady basis for the driving machinery for the telescope, as well as furnish timed current for electric clocks all over the settlement.

Three generating units had been decided upon so that there would always be at least one spare. Two were of 75-kw. capacity and the other of 150 kw. Ordinarily a single small unit would be enough to carry the operating load of the observatory; even with everything going full blast on the mountain the large one would do it easily alone. This meant that one of the three machines could be hauled down for repairs whenever necessary without interrupting the astronomers' schedule.

At the farther end of the power house McDowell fitted out a machine shop completely equipped to do any overhaul work that might come up. He included in this an electrician's department, a small foundry and a stockroom with a full line of spare parts and raw materials. Outside he installed two large fuel oil tanks with capacity enough to keep the engines running for several months without replenishing. All power lines to the observatory and other buildings he put in underground conduits to protect them from the weather. When it was all complete he had a self-contained electric plant the equal of the best city system, and capable of going on its own for years at a time. It was soon affectionately known to everyone as "Utility Hill."

Another important part of the establishment was communications. A fully automatic dial telephone system was laid out, with stations in every building on the mountain—twenty-two of them in all. No operator was needed. The switchboard fitted into a small glass cabinet in a corner of the power house; the resident electrician would provide whatever servicing might be needed.

A more difficult part of the communication problem that came up early in the proceedings was the telephone line between Palomar and Pasadena. Anderson and McDowell did most of their work in the Cal Tech offices, but had to be in constant touch with the work on the mountain also. There were continual problems of design and construction to settle, orders for materials to be sent out, new men to be hired. A direct private wire alone would suffice. McDowell went to see the telephone company about having a pole line run up the mountain. In the back of his mind he had the idea of using radio but felt that it would be too expensive. And the telephone people would hardly warm to a scheme that would rob them of paying business.

The first thing they said to him was:

"Why don't you use radio?"

"You mean you *advise* it?" Captain Sandy stammered.

Certainly, they told him cheerfully. A telephone line up Palomar Mountain would be just as vulnerable as a power line would have been and service over it could not be guaranteed. But with radio it would be simple.

"Much cheaper than wired communication for a job like this," explained the telephone company. "No operators will be needed. The whole outfit won't take up any more room than your present automatic system on the mountain."

And so, after a short time, two-way radio communication was set up between Palomar and Pasadena. A small room off the Optical Shop and a corner of the power house were all the space required. The stations were temporarily licensed as W6XKX and W6XKY by the Federal Radio Commission, and were soon in regular operation. The two standard Western Electric units comprised a transmitter and receiver operating on a wavelength of 7½ meters. Small rods erected on the roof were all that was necessary for aerials. A ringing system similar to the ordinary telephone bell was included. It was as simple to operate as the standard instruments. It was only necessary for someone to be within sound of the bell.

A schedule of calling hours was worked out and it was arranged to have someone in the vicinity of the radio sets at those times. When the bell rang the watcher simply turned a switch on the outfit and started it up; then lifted the receiver on an ordinary desk telephone set and began to talk. When the conversation was over both sets could be shut off. To put a call through ninety-five miles of air to the mountain took considerably less time than obtaining an ordinary long-distance connection, and there was no risk whatever of interruption from storms or delays due to heavy telephone traffic.

While the engineering construction got under way Russell Porter turned out complete architectural plans for housing the observatory staff. In this he had the able assistance of R. D. Batchelder, who was brought out from M.I.T. to do the detail designs. The principal unit was to be the "Monastery." Bachelor life had worked so well on Mount Wilson that the principle was to be adopted here. Most of the astronomers would visit the mountain for only a few days or a week in every month; it was unnecessary to provide quarters for their families.

The Monastery was to be set off to one side over the brow of the hill in a grove of trees, and would be the equal of a beautifully appointed club. Designs called for eight bedrooms upstairs; large living room, library and recreation room below. Complete kitchen equipment was included, with quarters for a man and his wife to run the place.

Porter got the Council to agree to the most modern possible construction for the Monastery, on the theory that it must provide the utmost in comfort and relaxation and be adequate for the severe winter climate. It was to be built entirely of prefabricated steel, welded together, the walls and floors filled with rock wool insulation, the roof covered with copper. It would be fireproof, termite insulated and earthquake resistant. An automatic heating and air-conditioning system, electric cooking and refrigeration, and telephone connection with the Observatory would make the Monastery the last word in off-duty astronomical ease.

While the ground was being prepared for this, five permanent cottages were quickly put up near by, for the resident operating staff and their families. These were designed on the same plan as the Monastery, but of bungalow size. Porter spotted them around among the trees with plenty of land around each one and good care to provide a view off over the edge of the mountain.

The gem of the whole collection, however, was the "Residence," which he persuaded the Council to include to house distinguished guests. He designed this as if to entertain royalty. Two master bedrooms with baths, living room paneled in natural wood, big fireplace, air conditioning, complete kitchen and two-bedroom servants' quarters, garden—everything—as fine a little house as any to be found in Southern California. When it was done one of the first guests to be quartered there was ex-President Hoover. His night there, he remarked, was more comfortable than any he had spent in the White House.

Although it looked as if the astronomers were more interested in their accommodations than in the telescope, this was not the case. From the start work had been going ahead on the observatory site itself. The early part of the job was slow because there was a good deal of grading to be done. The top of the mountain had to be scraped bare and worked down to a flat shelf of granite for the foundations.

The observatory was to be of the conventional circular type with a hemispherical dome. One advantage of the short focal length of the telescope was that the observatory would be comparatively small—much less than twice as big as the 100-inch dome on Mount Wilson. Nevertheless, it would be big enough to be imposing: one hundred and thirty-seven feet in diameter and one hundred and thirty-five feet high—as tall as a twelve-story building. McDowell computed that the steel work in it would total about 2000 tons.

First the exact location of the mountain top was found on a topographic map and the latitude noted (33°21'20" N) and verified by checking on Polaris. Then twenty-three five-foot holes were sunk into the solid granite in a wide circle and heavy steel columns were footed in them and bedded in concrete. A stiff girder was run around on top of these columns to form the upper sill, and the interior was filled in with more steel work and riveted up into one rigid mass. This cylindrical skeleton comprised the lower or stationary part of the observatory. Beams and bracing were made exceedingly heavy in order to provide the stiffness required to withstand earthquakes. A square opening in the center was left for the undercarriage of the telescope to pass up through without touching the rest of the building. The base of the instrument would be set on its own foundations and thus be insulated from all vibration originating in the dome.

A reinforced concrete wall thirty feet high was built around the outer framework and twelve inches inside this a second wall was put in and covered on its inner surface with asbestos insulation. The air space between the two walls would later connect with a similar space in the double-skinned dome above, giving the entire observatory an insulating blanket of air. Every evening before observations began this air, warmed by the heat of the Sun on the walls outside, would be pumped out at the top of the dome and new, cool air drawn in below. Thus the interior of the building could be held within a degree or two of night temperature all the time.

Around the top of the stationary shell of the building a circular track of two heavy railroad rails was laid down, on which the dome itself was to roll. In order to insure vibrationless operation the rails were welded together to eliminate joints and then polished absolutely level and smooth. For this purpose McDowell used an electric grinding car which rode around slowly on the rails themselves and polished off all bumps and uneven places. So important was it to have the job done right that Johnny Kemple, the veteran machinist who had polished the dome rails at Mount Wilson, was brought down especially for the job.

The dome was to roll on thirty-two four-wheeled trucks, somewhat similar to the trucks under a Pullman car. These were fitted with heavy coil springs and prevented from jumping off the rails by clamps inside and horizontal wheels outside. The outer rail was lower than the inner one, and the wheels resting on it were correspondingly larger, to avoid slip and screech on the circular track. When all trucks were assembled, a massive ring girder was built on them to furnish the foundation for the dome.

Like Serrurier's telescope tube, the dome was an innovation in observatory design. It was the product of the whole engineering staff, backed by Martel and von Karman. Months were spent by the Council and its various technical committees in thrashing out every feature, and Russell Porter was responsible for many of the details. He made hundreds of drawings in his inimitable cut-away style and many times ended an argument by appearing and pinning up a picture of some controversial part that demonstrated at once how it would work.

Von Karman, who headed the Institute's aeronautical department, persuaded the Council to borrow the monocoque design from the airplane wing, which derived its main strength from its skin, like an egg shell. This would save tremendously in weight, for only very light structural bracing would be needed. Following this principle, two huge box-girder arches were first erected on the ring at the base of the dome, thirty feet apart. These formed the portals of the slot through which the telescope would look out upon the sky. Then the rest of the circumference was filled in with thin built-up beams rounding up to the crown at the top. On this skeleton the skin plates would be supported. A one-hundred-foot erecting crane had to be installed to lift all this material into place.

The Nigger Grade and the roundabout road in from the south still gave the only access to the mountain top, for the promised "Highway to the Stars" was only just begun. Every ton of steel had to be hauled up on trucks and trailers over treacherous grades and serpentines scarcely wide enough to let them pass. The crane itself had to be broken in five pieces in order to get around the hairpin turns, and then put together again at the top.

When the skeleton was in place the steel plates were laid on

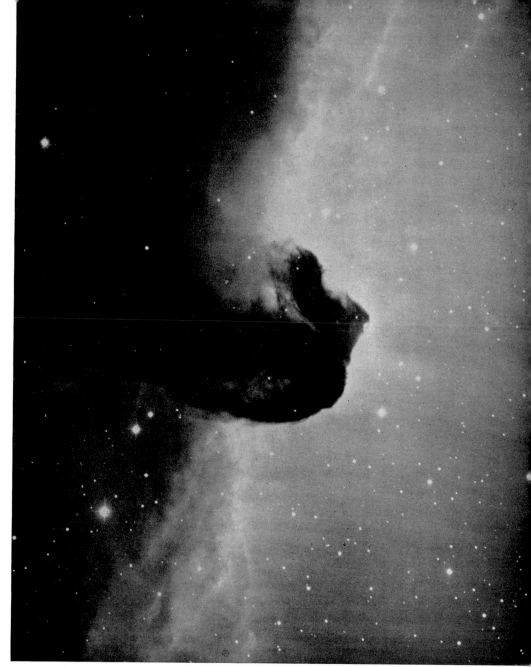

*Mount Wilson and Palomar Observatories*

The famous "Horsehead Dust Cloud" in the constellation of Orion. Entirely invisible to the naked eye, this has been photographed by many telescopes, but not until the 200-inch took this picture in 1951 was the detail so clearly seen. Gigantic clouds of "cosmic dust" apparently float through space—possibly all that is left of huge stars that have exploded and died.

This dust cloud, like the Horsehead, lies within our own Galaxy or Milky Way. It has fancifully been called "Madonna and Child." It is apparent that what we think of as empty space is actually filled with terrible turmoil and activity. The halos and rays seen around the brighter stars are effects caused by the structure of the telescope and halation in the photographic plate.

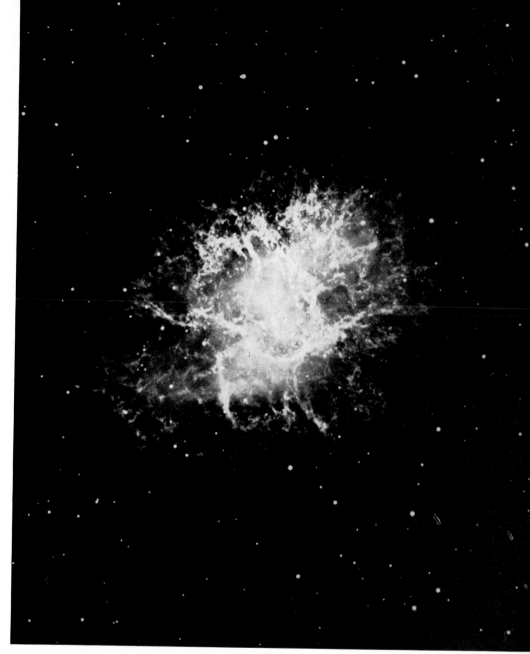

*Mount Wilson and Palomar Observatories*

This is the "Crab Nebula" in Taurus. It was originally seen in broad daylight by the Chinese in 1054 A. D., as a very brilliant star. We know now that what they saw was that rare event in our Galaxy, a stellar "atomic explosion," or supernova. Having burst, the substance of the star flew outward in all directions. It is still expanding at enormous speed **after 900 years.**

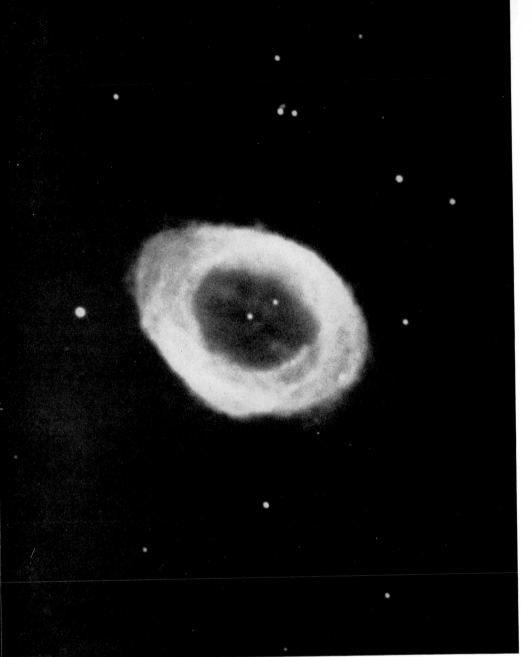

*Mount Wilson and Palomar Observatories*

The "Ring Nebula" in Lyra. This has been known for a long time, but earlier observers mistook it for a single bright circle of gas. The new pictures identify a central star, around which the illuminated dust cloud seems to be arranged. The Ring is still a mystery, for it does not seem to be flying apart as the Crab is doing.

*Mount Wilson and Palomar Observatories*

Out beyond our Galaxy in the deeps of space, millions of great conglomerations of stars move at bewildering speed. In the narrow space measured by the thickness of a pencil point held at arm's length the 200-inch finds this picture of four separate star-worlds. They represent four types of nebulae: the globe and three phases of the spiral nebula. We ourselves are of the disk type, without protruding arms.

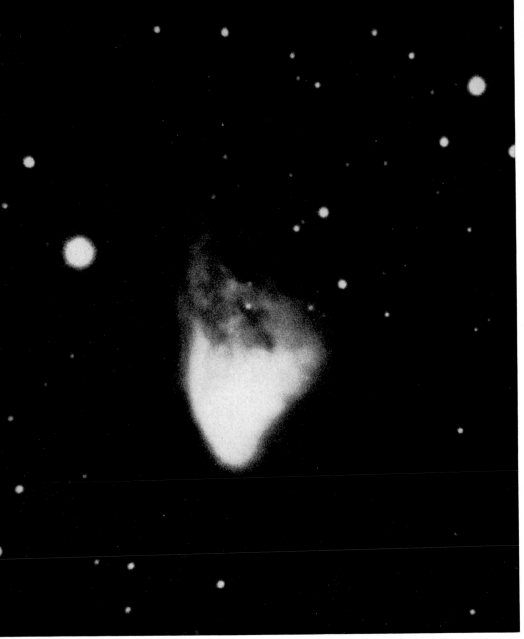

*Mount Wilson and Palomar Observatories*

This V-shaped spurt of flame is the first photograph ever taken with the 200-inch. It is called "Hubble's Nebula," after Dr. Edwin P. Hubble, who first identified it at another observatory years ago. The minute the 200-inch was ready, Hubble turned its great eye on this early discovery, and found it to be a wisp of illuminated gas, possibly the beginning of a new star or the death struggle of an old one.

*Mount Wilson and Palomar Observatories*

*Upper picture:* A typical nebula in space, like our own Galaxy. The intense glow at the center represents billions of stars, some of them perhaps accompanied by planets like our sun. The dark rim in the middle is simply the thin disk-edge of stars, black by comparison, that cut off the light from the inner cauldron.

*Lower picture:* The well-known nebula in Andromeda—our nearest island neighbor. It is the only one visible to the naked eye and can be seen in Andromeda on a dark summer night. The 48-inch Schmidt took this picture with such remarkable detail that individual stars can be identified, though the nebula is some 900,000 light years away.

*Mount Wilson and Palomar Observatories*

This puzzling photograph is the extreme achievement of the 200-inch telescope. When the original negative is enlarged to the maximum, a host of faint bodies can just be seen. Typical ones are indicated by pairs of white lines drawn on the print. The light from these remote worlds traveled a billion years to reach Palomar mountain. Faint as they are, enough can be seen of them to measure their size, identify their shape, and guess at their spacing. It may never be possible to look farther afield than this. Here photography and optics have been pushed close to their ultimate limit.

and welded edge to edge. These were so large that they had to be ordered from Chicago, where they were "bumped" in a special press which formed them into parts of a sphere. Each plate weighed a ton. Although the skin thus formed was only ⅜ths of an inch thick, it made a smooth streamlined shape guaranteed to withstand the heaviest wind and weather. The total weight on the truck wheels was about 1000 tons, but so perfect was the alignment and so smooth the rails, that a 200-lb. push would set the whole dome in motion.

To give the dome the same double-skin feature as the base of the observatory an inner plating of aluminum panels was used, secured to the arched roof beams with hooks and bolts. These panels were made up like hollow boxes out of sheets of the metal, and filled with crumpled aluminum foil to provide the greatest possible heat insulation. For the first time an observatory was to be sheathed inside with gleaming silver instead of the conventional dull black. The astronomers insisted that light reflections would not be troublesome because at night there was no light to reflect. Later on, all the photographic laboratories and darkrooms were painted white with the same idea.

Eighty men worked for two years assembling the observatory shell and the job, like the telescope itself, bristled with innovations. One of the most interesting of these was the method of driving the dome around: the invention of a young Cal Tech engineer named Ed Grant. In previous installations such as Mount Wilson, the wheels on which the dome rested were driven by motors after the manner of a trolley car. A still more venerable scheme, used at Yerkes and Lowell, pulled the dome around by cables wound on a drum. Neither of these was smooth enough for Palomar. So Grant tried something new.

Just above the trucks inside the dome he attached a smooth welded steel band a foot wide, standing on edge. On the stationary foundation he placed two pairs of 5-h.p. electric motors with vertical shafts carrying rubber-tired auto truck wheels. A system of spring supports pushed the wheels against the dome band under a pressure of several tons and the traction was enough to set the dome in motion and carry it smoothly to any position desired. All the clatter and vibration of the old gears was thus eliminated; by adjusting the tension of the springs there would be enough slip at the start to prevent the objectionable jerk and jar. The new system also provided a brake so powerful that the dome could be held stationary against a ninety-mile wind.

Grant had a hand in one or two other innovations also. He was one of the youngest of the group and quite lacked the spirit of self-effacement that most of the others possessed in too great degree. This lack was enhanced considerably when he won a $1500 prize from a manufacturer for an essay on welding. When the check came along a friend promptly photographed it for him and put it in circulation. The gang at Palomar gently chided him for it by labeling a part of his dome drive "Grant's Coffin."

Meanwhile another young Cal Tech man was doing his work quietly and well on Palomar. This was Byron Hill. He arrived on the mountain in 1936 and became the fully responsible Superintendent of Construction.

During that year the girders for the telescope substructure were dragged up the hill and set in place, and by the end of the winter of 1937 the last steel plate was welded into the dome and the observatory closed in. While this was going on a little gang of men put up the baby observatory for the 18-inch Schmidt camera near by. Some of the astronomers at Pasadena had become mildly impatient with the long wait and desired to begin practical work on the mountain as soon as possible. Sherburne built the instrument in the shops to Russell Porter's designs and the opticians made the mirror and correction plate. The camera was in effect a successor to the old Bruce camera of Mount Wilson days, only many times faster. It was soon installed in its little 20-foot dome and Fritz Zwicky of the Physics Department, with others, began taking photographs of large sections of the sky. The results were of immediate and startling interest.

Not only did they find on their plates numerous evidences of the "gravitational lens" effect of certain nebulae, which bears directly upon the proof of the Einstein Theory of Relativity. More important, Zwicky began to pick up the mysterious flaring suns known as "supernovae." Within three years he had discovered more of them with this powerful new camera than all astronomy had found in the years before.

Thus, even before the new observatory was complete the name of Palomar had begun to bring a disquieting influence into astrophysics. What would happen when the 200-inch itself was turned upon the sky?

# CHAPTER XXXI

## MAN BITES GLASS

IT used to be news when a man bit a dog, but it isn't any more.

But when a farm boy without education or experience turns himself into a skilled optician and persuades a man like John Anderson to let him make a mirror out of a glass disk worth one hundred thousand dollars—that *is* news.

In behind the windowless walls of the Laboratory at Pasadena a group of silent young men in white uniforms were writing a new chapter in optical history. They were tackling the toughest job of mirror making ever attempted, and were getting away with it by learning how as they went along. This was neither a paradox nor a miracle, but the result of astute planning by Dr. Anderson, who had taken sole responsibility for creating the 200-inch mirror. He had chosen the right man to do the job. His name was Marcus H. Brown, and he came from an egg-ranch at Long Beach, California.

To anyone in his senses it would seem evident that the delicate task of making the mirror could be entrusted only to the most expert optician in the world. In the days of the famous refracting telescopes this certainly was the case. Alvan Clark, father and son, Fecker, Brashear, Lundin—all were lifelong experts, trained from childhood in the shaping of glass. When an important lens came along one of them was naturally chosen to make it.

But with mirrors it was a trifle different. There was a tradition that they should be home-made. Newton, Herschel, Lord Rosse and many another pioneer had battled with their own reflecting surfaces and learned by painful trial and error how to make them behave. When Hale came along this was still true. He hired Ritchey in the early Yerkes days because he was good with his hands and seemed a careful and conscientious work-

man. Later, at Mount Wilson, George Ritchey made himself
into as fine a mirror maker as any in the world. And as the years
went by he used the same principle himself and took on one
assistant after another, training them for mirror making solely
by making mirrors.

Ritchey was originally a cabinet maker and had the idea that
only cabinet makers could be turned into successful opticians.
It hurt him considerably to find that an electrician made a good
one also. But when Anderson's turn came he was not so conventional. The process of choosing the man to make the new
mirror had evolved still further. It was not even necessary to
pick an electrician. It was only important to get hold of a young
man of the right temperament and spirit and train him from the
ground up. The man Anderson chose was a truck driver.

But the credit was not altogether Anderson's. Brown was a
truck driver by necessity. It was his own idea to become an
optician, and he carried it out against great odds. The very fact
that he carried it out was what made him eligible to do the 200-
inch glass.

Back some thirty-two years before, when Marcus Brown was
a kid on his father's ranch, he discovered that he did not like
farming and particularly abhorred raising hens. It did not give
him the chance to tinker with machinery that he wanted. So
he struck out for himself. After graduating from Sixth Grade
by the skin of his teeth he tried all sorts of things—helper to a
cable splicer, errand boy in a packing house, day laborer—anything he could get. But he liked nothing well enough to stick to
it. Then he fell into a piece of luck.

Hale was building his private solar observatory on the grounds
of the Huntington estate in Pasadena to continue as well as he
could with his shattered health. It happened that Brown's
brother-in-law was a gardener there. The 80-foot excavation
for the observatory was in the charge of George Jones, who had
been superintendent of construction on Mount Wilson since
1904. Jones was having a difficult time with the gang of Mexi-

cans that was digging the hole, and finally his truck driver quit, saying that it was too dangerous. Through the brother-in-law young Brown was suggested and Jones, skeptical of nepotism, said he would give him a week's try. Brown was soon invaluable, for he talked Mexican like a native and could back the truck up to the brink of the excavation without turning a hair or frightening the diggers below.

When the job was over Brown followed Jones back to the Mount Wilson shops and begged to be taken on. It was too good a chance to miss.

"Can you drive a truck up a mountain?" Jones demanded.

"You watch me!"

So Jones took him on, albeit with some misgivings, and Brown went to work piloting a truckful of telescope parts up and down the tortuous nine-mile carriage road on Mount Wilson. He had never taken any such responsibility before but he taught himself how to drive it, soft shoulders and all, and never had an accident in five years.

Brown hadn't been on the job long before he began to look around for something better. Truck driving hadn't much future. He would like to get into the shops and settle down to the precision work he knew that he could do. At one time or another most of the astronomers on the mountain rode on the seat beside him and Brown made a point of asking their help to get a job in the shop—especially a job on glass. They gave him little encouragement; the Laboratory was already supplied with the best experts in the world. He had a good job, they thought, and had better stay where he was. So Brown tried another tack.

Between runs up the mountain he hung around the shop on Santa Barbara Street making friends with the opticians at work on the lenses and mirrors. One of them was an old fellow named Kinney, who had helped Ritchey make the 100-inch Hooker. Kinney was going to retire in five years and Brown decided to prepare himself for the old man's job. So he began systematically to study glass at home, getting books out of the library and struggling with the theory of optics—substituting midnight oil and enthusiasm for the higher education he had missed.

For several years nothing happened, except that he won Kinney's friendship and the respect of everyone in the Laboratory. He kept quiet and listened, determined to say nothing till the time came. Then, in 1928, a rumor swept through the Laboratory that Hale had gained the support of the Rockefeller Foundation and that a 200-inch telescope was soon to be built. Brown was immediately in a dither. This was the opportunity he had been waiting for. He rightly guessed that Kinney and the other opticians were too old to be chosen to grind the new mirror. But he was afraid to ask for the job; it wasn't supposed to be known yet.

Nearly six months Brown waited, and spent his time talking it over with his friends the opticians.

"I'd rather you tackled anything else in the world but that 200-inch mirror," said one. "It'll finish the man that tries it!"

Brown wondered if this was genuine solicitude or had a tinge of envy about it. He hunted up Kinney in his special workroom and asked him what he thought. The veteran of a hundred mirrors stared at him over his spectacles for a moment.

"What do you know about glass?" he asked finally. "Look at me. I've been at it twenty-five years and I don't know much about it myself."

"I guess you think I'm crazy," said Brown.

"I *know* you are." Kinney slipped off his stool and went up to him. "But then, so is glass." Then he began to chuckle. "I tell you what you do. You go in and tell 'em you want the job and see what they say."

"Gosh," said Brown. But that settled it. He would go in.

In the summer the decision was finally made. A six-million-dollar observatory was to be built on or near Mount Wilson. The same day the announcement was posted Brown went in to see Anderson and asked him point blank for a position as an optician in the Laboratory. He hinted pretty broadly that he would like to get in line for work on the new telescope.

Anderson was not very enthusiastic. "You'll make more money driving the truck," he told him. "I'd have to start you in as a green apprentice."

"That's all right," Brown said instantly. "That's what I want. I've thought it over and I know."

"Well," said Anderson. "You have the right spirit. Suppose I put you on here at Mount Wilson with the understanding that if you are capable of becoming an optician you can have steady work. No specific job promised. Just steady work with glass, *if* you make good. How will that do?"

"Dr. Anderson—" But Brown couldn't say any more, and to save making a fool of himself, fled.


Then he began to "lean on it" in earnest. He and a youngster named Schroeder found themselves apprenticed to Kinney and Dalton, his assistant. In a week they were both buried in grinding compound and streaked with rouge, doing the dirty work around the machines that were turning out a steady stream of optical instruments for Mount Wilson. That lasted for only a few months, however, for Brown's determination sent him ahead at top speed. Presently he was taking responsibility of his own and making mirrors all himself—minor ones, but still mirrors. When the time came to build a 12-inch reflecting telescope for special seeing tests on Palomar, Brown was able to turn out the mirror single handed. From that he went on to spectograph gratings and the lenses and mirrors for the solar furnace that Hale was building for the Astrophysical Laboratory roof.

But all this time Brown was without portfolio. He just "worked there." And he worked hard for three years, not knowing whether he was coming up to Anderson's original requirement or not—not daring to think about the 200-inch job at all. But he wasted no time thinking about it; he kept quiet and ground glass. The minute work was over for the day he rushed home and got out his books and studied half the night. He was in a race and he knew it. The only thing that worried him was that there was so much to learn and so little time to learn it.

He put in hundreds of hours of his own time studying up on every possible angle of glass grinding and polishing. Optics is no plaything for anybody, but he mastered the rudiments of it. He learned to make Foucault tests and interpret the shadows; he absorbed the theory of grinding machines and the mechanics of cutting a parabolic curve in a disk. He experimented with tools of wood and tools of steel and invented a design of his own against the day when the 200-inch should be ready to cut. He investigated lap material and grit and rouge. And he kept quiet.

To make doubly sure that he would know how to make mirrors he built a grinding machine of his own at home, designing it from the ground up. He had no money to spend on it and concocted it out of whatever odd parts he could pick up. The driving mechanism was a Ford rear end, the tool carriers were pipe fittings. He used spare parts out of a thrashing machine and a disk cultivator on his father's farm, and pulleys that had served in his Dad's shop fifty years before. He got it built, finally, and it worked. But he never did much with it, then, for his luck changed once more and he didn't need a home-made grinder. Later on it came in handy, and today it is making some of the small mirrors for the Giant himself.

Brown was pretty lonely in those years, shut in by himself grinding glass, glass, glass. Occasionally he was a trifle bitter about it all. It struck him that with him trying so hard somebody ought to take a little more notice of what he was accomplishing.

"There's only one person in the world who will look after a man's interests and that's himself," he muttered once. "Or maybe two. Himself and his wife—if she's any good—"

Brown's wife was. In those early years when he would stay up late in the shop fighting the glass, she would take her three kids and walk the two and a half miles to the Laboratory with his supper, then wait around with the youngest asleep in her lap till "Browny" was ready to close up for the night and drive her home. But what Brown mistook for isolation was the fact that Anderson was wisely letting him find himself. He didn't know whether this chap could make the grade or not, but if he could he must do it alone.

In 1931 the matter of who was to be head optician on the big mirror was still in the air—at least, so far as Brown knew. But Anderson had long ago settled it. He had, as a matter of course, offered Kinney the job, and then Dalton. But Kinney said he didn't want it and Dalton was not well. So it logically went to Brown. The first he knew of it was when he was moved down to the Cal Tech campus to the basement of the Instrument Shop, with one assistant, and told to start work on the 30-inch ribbed Pyrex disk that had just come from McCauley's hand at Corning. The next he knew Porter and the other architects were consulting him about the design for the Optical Shop.

There was no doubt after that that the ex-truck driver was on the 200-inch project. As for being "in charge" of the mirror work, he never was officially told that he had any title. Several years later he discovered his name in the Institute directory as Optician in Charge. That seemed to settle it.

When the 200-inch disk arrived at the new Optical Shop that evening in April, 1936, Brown bossed the unloading of it from the trailer. Then he swung the great doors shut and for four years disappeared from the outside world. During all that time the immediate responsibility for the welfare of the great disk was his. In the high-vaulted, air-conditioned building that Porter had designed especially for the grinding operation Brown, with a crew of twenty-one men whom he picked himself, lived with the disk continuously, working toward the goal of the most perfect astronomical surface ever made.

The Optical Shop had only one door but the lock on it could

be opened with anyone's pass key. This annoyed Brown so much that he finally asked Dr. Anderson if he might change the combination. Anderson told him to go ahead. The lock that has been on that door since is a special one indeed. Only Brown and his gang and Anderson have the keys. No one else whatever can get in without one or the other to help.

Years ago Ritchey had locked himself in with the 100-inch disk in the same way. Although equipment and methods were better now the tradition of care was as potent as ever. Not a scratch nor a blemish was to be permitted; not a single inaccurate spot in all the huge area of the disk. Brown knew what it meant to Anderson to have that mirror right and he guarded it with the jealous care of a mother. And Anderson reciprocated by letting him have, as much as possible, the sole authority over the great room in which it was housed.

But this privilege never made the erstwhile truck driver arrogant. He could have assumed a dictatorial air, with such an important job under his care, but it wasn't in Brown to do it.

At the end of the shop there was a glass-enclosed observation gallery where visitors could watch without contaminating the sacred air. One evening after a hard day he happened to look up there from the floor and saw the janitor struggling with a convention of visiting salesmen who wouldn't go home. So Brown went up to help him out. The drummers captured him instantly and began asking questions, which Brown tried modestly to answer. One chap was particularly effusive in his attentions, called him Doctor Brown and said he'd sure let people know, back in New York, how he was shown around in Pasadena by the head man.

"By the by, Doc," he asked, "exactly what is your title?"

"Me?" laughed Brown. "Oh, I'm just the janitor's assistant."

The remark dropped like a lead weight on the salesmen's convention. Their spokesman cleared his throat.

"Come on, fellers," he said brusquely, "let's get out of here."

"The janitor and I nearly died laughing," said Brown.

# CHAPTER XXXII

## TWENTY-ONE MEN IN WHITE

FROM 1932 to 1936 Brown—always with Anderson in the background—perfected the organization of the Optical Shop and made the first of the auxiliary mirrors for the telescope. Experienced as he was, he still spent his time learning, and the most important thing he learned was how to train others to follow his lead.

The Optical Shop didn't advertise for help; it didn't have time to. Instantly word was out that Cal Tech was making its own mirrors applicants swarmed in from everywhere. Amateur astronomers, machinists, garage mechanics, carpenters, electricians, gas station attendants—everybody who had even the mildest reputation for accuracy or manual skill. And some who had no mechanical trade at all.

"All I'm looking for," Brown told them, "is men with interest and the ability to catch on. And I want 'em young. Youth helps, for it takes confidence and a little conceit to get away with this job. Never mind what you know or what you've done; it's what you can *learn* that counts."

He knew too well what an optical worker must have, to be fooled by anybody. Nine out of ten applicants he eliminated with a single interview. The tenth man he kept for observation, and put him through the same make-good-or-bust training that he himself had survived. Half of the candidates stuck, and these he hired permanently. He didn't burden his pupils with instructions or fuss over them with warnings and advice. He just gave them a glass disk and a grinding machine and told them he wanted an optical mirror and let them see what they could do to produce it. "There's only one thing, boys," he said. "If you don't know what you're doing don't do anything till you find out."

For a while Brown gave his gang night school instruction, telling them all he knew about glass, trying to describe in advance how mirrors were made. It didn't work. He found it was better to tell them too little and let them find their way by themselves.

Twenty-one men he got finally, whom he dressed in white shirts, pants, socks and sneakers and ushered into the still, sterile air of the Optical Shop, filled with the fear of God and the passionate hope that they would not be found wanting. It was that hope Brown looked for most keenly; if a man wanted to succeed really badly he was a good bet.

One of the boys had sold insurance for seven years, but had never touched glass in his life. Brown put him on a 45-inch mirror. Another, who came to him from a Pasadena garbage truck, he put to work on a 36-inch job. This fellow was so afraid he'd do something wrong that he took five months to finish it. But when Brown gave him a second one he did that in four weeks. A third chap hadn't done much of anything before he came to the shop; he turned out the most promising of the lot.

In 1934 the 120-inch disk came out from Corning and the optical crew went to work on it. This huge glass was not to be a mirror in the telescope but a testing "flat" for the 200-inch—as nearly a plane surface as it was possible to achieve. A special grinding machine had been built for it by Sherburne and Brown got the ten-foot glass on it and began to grind. When he had it smoothed off he had to stop, for the big disk could not be made optically flat till the 200-inch itself was polished to a spherical surface for testing it. But the grinding operation was a success, and dispelled any lingering doubts that Anderson might have had of the home-trained crew.

When Belyea backed his trailer into the doorway of the Optical Shop with the Pyrex Giant aboard, Brown's real troubles began. He and three other men shared the responsibility of unloading it, but to him it was more than a responsibility—it was the beginning of his life work and must not go wrong. With the overhead crane he got the crate into the shop and stood it on the floor.

The shipping case which Corning had fitted to the disk was in three parts: a heavy steel band clamped tightly around the edge, and two reinforced steel disks bolted to it front and back. The band had eyes in the top and it was comparatively easy to pick the forty-ton load up without danger. A few hours' work with the glass in mid-air and the crate was dismantled. Brown carried it slowly the length of the room with the crane, and deposited it on the twenty-foot turntable of its grinding machine. Then, with equal care, he dismantled the band. There for the first time was the huge yellow-green Giant that he had waited eight years to see. From that moment on the glass would depend upon him for its very life.

The grinding machine was as big as a two-story bungalow. Its heavy iron frame held the turntable high off the ground, with powerful electric motors and driving linkages beneath. By a complicated system of gears and shafts the turntable could be tipped into a vertical position so that later on the disk could be stood on edge for testing. On top was a heavy horizontal beam called the bridge, which moved back and forth on wheels. This supported a carriage, also on wheels, and the carriage in turn held a vertical spindle downward over the turntable. At the lower end was a fitting for attaching the grinding tool.

In operation the disk on its table would be rotated about once in eighty seconds. The tool would turn faster and at the same time be moved two ways at once by the bridge and carriage. The motors driving all of these parts were linked together so that the tool could be made to trace any kind of a pattern desired, and hence distribute the grinding evenly over the whole surface of the disk. Engineers call these tracings "Lissajou figures," and the machine is the same in principle as the one that draws the intricate filigree work on a dollar bill. The principle was not new but the mechanical details had been brilliantly worked out by a combination of Mattson, Sherburne and Brown.

Before an actual start on the mirror surface could be made the 20-ton slab had to be smoothed up to a true disk, and its ribbing at the back prepared for the elements of the supporting cell. This was the worst part of the whole affair for Brown because the disk had to be picked up and turned over by the crane several times with nothing more secure than a wire rope sling

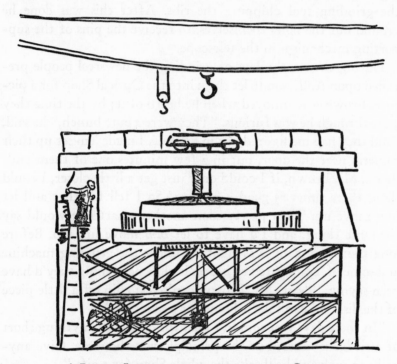

A ROUGH IMPRESSION OF THE 200-INCH GRINDER

passed around the edge to hold it. To turn the great glass over on the grinding machine required absolute co-operation of all hands, and there was always one critical moment when, with the turntable partly tipped, the crane had to pick up the burden without jerk or jar. A misstep, a bit of slack in the cables, a slip, and all would be over. For the disk to drop even a foot or two onto the concrete floor would mean a smash, with deadly slivers of glass flying in all directions. Anderson and Brown and everybody breathed a sigh of relief when the last of it was over and the disk was securely anchored to its cell. From now on nothing short of gross carelessness could damage the precious glass.

When he had got the top surface of the disk and the rim smoothed off, Brown did the same on the back, temporarily filling the cavities with wood plugs and plaster of Paris to prevent the grinding tool chipping the ribs. After this was done he ground out the holes themselves, to receive the pins of the supporting mechanism in the telescope.

During these early days of grinding the newsreel people prevailed upon Anderson to let them into the Optical Shop for a picture. Brown was annoyed when he heard of it; by the time they were through he was furious. "They were a cute bunch," he said, "and they had me figured out in no time. I made 'em set up their cameras near the door, but in a few minutes one of them said: 'Look, Mr. Brown, if I could only just get a little closer, I could shoot three times as good a picture.' So I fell for that and let him move up. Then pretty soon another smart one would say the same thing, and I'd have to let *him* move up, too. Before long the whole gang was right up under the grinding machine and some of 'em wanted to get on it. The next thing they'd have been saying, 'Please, Mr. Brown, can't you chip off a little piece of the disk so I can take it home for a souvenir!'

"In those days you couldn't hurt the disk with anything short of a sledgehammer, but the principle was the same. Give anybody an inch and he'll take the whole Shop for a gift."

As time went on Brown got even less friendly about intruders, and Anderson heartily concurred. It got so that even the astronomers themselves considered it a privilege to enter the Optical Shop and when they did they would huddle quietly at the far end of the room and step very gingerly so as not to shake any microscopic piece of dust from their clothing.

Presently it was time to begin the long process of making the mirror surface, first as a spherical hollow, then as a paraboloid. For the rough work of gouging out the glass Brown used a hollow, disk-shaped tool one hundred inches in diameter, welded up out of sheet steel and faced with Pyrex glass blocks cemented in place. It was his own invention. He set it in motion back and forth across the face of the disk with a long stroke, using a coarse grade of abrasive known as "Natalon." He did not have to worry about the shape of the hollow at first, for when two glass surfaces are ground together in this way the only shape they can take and still remain in contact, is part of a sphere.

With the surface roughly hollowed out, Brown constructed a full sized, 200-inch tool to smooth it down to a perfect spherical contour. Nineteen hundred and sixty-four glass blocks went onto this new tool, and it took several weeks to get it in shape before fine grinding could begin. Eight different sizes of grit were used now, each one finer than the last, and each taking off less and less glass. They were followed by two sizes of aluminum oxide as a sort of intermediate stage between grinding and polishing. Brown proceeded with unbelievable care, going over every inch of the great surface with a magnifying glass after each grinding to be sure the scratches from the larger sizes were all removed.

Barrel after barrel of Natalon went into the "soup" that did the grinding, and Brown got to ordering it by the ton. At first he tried to salvage the carbide grains and use them again. But the danger of scratches was too great. He abandoned economy and used his grit only once, then dumped the "muck" down the drain. By the time the grinding was finished, five tons of glass had been removed from the 200-inch disk and it had taken ten tons of Natalon to do it.

All that remained was to smooth up the spherical surface, then deepen it into a paraboloid—grinding and polishing off about $\frac{5}{1000}$ths of an inch more glass with a mixture of rouge and water. But Brown knew that "all that remained" meant at least three years of work of the most painstaking kind.

Now followed such a cleanup as would have made even Ritchey gasp. Brown spent three and a half months on it. First the men washed down the disk with hoses, scrubbed it, searched through every nook and cranny of it for the last grain of grit. Then they picked it up off the machine and stood it in a corner out of the way. Next they tackled the machine itself with hoses, hot soap and water, dry rags. And finally they began on the room.

The Optical Shop was one hundred and seventy feet long, fifty wide and forty high. Not an inch escaped. With rags and long-handled mops and vacuum cleaners the entire gang attacked it, working from the top down; over and over again till the paint itself began to come off. Then Brown sent them over

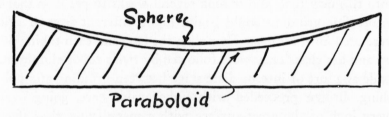

REMOVING THAT PAPER-THIN LAYER OF GLASS CAN TAKE A YEAR

it all once more with rags dampened with O'Cedar furniture polish, to give a smooth, slightly sticky surface that would catch whatever dust might fall.

When the room was done Brown laundered his crew, having them throw away every stitch of clothing and every pair of sneakers they had worn during the grinding process, supplying them with new outfits complete. Then he moved the disk back on its turntable and made ready to begin the polishing. It was not till months afterward that he realized that he had entirely forgotten the ceiling. "I sure intended to do it," he said, "but it got overlooked in the shuffle." Subsequent results showed that no harm was done.

For the main part of the polishing job the same 200-inch tool was to be used, but now the 1964 glass blocks were to have a surface of their own, made of a compound that Brown invented himself. He had been experimenting for eight years now with

polishing "laps" of a hundred kinds, and had tried every conceivable ingredient that might give that wax-like, smooth surface that would flow just a trifle under pressure and yet not
wear out too soon. His final formula consisted of rosin, paraffin
and cylinder oil.

The boys mixed the stuff up in small batches on a stove, then
poured it into wooden molds to cool like candy. After it was
hard they cut it into little squares and pasted these on the glass
blocks with the aid of a blow-torch and paintbrush wet with
the same material. After it was hard again, they trimmed and
beveled each square and cut channels in it, dividing it into still
smaller squares about an inch on a side. Thus the 200-inch lap,
when it was done, was a mosaic of nearly 8000 facets, with innumerable little canals for the rouge liquor to run through.

The polishing procedure Brown worked out as he went along,
trying out a hunch to see what would happen, then modifying
it as he learned. He would lower the tool onto the disk in the
afternoon and let it gradually press itself into shape by its own
weight. Then he would start his machine, the disk slowly revolving, the tool making "excursions" of only a few inches off the
center. One of the boys would pour the rouge liquor in from the
top with a soup ladle through funnels on the upper side of the
tool, letting it run through onto the lap, do its few moments
of polishing and leak out to the rim. This "run" would last no
more than half an hour, after which the lap would be left on the
disk for the night, with a "limit stop" on the spindle to prevent
it from sinking too far. In the morning the real polishing run
would begin.

One of the tensest moments in the whole building of the telescope came directly after polishing started. As soon as the
holes in the back had been bored out the disk was permanently
installed in its steel supporting cell. The question was whether
the ball-bearing supports that the engineers had designed would
hold the glass without causing distortion. There were thirty-six
of these supports, their coefficient of expansion identical with

that of the "Pyrex." In general principle they were cylindrical pins fitting snugly into the back of the disk with asbestos sleeves, but connected to the cell underneath through levers and counterweights hung on ball-bearings. When the mirror lay horizontally its weight would be evenly distributed on the heads of all the pins; when the telescope tipped the counterweights were expected to react through their levers just enough to keep the *side* of each pin sharing an equal part of the load.

Thus the astronomers hoped that the mirror would be floated in all positions with even support that would prevent strains and distortion. How successful the design would be no one would know till the mirror was smoothed up enough for an actual test with a beam of light.

Ever since the disk had arrived in Pasadena Anderson and the others had been worrying about the result of this test. Theoretical calculations had shown that the glass at the center of the mirror need be no more than four inches thick, but to be safe the optical experts had agreed upon six. At the last minute an accident in the annealer at Corning had made it necessary to lower the top surface of the disk by two inches, so when it came West it was back to the original theoretical thickness. But the Council felt that it was safe to go ahead.

The question now was, what would the pin supports do to the mirror surface so close above them? It was not a question that could be answered by exact calculation, for the mathematics of it were so complicated that only an approximate answer was possible. The Council asked the opinion of a prominent outside engineer. His rough figure indicated a distortion of some thirty wavelengths of light—enough to make the mirror worthless. Anderson hastily made a calculation of his own and it came out $\frac{1}{10}$th of a wavelength. Nobody knew who would turn out to be right. For nearly two years they had to wait till the mirror was spherically polished to get their answer.

Finally the day came; it was a silent Anderson and Brown and Porter who crouched on the platform by the Foucault knife-edge apparatus and stared at the huge disk, tilted on edge in its cell at the other end of the room. Would it be thirty wavelengths or one-tenth? Would the hundred-thousand-dollar glass become a mirror or a dud?

The tiny beam of light shot down the length of the laboratory and back. Anderson sat down at the instrument, put his eye to the knife-edge and bobbed his head back and forth to catch the telltale shadows.

"H'm!" he said.

"Well?" the others demanded. "What do you see?"

"You look," said Anderson, moving aside.

Brown jumped into his place and stared past the knife-edge, wobbling his head around this way and that, and then *he* said "H'm!" Then Porter followed suit.

"What do you make of it?" Anderson asked.

"Darned if I see any strains at all," Brown admitted.

Anderson sat down and carefully made the adjustments all over again. Then he stared long and silently at the shadows.

"What does it mean?" Brown demanded at last. "Have *I* done something?"

"In my humble opinion," said Porter, who had been looking past knife-edges for twenty years, "it means that there are no strains to see."

Then all at once the three of them burst out laughing, and the measure of their relief echoed down the long windowless hall.

The mirror grinned back complacently; Brown gave one of his boys such a joyous clout on the shoulder that he had a backache for a week.

# CHAPTER XXXIII

## IN THE OPTICAL SHOP

DURING the four years of its making the 200-inch disk was completely removed from the contamination of outsiders. Yet visitors were always able to see what was going on from the observation gallery which the astronomers had thoughtfully provided.

I had a date there one afternoon with Brown, during the long months of the polishing. But he was getting the disk ready for a Foucault test and was late, so I went up ahead to have a look.

One climbed a stairway outside the main room to a neat little foyer with pictures on the walls, rugs on the floor and a full complement of rest rooms in the background; then through another door came out into a long gallery with heavy plate glass windows on one side. This ran across the whole width of the shop and commanded a view of everything that was going on within. Everything but the sounds, for the glass was so thick that the work proceeded in silence, like a pantomime.

Partly because of the glass, one got an extraordinary illusion that the big laboratory was only a small room and the men and machines but miniatures. The clean, still air, and the strong light that flooded down over everything from dozens of lamps sunk in the walls, killed the shadows and destroyed the perspective, bringing everything apparently within hand's reach. A hundred and fifty feet away at the end of the room (it seemed only a few yards) the great disk lay on the turntable of its grinding machine. Its crew, all dressed in white, were swarming over it, with mops and hose, swabbing its limpid surface clean of the last stain of rouge. Near by stood the full-sized tool, upright in a wooden easel, and a man perched on a step ladder was touching it up with a blow-torch. Opposite, nearer at hand, the 120-inch disk and its grinder seemed to be waiting for the rest to catch up. The foreground was filled with an orderly clutter of small grinders, mirrors, blank disks, testing machines, barrels of rouge and piles of supplies.

Two or three men near by were grinding away on smaller disks, standing in apparent idleness while the arms of the machines slowly pushed the tools back and forth, streams of brick-red rouge running down all around. At a sink in a corner two others were wringing out pink-stained cloths in an old fashioned clothes wringer. A third was scrubbing himself severely with a bristled brush. At the other side of the room another optician in the inevitable white uniform was setting up a screen with a sign on it that said: "Keep away from this Machine." He was preparing for a test, lining up the center of his mirror with a string stretched to the eyepiece of a Foucault machine. It was all very complicated and very busy; these were the men who had never touched glass before, moving efficiently about at their work as if they had been born to it. Not a sound came through the window, yet there was a feeling of swift, smooth activity going on everywhere, like a tense scene in a hospital operating room.

At that moment one of the boys leaped up the ladder to a little platform on the side of the grinder and seized a control handle. The turntable gradually tilted up. Suddenly the disk, which had seemed a small thing in profile, looked enormous as its full face stared down the room. Brown could be seen now, standing apparently at ease off to one side, giving an occasional order with the swing of an arm. No more than a minute seemed to go by, then the disk stood on edge, the pale shimmering green of its interlaced ribs showing through from the back like a magnified piece of honeycomb done in ice. It was a beautiful sight—too soon to be hidden for good in the heart of the telescope.

Some time later I found Brown at my elbow. "Sorry to be late," he said. "The boys can do it without me perfectly, but I don't like to hold them responsible, so I'm usually there."

One of the routine knife-edge tests was about to be made.

Under the window on a sturdy wooden platform Millikan and Anderson were lining up the instruments, aiming them at the disk one hundred and ten feet away. The Foucault machine, as Anderson had designed it, was mounted on a high platform level with the center of the disk. It could be raised and lowered or moved sidewise with a simple turn of a handle. The apparatus looked like a small lathe, with a hooded electric light and the adjustable knife-edge held in a ring close beside it. In front of the light was a pinhole—nothing more than an artificial star. The pinhole, as Brown explained, must be not more than $\frac{1}{1000}$th of an inch in diameter, pricked through thin metal with a fine-ground needle by an expert hand. The knife-edge, likewise, must be cut from spring steel and be microscopically accurate.

When the test is set up the pinhole is placed as nearly as possible at the center of curvature of the mirror's spherical surface —the point out in front where its imaginary radii meet. The observer now brings his eye as close alongside the lamp as he can. If the curve is nearly true, he sees the whole mirror filled with light, since every point in it reflects the light back to him along some radius of the curve. Next he moves the knife-edge slowly in from the side, cutting the line of sight and blocking the rays returning to him from the glass. If the mirror is part of a perfect sphere it will suddenly go dark all over while still visible in outline, for the knife-edge will have cut off all the returning rays at a single point. But if the curve is irregular, the rays are not concentrated quite to a point and some will be cut before others. What the observer sees now is a remarkable set of lights and shadows on the disk. Suddenly the whole surface seems to stand out in relief, with hills and valleys clearly marked, as if strong illumination were being cast in from the side, obliquely. Irregularities of a few millionths of an inch are as plain as the ruts in a muddy road under the glare of headlights at night.

The test is the same, whether the mirror be three inches in diameter or seventeen feet. But the interpretations are not easy; one must be highly skilled to translate shadows and highlights correctly, and know where next to polish off glass after the test has been made.

Half a dozen Foucault machines were scattered around the room out there, mounted on rolling easels. Every one of the crew

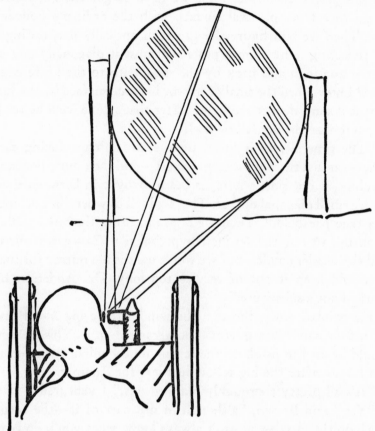

THE FOUCAULT TEST

was expert in their use. "The darn things are so accurate," Brown explained, "that they detect errors you never could work out of a mirror. The best surface you can make looks terrible with those knife-edges, and the boys used to fuss over a mirror for weeks after it was plenty good enough. So now we stop them a little *short* of perfection—about a hundred years short."

I asked him what the 120-inch glass was for. "The final parab-olizing test," he said. "We have to have parallel light rays the same as from a star to prove that the mirror will focus to a point. The 120 will provide them.

"It's pretty elaborate. First we have to get the big mirror down to a true spherical surface with the ordinary Foucault test. Then we will figure the 120-inch optically flat, testing it by reflecting light from a pinhole against it diagonally and on to the 200-inch and back by the same path to the knife-edge. We'll know when the smaller mirror is a true surface by the fact that it doesn't distort the light. After that's done we'll be ready to parabolize the big fellow itself.

"The general idea is to set up the two mirrors facing each other—at just the right distance apart—and then put a Foucault machine at one side, sending a beam of light in between them with a small diagonal mirror. That will tell us when the 200-inch is a true paraboloid. Then we'll go on, using the same sort of hook-up, to test the 60-inch hyperboloidal Cassegrain mirror and the smaller coudés. But we won't use the big mirror for that. It would keep it out of service too long. Dr. Anderson has worked out a substitute."

He pointed down through the window at a big metal easel with four good sized mirror disks arranged on it. This, he said, would be used to finish up the testing on the minor members of the family after the big fellow had left for Palomar.

"It's all pretty thoroughly planned out," I ventured.

"Yes," said Brown, "although in my part of it—the actual work on the glass—you can't always know what you'll do from day to day. Glass is a funny thing—human almost. You've got to move fast to keep up to it. Fast but carefully. Dr. Anderson knows what he wants and I try to give it to him. But I have to cut and try a lot to do it.

"Take that mirror out there, now—the polishing of it. I study something out and seem to get an impression of what to do about it and that's what I do. Maybe I'll start on a half-hour run and then stop at the end of five minutes on a hunch that something isn't right. I never pass up a hunch; I obey it immediately. Usually I'm glad I did.

"It's a matter of run and test, run and test. A long run is bad —it's too risky. You can't do any harm by making short runs, just waste a little time, that's all. Time is cheaper than glass. *Grinding* a mirror is easy—you know what to expect. But with polishing and figuring you never can tell what the tool will do next. One day it works one way, next day it's entirely different. A lap is just as temperamental as an optician and you can't get it to talk, either. You're working blind till you take the tool off and see what it's done to the mirror. Then you give it a test and see what to do next. . . . One thing, though: we're a lot better off than Ritchey was. Five minutes of polishing at a time was all he could do, and even then the disk had to cool for hours before he could make his tests. This 'Pyrex' is so thin that it cools practically as fast as you warm it."

All the time we stood there talking, a man was going back and forth over the floor of the shop with a big carpet sweeper. Brown said it had a magnet inside it, for picking up steel chips. The fellow did nothing else, eight hours a day. Every night he brought in the sweepings in an envelope and Brown analyzed them with the utmost care, trying to decide where they came from. Ever since the start, these mysterious chips had been turning up on the floor and nothing they could do would stop them or reveal their source. "One little chip," he explained, "riding through a run under the tool would plow a furrow hopelessly deep in the disk. So far, it hasn't happened," he shrugged. "There's luck for you, again."

I said I thought it was care.

"Well, we *try* to be careful," Brown said. "But if we took every precaution that suggested itself, we'd never get anything done. We started taking chances when the disk was delivered, and we still are. That is, we seem to be. I expect if you talk to Dr. Anderson you'll get a different impression. . . . There he is now, signaling to me to come down. I'm sorry—I'll have to go."

And off he went, as quickly as he had come.

I was curious to know Dr. Anderson better—this man who had so quietly assumed the responsibility for the whole optical success of the telescope. As it worked out I got the chance on the next Sunday morning, when he invited me into the Optical Shop itself. But if I expected him to demonstrate himself I was wrong, for he remained as quiet and unassuming as ever. It was the magnitude of this great room and the machines in it that told his story for him—the magnitude side by side with the overpowering minuteness of the accuracy on every hand.

We sat on a bench outside the door with the special lock, and changed to sneakers—they had almost a whole shoe store there on a shelf for the convenience of the privileged visitor—and presently were stepping into the hushed, still atmosphere where the giant glasses were being born. What an improvement this was over the long corridor at Mount Wilson that Ritchey had to use for his tests! What he thought was a fatal weakness in the 100-inch disk was only the freakishness of the warm air currents drifting through the hall. He might as well have tried to read a newspaper across a hot stove.

But here in the Optical Shop there was none of that—none of anything that might impair the success of the work. The gray-painted grinding machines stood around in a friendly clutter, and mirrors in every state of completion crowded in on every hand. But you knew that nothing was out of place and you realized above all that everything was *clean*.

Anderson led the way up the ladder to the Foucault platform, and aimed the little instrument down the room at the disk, which was looking at us with Sunday morning calm. As he was getting things lined up he explained about the tests and shadows. I told him I had made a mirror myself and knew the rudiments of the game. He warmed up immediately. "That's fine," he chuckled. "You know, everyone who's interested in astronomy ought to make a mirror. It's a kind of kindergarten course one needs to establish the right point of view." It was a matter of language, then. When he found someone who talked his own he was no longer reticent; he let you see inside his mind.

I was looking past the knife-edge now, at the face of the mirror for the world's biggest telescope. There were the shadows—the lights and shades that told within a millionth of an inch where that surface was. I was amazed. I could imagine myself at home, looking past the edge of an old razor blade at the optical landscape on my own six-inch mirror. It was the same.

But what they did about it was not the same. Through the week Brown and the boys worked along with the polish-and-test schedule at their own rate, up until Friday night. Then, on Saturday morning at eight—not a minute after—Anderson and Brown would begin their detailed summing up of the mirror's condition, working usually till late afternoon. Every square inch of the great surface would fall under the searching test and a chart would be drawn up to show where the high and low spots were. Then, in the following days the gang would go to work again, leveling off a little here and a little there, gradually polishing down toward the perfect sphere.

This, said Dr. Anderson, was only the start. When it came time to parabolize, alternately with fine grinding and polishing—then the real work would begin.

"Will you finish on schedule?" I asked. But it was a foolish question. There was no schedule, he said. There were too many unknowns. They would finish when the mirror had a surface that satisfied them all. They were about six months ahead of expectations, however, Dr. Anderson said without visible pride. When they made their tests after the first light polishing they were much nearer than he had hoped they'd be. The mirror was to have a radius of curvature of one hundred and eleven feet and two inches. It came out just one hundred and eleven feet. The radius at the center was shorter by a tenth of an inch.

A tenth of an inch in 111 feet for a first rough approximation is not bad—an error less than $\frac{1}{100}$th of one per cent. Those other wizards of astronomical figures—the politicians—might well take notice.

We walked up the long room and stood in the shadow of the Giant, his great green flank soaring above our heads. The glass was beautifully transparent and the slight milkiness of the Pyrex composition gave a fairy-like background to the weird reflections in its surface. I had walked on its mate at Corning but dared not so much as lay a finger on this. Anderson assured me that I could not hurt it. In fact, the men walked on it regularly every day, swabbing it off.

"Suppose a grain of dirt—"

"We have to walk on it whether we like it or not," he said calmly. "So we keep clean and don't worry. Nothing has happened yet."

Was he talking about luck, as Brown had? No, I decided. Anderson didn't do anything or allow anything to be done unless he was sure. As sure as a man with fifty years of scientific training could be.

"Can't you tell me more about all this?" I urged him.

"There isn't much to tell," Anderson hedged. What he meant, of course, was that there was too much to tell even to make a beginning. But he saw me examining the glass center plug cemented into the disk to make the polishing even, and ended our interview with a story.

The plug was forty inches in diameter and weighed a ton or more, and when it came time to lower it into place—a snug fit in the hole—no one knew just how to do it. There was no precedent, for it had never been done before anywhere. They had a consultation about it in the office. It was not possible to let the plug down with the crane because there was no room for the cables. And it couldn't be pushed up from below because the mirror cell was in the way. What, then?

Ice. Sinclair Smith's uncle, who was a contractor, had once got a job from the Southern Pacific dismantling a tall water tank that had been weakened in the Santa Barbara earthquake. It was wavering high in the air on its twisted legs and was a menace to the railroad. He didn't dare send his men up to take it apart piecemeal. Then he thought of ice. He bought a train-load of it and piled it up from the ground in a great pyramid, then jacked the tank off its legs and let it rest on the chilly foundation. Then he waited for the California climate to do the rest.

R. W. P. + D. O. W.

In two weeks the tank had come down and Smith's uncle joy-fully cut it up for scrap.

Why not do the same with the glass plug? Anderson agreed. He didn't tell them that he had just figured out the same thing himself, starting from scratch. Next day Brown suggested the same principle, using photographic hypo crystals melted down with water. That afternoon R. A. Wood of Johns Hopkins happened in and took a shot at the problem.

"Why not use melting ice?" he proposed after a minute.

"Ice it is," said Anderson. And the plug slipped into place without a hitch on a couple of hundred pounds of ice "bought at the corner drug store."

So it goes when scientific minds get together on a problem. Some simple thing, no matter how crazy it seems, usually holds the secret of success. And no solution is too lowly to be used, so long as it works.

# CHAPTER XXXIV

## INSPIRATION

WHILE Brown was closeted with his mirrors, a good deal was going on in the Instrument Shop next door. Sherburne, in fact, considered that he had a job just as hard as Brown's, even if less spectacular. This was the cutting of the three gigantic driving gears for the telescope tube and yoke.

Sherburne and his men had already solved many tough construction problems that required the utmost in machinist's skill: the pin supports for the mirror, the huge mirror grinding machines, the 18-inch Schmidt camera, the Sun telescope for the Astrophysical Laboratory, the tenth-scale model, and many more. But the gears were the most important of all. Unless they were very nearly perfect the telescope control—the last word in automatic operation—would be useless.

The gear blanks had been cast and rough-machined in the East from designs contributed by Prof. Earle Buckingham of M.I.T. Each one was fourteen feet in diameter, split edgewise into two parts and then bolted together with utmost care. So accurately had they been made that the two halves of the blank could be taken apart and turned with respect to each other and then bolted up again without changing the alignment. This drive was to be of the worm-and-spiral type. Sherburne's job was to cut a set of teeth on the rims so exactly uniform all around that the gear could be set reliably within four seconds of arc or $\frac{1}{324,000}$th of a revolution—an error of less than four ten-thousandths of an inch in machining.

"I don't say we can do it," Sherburne admitted mildly, "but we're going to try. Maybe we can do better. What gets my goat is to have somebody publish an absolute statement saying we *will* get that accuracy. The old gear firms laugh at us. Then they send somebody out here in a hurry to see how we're doing it. There's no secret about it; our cutting method is so old it's got whiskers. We're just spending more time and money than commercial firms can afford, that's all."

But it is doubtful if gears of that size and accuracy could have been made outside. A firm in Europe asked several thousand dollars for a four-foot gear cut to the standard required. A fourteen-foot one they could not manage at all.

Sherburne mounted the gear blank horizontally on a spindle, then cut the teeth in the conventional way on a milling machine erected alongside. Then he devised a special polishing "hob," and began the truing up. After the teeth all around the gear had been made as smooth and accurate as possible the halves were split apart and reassembled at one hundred and eighty degrees from the original position. Then the teeth were polished again. The process was repeated, alternately splitting the gear, shifting its halves by an angle that was less each time, then bolting it together and repolishing. In this way the errors introduced in each operation were eliminated in the next, until finally the teeth were identical around the whole circumference. To do it, Sherburne had to build an asbestos-lined shed enclosing the gear and its cutter complete. Air-conditioning machinery was installed inside and the temperature kept constant night and day within one degree Fahrenheit. When the gears were finally finished he tested them with the finest precision gauges available. He found that he had achieved an accuracy nearly four times what was required.

Meanwhile, in the Astrophysical Laboratory across the campus, much of importance was going on, too. The laboratory was Hale's last great contribution to the telescope project, without doubt the most complete of its kind in the world. On its roof a 36-inch Sun telescope had been built at the top of a tower resting on rock one hundred and thirty feet below. A seventy-five-foot spectrograph was placed in the tower and below ground, fanning out in all directions, were more than twenty laboratories and darkrooms fitted with every kind of apparatus for supplementing the work to be done on Palomar.

On the roof, too, Sherburne had installed the tenth-scale model, fitted with mirrors that Brown had made. Every detail of the 200-inch Giant was here reproduced in miniature. It was intended for use as a testing ground for each of the innovations adopted by the Observatory Council and was found especially valuable in ironing out the wrinkles in the almost human automatic control system. In a cabinet near by the intricate maze of switches, motors and electronic relays were kept at constant temperature—a new system invented by Robert McMath of Detroit. Night after night Anderson and Porter tried it out on the stars and, veterans though they were, could not but marvel at its smooth performance. It augured well for success later on.

Hale had insisted all along that it was no use to spend six million dollars on the project unless all the supplementary instruments for the great telescope should be developed to their highest possible efficiency. One of the most important offices which the 200-inch would perform, he said, was to act as a stimulant to scientists everywhere, and as a general clearing house for telescopic discoveries and inventions. Everything inspired by the Giant could be applied immediately to the improvement of astronomical technique throughout the world. His vision was rapidly becoming fact.

Already McCauley's success with ribbed Pyrex disks at Corning had revolutionized the making of astronomical mirrors throughout the world. Already Frank Ross had developed a corrector lens to improve the field of the 200-inch mirror and had found it of great advantage on the large instruments at Mount Wilson. Already W. B. Rayton of Bausch and Lomb had devised a lens of the unheard-of speed of F:0.59, for use in measuring the very faint spectra of distant spiral nebulae. He designed the lens on the principle of a microscope objective and actually put the photographic film in contact with the back of the glass.

"It is with this lens, attached to the spectrograph of the 100-

inch reflector on Mount Wilson," wrote Hale proudly, "that the law of the 'expansion of the Universe' has been found by Hubble and Humason. It has nearly doubled the range of the 100-inch telescope. And a still more rapid lens of a similar type is being

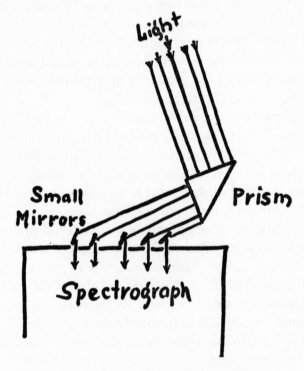

SCHEME OF THE BOWEN IMAGE SLICER

developed for us by the British Scientific Instrument Association."

It might be interpolated here that Milton Humason, who shared in this epochal discovery, began as a pack-train driver on the old Mount Wilson trail.

Professor Bowen of Cal Tech had come out with a little device which he called an "image slicer"—an arrangement of tiny mirrors smaller than toothpicks, which gathered the light from a star and concentrated it on the slit of the spectrograph. It had seemed so promising that he had taken it to the Lick Observatory and had spent all one summer testing it out on the 36-inch refractor there. Results were amazing. With ordinarily good seeing the image of a star cast on the spectrograph slit is so large that not more than ten per cent of all the light can squeeze through the tiny opening and be reflected onto the photographic plate. Bowen's invention gathered in the light that missed—most of it—and increased the efficiency of the spectrograph by as much as five times. All astronomy was sure to reap the benefit.

Meanwhile, Anderson, with the help of Frank Ross, Zwicky and others, had developed the Schmidt star camera to an extraordinary degree. This instrument had come over from Germany some years before and had been taking the astronomical world by storm on account of the large star field it could photograph clearly on a single plate. Its optical system consisted simply of a mirror with a spherical curve, and a "correcting plate." But the plate was so difficult to make that large cameras had not been possible. Now, under the stimulation of the 200-inch, a Schmidt camera with a correcting plate four feet in diameter and a speed of F:5 had been successfully designed. "It will be so fast," said Max Mason, "that it can be used as a general view-finder for the 200-inch or any other big telescope, bringing forth out of the heavens in a few minutes important phenomena for study that previously took months or years to find."

Everywhere, in and out of Pasadena, scientists in many allied fields were breaking down barriers and making fresh discoveries. New high-speed photographic emulsions of especially fine grain were coming out of Dr. Mees' laboratory in Rochester, together with plates for the first time sensitive to extreme infra-red rays. Pettit and Nicholson had developed a thermocouple many times more sensitive than anything previously available for measuring the temperatures of bodies like the Moon and the planets. Wood had established an entirely new standard in diffraction gratings and made them so sensitive that the element titanium had been discovered in the dark of interstellar space. Stebbins and his associates were bringing forth photo-electric amplifiers with which the 100-inch telescope could pick up light no brighter than a candle three thousand miles away. Zworykin of television fame was experimenting on "light-amplifiers" and with Sinclair Smith was investigating the idea of electronic guiding of telescopes. And Smith and C. G. Abbot had produced radiometers for use in the infra-red, sensitive enough to measure the heat of a man too far off to be seen—and the minute heat of a star.

With all these and many more added to the tremendous light-gathering power soon to be realized on Palomar Mountain, Hale cheerfully agreed with Max Mason that "the whole course of astronomy might well be changed."

These were developments the seasoned scientist had made. But perhaps the most interesting of all came from a young scholarship student at Cal Tech named John Strong. He had arrived at the Institute some years before to carry on a research in infra-red spectroscopy. But while waiting for his equipment to be built he had begun "playing round," as he said, with the coating of glass objects with thin films of quartz in a vacuum. Back in undergraduate days at Michigan University he had heard the Dutch scientist Ornstein lecture enthusiastically on the subject and urge that further research be done. Several students had tried it and decided that it was not a practical scheme. Strong tried it himself, with a method of his own, and decided that it was.

So now at Cal Tech he took up the experiment again, and applied it for the first time to the coating of astronomical mirrors. Beginning with a six-inch glass which an amateur astronomer friend provided, he found that he could lay on it a beautiful thin film of quartz which protected the silver reflecting surface and made it last for a long time without renewal.

Whenever an amateur did anything interesting he invariably told Porter about it. And this time Porter told Anderson. Young Strong was soon summoned to the office to explain how his process worked. He explained in detail and suggested hopefully that it might be developed for use in the larger telescopes. Anderson doubted it; the quartz might save tarnishing but once a mirror was coated with it, it could never be got off. Nothing came of the interview then.

It was the depth of depression and Strong's scholarship money was running low. He needed to drum up a job. Suddenly he thought of aluminum. Why not coat mirrors with that, instead of the conventional silver? It had a far higher reflective power than silver in the important ultra-violet region and was practically untarnishable. Aluminum, he thought, could be deposited by his process just as readily as quartz. He went back to Anderson and put the scheme before him. Anderson told him to work out an apparatus that would coat a large mirror evenly. Strong was soon back with the plans. They both went to see Millikan.

The upshot of it was that Strong abandoned infra-red spectroscopy and was given a room in the Astrophysical Laboratory to work out his process. It gave immediate promise of success. He was soon aluminizing mirrors as large as twenty-four inches in diameter. Dr. Wright at the Lick Observatory heard of Strong's work and asked if he might send down the 36-inch mirror of the veteran Crossley reflector for treatment. Cal Tech cordially agreed and the big glass arrived from Mt. Hamilton soon after. It took the new metallic surface as perfectly as the others had done. Then Strong asked for the thing he had wanted all along—to be allowed to aluminize the two big mirrors on Mount Wilson.

He was only twenty-seven years old but the Institute had such confidence in him that it gave him an expense account and told him to go ahead and develop a machine for the job. Singlehanded he designed and had built a steel tank big enough to enclose the 100-inch mirror and seal it in tight. Then he constructed a system of vacuum pumps, along the lines of the old diffusion pump devised some years before by Metropolitan Vickers in England. Next he undertook experiments in applying his principle of aluminizing to so large a surface.

There was an ironic similarity between this outfit, which worked, and the one invented at Lynn for raining fused quartz on a big disk—which failed. The difference between them was that Strong only needed a microscopic layer of aluminum—less than a millionth of an inch thick—whereas Ellis had required nearly an inch of quartz. Moreover, Strong was a physicist while Ellis was only an engineer. Strong's method consisted of coating a number of coils of tungsten wire with pure aluminum, suspending these above the mirror in the tank, creating a high vacuum, then boiling the aluminum off in a shower upon the disk by passing an electric current through the coils.

It was not as simple as it sounds in description. The first problem was to get the coating on evenly. This meant developing a mathematical equation expressing the behavior of aluminum mist evaporated from hot tungsten under vacuum; then, testing this equation in the laboratory to prove that it was valid; then determining how many coils would be required and where they must be placed. The next problem was to obtain and hold the necessary vacuum. This meant designing the tank in such a way that the joints between top and bottom could be sealed; then finding a wax compound which would effect such a seal; then covering the whole interior of the tank with the wax at a temperature higher than boiling water to stop up microscopic leaks; then rigging a gang of mechanical air-exhaustion pumps powerful enough to evacuate such a large space; then building the battery of electrical condensation pumps that would improve the vacuum to less than one seven-millionth of ordinary atmospheric pressure.

After all this preparation Strong had to discover a way to clean the disk, not "surgically clean" only, but literally, *atomically* clean. That took him into chemistry to find a solvent for grease, and then into physics to find a method of scrubbing the glass surface with an electric discharge.

Strong was no magician; he was a hard-working investigator who took each problem up methodically, steeped in its literature, experimented month after month to be sure of his ground before taking the next step, and then modestly gave credit to everyone under the Sun who had contributed even a farthing's worth of help. Like Hale, he was the living embodiment of Whitney's ideal: "The impossible is that which we have not yet learned to do."

And in the end he coated the Mount Wilson mirrors with aluminum and gave them such a beautiful permanent surface that they have never had to be recoated since. With them the tiny companion of Sirius could at last be studied in detail.

After this he would like to have gone back quietly to his chosen work in the infra-red, but that was impossible. The Strong aluminizing process had traveled around the world. Letters began to pour in from observatories all over America; and from Europe, Asia and Africa, asking for advice on how to coat mirrors. He answered them all the best he could, struggling with numerous foreign languages, reminding everyone that the process was free to all who might want it, and was already completely described in the scientific prints. After that came the horde of self-interested little manufacturers who desired to borrow or pirate the process and make some money coating mirrors for amateurs. Strong had to untangle them as well as possible and try to make sure that they were at least competent before they exploited his discovery. He could not patent the process himself, being a special scholarship student, and so got no money out of it beyond his salary as a member of the Astrophysical staff. The possibility that some large concern might patent the idea and actually freeze him out of his own claim to it did not bother Strong at all. He had achieved something that would help all astronomy and that was enough.

Then, to make the honor complete, the Observatory Council asked him to design a machine to be built into the observatory at Palomar to aluminize the 200-inch Giant itself.

# CHAPTER XXXV

## A MARTYR TO THE CAUSE

ALL the while that the mechanical and optical parts of the telescope were under construction the engineers and scientists of the Astrophysical Laboratory were devising the most completely automatic control system conceivable. The man who had charge of this intricate development was Sinclair Smith, an astronomer and engineer and a most brilliant inventor besides.

Smith knew that the seeing on Palomar would probably not permit the 200-inch to be used to full advantage on more than fifty nights in a year. Therefore, every minute possible must be given to actual observation. The work of setting the telescope on a star and keeping it there must be done by an automatic machine with the minimum of delay. No time could be wasted in hunting for an object in the finder first, then jockeying the great instrument back and forth continuously with electric push buttons to keep it in position. The astronomer must be able to set some dials, press a button, wait a moment, and then begin to observe.

The plan read like a fairy tale, and until Smith solved the problem it was one. To replace human judgment in aiming the instrument, he required a robot that could practically think for itself. When an astronomer guides his telescope he unconsciously compensates for many factors at once. The robot would have to do likewise.

Brilliant work had already been done with mechanical "thinking machines" of this kind, and Smith turned to it as a precedent. At Massachusetts Tech, some years before, Professor Vannevar Bush had invented the "integraph"—a computing machine that was almost human. It consisted of a complicated assembly of motors, gears and electric circuits into which the variable factors of a mathematical equation could be "fed" by setting dials. The machine would then add up or integrate all these factors and turn out, in a few minutes, an answer which would have taken years to reach by computation. Later on, McMath had applied the principle to a small observatory of his own, and with Bush had developed the automatic telescope control scheme tried out so successfully on the tenth-scale model.

For the 200-inch instrument Smith sought to apply the Bush-McMath principle with improvements of his own. The problem was to hold the telescope on some particular spot in the heavens with an accuracy of a single second of arc—equivalent to aiming a rifle at a moving 25-cent piece three miles away. To do this, a group of variable factors, depending on the star under observation, must be continuously added up and their combined effect fed to the motor drive. The first of these factors is the change in star position caused by atmospheric refraction—a function of the height of the observatory plus the altitude of the star. The next factor is the change in refraction due to the weather. This change is compounded from the temperature, humidity and barometric pressure at the time of the observation, and is modified by the height of the star above the horizon. Then there is a variable introduced by small unavoidable errors in the driving gears—errors which even a Sherburne could not get out. These must be learned by experience and compensated for continuously. And finally come the errors due to the deformation of the telescope under its own weight—errors too small even for a Serrurier and his colleagues to prevent. None of these factors would be large, but unless each one was properly included, the telescope could never find the star or keep on it of itself.

The method which Smith worked out was a combination of electrical and mechanical devices that would have defied an Einstein to unravel. It took him four years and he died before he had finished.

Dr. Bush made two trips to the Coast, bringing with him Hannibal Ford and Edward Poitras. Ford had been doing closely guarded secret work for the Navy for many years and Poitras, as his assistant, was familiar with every detail of it. With Smith and Bush they represented the world's greatest team of electrical control engineers.

The solution of the telescope drive problem lay in two "computers," one attached to the yoke drive and the other to the drive for the tube. The two were to be connected together electrically in such a way that they modified the position of the telescope just enough to compensate for all the errors. In principle a computer consisted of a group of mechanisms such as cams, differentials and other intricate gearing, each representing by the position of its shafting a single error, to be set up on it by the operator from outside. These various shafts were connected together through differential gearing of the kind found in the rear end of an automobile, and were thus "totaled" onto one master shaft. This last did not revolve like the shaft in a steam engine, but maintained an angular position representing the summation of all the errors fed into the machine. It was connected by means of a "Selsyn motor," or electrical position transmitter, to the main timing clock of the telescope itself and thus slightly modified the latter's driving rate. The telescope, therefore, would not be pointed where the star actually was, but at the place in the sky where it seemed to be, and where an observer would see it.

The right choice of a timing mechanism was the secret of Smith's brilliant plan. Previous telescopes had used some form of pendulum clock or flyball governor to insure an even rate of drive. The new clock would be wholly electrical. Borrowing the frequency control principle from radio broadcasting he decided to use a quartz crystal oscillator for his master clock. The crystal would be kept in steady vibration by an alternating electric current furnished by vacuum tubes, and would maintain a constant period of oscillation or "note," like a tuning fork. This note would control the electric circuits which supplied the driving motors. Then, by interposing the computers between crystal and motors he could change the telescope's position just enough to compensate for the errors.

A "Selsyn motor," it should be explained, is a motor only in looks. Its shaft does not revolve continuously but stands practically still. When several of these devices are connected together on the same electric circuit, their shafts will maintain identical angular positions all the time. If one shaft is turned by some outside force through a certain angle, the companion machines will follow, forward or backward, in exact unison. So long as they are connected by the proper circuits they will maintain this companionship indefinitely even if miles apart. Smith planned to use dozens of them for the telescope control. Not only were they necessary for the computers, but they afforded the best possible means of transmitting dial readings all over the observatory. Any number of Selsyns could be connected to the same circuit, controlled by the master machine. Thus, indications of the telescope's position would be given simultaneously on dials at the control desk and at all observing stations as well.

The principle of electrical control is widely used in elevator drives, in the steering of big ocean liners, in the Navy, in industry, and in the Bush integraph. But Smith's application of it to the telescope drive is so involved and so technical that it would seem hopeless to explain it outside of an engineering meeting, and even there it would be intelligible mainly to specialists. Nevertheless, the story of the Glass Giant of Palomar would not be complete without one thoroughly incomprehensible passage. As Bush himself once advised the writer, "Give 'em something they don't understand and make 'em dig for it!" For those who like to dig, then, here it is, quoted from Edward Poitras (Smith's able successor), who tried to describe the final control system so the layman could "understand."

"The drive in right ascension will be controlled by a quartz crystal oscillator at fifty kilocycles. This will be stepped down by vacuum-tube multiple vibrators to fifty cycles, and amplified enough to run the fractional-horsepower motors for the drive itself. There may be a motor-generator set interposed to furnish enough power. The crystal set will drive a comparison motor. The computer will be connected to a variable-frequency string vibrator (a metal string with a weight on it) set to vibrate at fifty cycles with a five-percent leeway above and below. This leeway will be modified by the results from the computer so that the vibrator will oscillate at all times somewhere between 47½ cycles and 52½ cycles. Variation of frequency is produced by electromagnetic force on the weight of the standard, by means of a potentiometer. This vibrator controls, through vacuum tubes, the clock motor of the drive.

"This clock motor and the comparison motor driven from the crystal standard are compared for angle with a differential. The output of this differential is in turn compared with the output of the computer by a second differential. This difference will operate a potentiometer (voltage control unit) which will control the frequency of the string vibrator, so as to bring the potentiometer toward zero at all times. This is the 'null' method, and is self-balancing. The purpose of this apparently roundabout method is to insure perfectly smooth telescope motion in spite of possible slight irregularities in the output of the computer.

"At the desk control station, located at the north pedestal, will be the various control switches, indicators for right ascension and declination, telescope zenith angle, wind screen position, sidereal and standard time clocks, etc. Here are located the Selsyn transmitters on which the night assistant will set up the next desired star position, ready for automatic setting at the observer's command. Pressing an 'execute' button causes the telescope to assume the position set on these dials."

And, it might be interpolated, pressing another button, which is found in duplicate at every observing position, will stop the whole works instantly, in case something jams or the observer falls overboard. Mr. Poitras finishes with a flourish:

"Each observing station will have banks of three Selsyn dials for right ascension and declination; rough, intermediate and fine settings will thus be indicated. The observer can always read his dials and tell just where the telescope is pointing, though he can't see the telescope itself (being inside of it). When he is through photographing one star all he needs to do is pick up his telephone and say to the night assistant at the control desk: 'O.K., Joe, next star.' "

And all his worries will be null and void thereafter forever-more.

But the detail work on the control system was no light matter for Sinclair Smith. He had been ill of a serious affliction for a number of years and now began to get gradually worse. But he kept on as if nothing were the matter, poring over his diagrams and charts day and night, taking little rest and no recreation. By and by he was forced to have an operation. He consented only because he thought it would increase his efficiency.

But it did not. He began to have severe pain, and soon had to submit to a second operation. When that was over he felt better for a time and threw himself into his work even harder. His doctors urged him to slow down, but he refused. He was the only man who understood this control mechanism. Dr. Hale and the others were relying on him to bring it through.

"But you've got to stop, young man!" his physician cried. "You've got to give nature a chance!" He looked Smith straight in the eye, then patted him on the arm. "Now be sensible," he said. "The telescope isn't worth it."

Smith returned the look without flinching.

"It's cancer, isn't it?" he said steadily.

"Yes."

"How long—?"

"A few months—maybe a year, if you do what I tell you."

Smith walked to the door of the doctor's office, then turned and stood for a moment with great dignity.

"I have an important job to do, doctor. I'm going to work this thing out in my own way."

"Now my dear fellow—"

But the young astronomer was gone.

Then, month after month Smith raced with death. Inconvenience, suffering and terror he put aside in the resolute fight to finish the job he had started. Six months went by, and a year. Still he continued, little by little solving the unbelievable complications of the control problem, gradually getting his design on paper. His year of grace was lengthening into two and he was nearing the end of the work. Six months more—

His colleagues watched him silently, nervously; meeting him in the hall they would beg him to take a rest, try at least to make him slow down. Smith would only smile a little, lay a hand on their shoulders, then go silently back to his office and shut the door.

Finally they prevailed upon him to go to the hospital for further treatment, thinking that once out of the office they could persuade him not to return. It was unnecessary; within a few days he was dead.

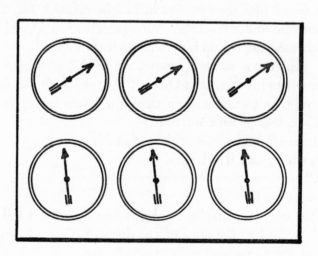

# CHAPTER XXXVI

"THEY LOVED THE STARS TOO FONDLY,
TO BE FEARFUL OF THE NIGHT."

IT was a sad time, that spring of 1938, for the Observatory
Council and the scientists of Cal Tech. In the space of four
short months Smith died, and Pease and Hale.

Francis Gladheim Pease had been one of the first astronomers
to measure the diameter of a star. In the early 1920's, Dr. Michelson had come out from Chicago to test his newly developed
interferometer on the 100-inch telescope at Mount Wilson. All
of the astronomers helped him, but it was Pease who did the
most. For his temperament was the best suited to the infinite patience required. Before long he and Michelson succeeded in making the first actual measurement of a star's diameter.

Two years before his death Pease announced that he had measured the diameter of the star Epsilon Pegasi, and found it to be
86,000,000 miles—one hundred times the size of the Sun. The
50-foot interferometer which he used was of his own design—
a great steel beam carrying two small mirrors which reflected
the light of the star to a large mirror and thence to an eyepiece.
Here the two rays of light were superimposed, and so gave rise
to interference fringes of bright and dark lines. As he moved
the two mirrors outward on the beam, the fringes weakened,
and finally disappeared, and the diameter of the star could be
calculated from the separation of the glasses.

It was exacting work, for the best of seeing was required and
every detail of the machine must be in perfect adjustment. All
night long for weeks on end Pease would perch on the little chair
at the top of his instrument, adjusting, readjusting, trying to
achieve that perfect state of co-ordination between hand and
brain that would finally reward him with a glimpse of the elu-

sive fringes. Then with the delicacy of touch born of forty years with the stars, he would begin to move his mirrors outward, with rigid self-control holding his mind from jumping to its conclusion too fast, jockeying back and forth hour after hour, eliminating himself to the utmost from the measurement. And time after time, just as he had got to the point of final disap-

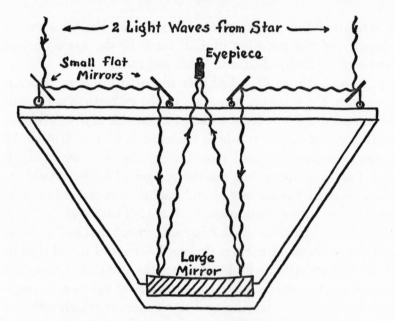

PRINCIPLE OF THE MICHELSON INTERFEROMETER

pearance of the fringes a cloud would cover the star, or some slight fault in the machine would interpose itself to spoil the result.

After he had died the interferometer stood alone, little used. It would be long before anyone else developed the peculiarly delicate touch necessary to make the instrument effective.

Pease was a precision workman and a dreamer besides. The credit for the earliest 200-inch designs was his; and his sketches and calculations helped Hale to bring his vision of a giant telescope into focus as a reality of glass and steel. Like Barnard,

Pease spent his life in a world that was meaningless to common men; like Barnard he gave it away in exchange for the secrets of the stars. And when he went, early in February, 1938, according to his wish there was only the most simple funeral; then his ashes were borne by the California winds into the sky he had served so well.

Three weeks later, Hale, perhaps the greatest astronomer of his time, followed after.

It used to be a matter of resentment at Harvard that Charles W. Eliot received only cursory mention on the inside pages of the newspapers when he died, while banner headlines lamented the loss of Rudolph Valentino on the same day. At sixty-nine, George Ellery Hale was one of the most honored men in the history of science, yet less well known to the world than many a local ward boss. He slipped out of life with scarcely a ripple. Even in gaudy California his passing went largely unnoticed, except for the dignified mourning of intimate friends.

His work was done; more than most men he had achieved the things he fought for in life, and succeeded in leaving behind a group of vital projects, all in the hands of able young men. Yerkes, Mount Wilson, the National Research Council, the International Astronomical Union, Palomar—each was a monument; yet each was much more. These things were not merely memorials to a man of genius, they were indestructible parts of his spirit which would live on after him, profoundly modifying the course of all science.

To his colleagues Hale was primarily a scientist; his greatest desire, they felt, was to shut himself in his laboratory and work, as they worked, toward the common goal. To them it was his tragedy that his health would not permit this; that his fiery energy wracked him less when it was spent in the broad field of organization, arranging that others might achieve instead.

"Although a great organizer," said Dr. Adams, "he was first of all a great investigator. The spirit of research was dominant in him." Yes, the spirit of research was dominant in Hale, but there was more than that to his genius. There was the ability to integrate the talents of others into great projects for the advance of knowledge. His title of "Doctor" fitted him best in the ancient sense: he was a teacher—a pioneer in scientific thought. His was the power to inspire, to create dissatisfaction with ignorance. The three great observatories that Hale built were more than beautiful machines for research, they were symbols echoing his lifelong cry of "Light! More light!"

The scientist buried in his laboratory is apt to measure his own value in terms of specific achievements. The breaking down of a single mystery, the statement of one law, before unknown, in his view constitute the ultimate goal for a dispassionate mind. But there is a wider usefulness to which the technical thinker may aspire: the faculty to envision knowledge as a whole and to plan voyages of discovery toward the vast frozen North of human wisdom. In that category Hale lived and died. Even his associates scarcely knew how great he was.

The very fact of his illness forced him to go beyond himself. Had he been well he might have contributed one or two more advances to science than he did. Ill, he projected the need for a thousand advances upon all whom he touched, thus multiplying the power of his own technical ability a thousand fold.

Hale invented the spectroheliograph and the spectrohelioscope and inspired their use throughout the world. He was a pioneer in astrophysics—the man who established the importance of our Sun as the nearest cosmic laboratory. He demonstrated the magnetic fields in sunspots and pointed the way toward the theory that storms on the Sun give rise to the aurora and to the fierce magnetic storms we have on earth.

Yet his value to the world lay less in these achievements than in the example of his energy and the forcefulness of his attack upon problems in general. His extraordinary talent for raising money and for surrounding himself with others who could raise it did not spring from an ability as a supersalesman, but from the burning fire of his example. "Hale was forever eager to be on his way," said Dr. Seares of Mount Wilson. "Once his decision was taken let something be done! Ignore obstacles, make a beginning in the faith that difficulties will disappear!"

"The gods bring threads to a web begun," Hale often quoted, and many were the webs they wove for him and are weaving still. Perhaps the greatest of these is Palomar.

Albert G. Ingalls of the *Scientific American* once jokingly pointed out to Porter that the 200-inch observatory building was almost identical in dimensions to the Pantheon in Rome, built in the time of Christ. "I hope," he remarked, "that your observatory will be in as good a state of preservation in 2000 years as the Pantheon is now."

In his last years Hale began to worry profoundly over the fate of science, not in 4000 A. D. but in the near future of the Twentieth Century. All his planning, all his visions for the coming generations seemed jeopardized by the rising tide of brute force—the sinister insistence of political demagogues on their right to destroy independence of thought both here and abroad. He deeply feared the return of the Dark Ages: the resurgence of the ignorant; the clamoring for power of the moron mind.

Over and over he heard the insolent question: "How can it be justifiable to spend six million dollars on a telescope when thousands are starving?" And more and more he realized that the world of the future might not understand the simple answer of "Light! More light!" Food, more food! was the cry. Sadly he prepared to leave science at the mercy of a race of men with crying stomachs and sleeping heads.

A great English statesman once objected that the money that Michael Faraday was spending on his electro-magnetic "toy" might better have gone to the poor. "Some day, Sir," said Faraday softly, "you may be able to tax it." The dynamo, which came out of that toy, today is the basis of electric power and whole governments are fighting for its control.

We can only hope that when Hale looks down from the stars through the great mirror of the Palomar Giant he will see that the battle for knowledge is still going on; we can only believe that with Faraday he will be able to say:—in another 2000 years— "This is the little toy which your demagogues scorned!"

# PART IV

# THE VOYAGE BEGINS

# CHAPTER XXXVII

## IN THE GIANT'S BOSOM

AND so we return to the present on Palomar Mountain, where the final touches are being put on the world's largest telescope.

Up the new county road we come, up the long hogback of the south shoulder, through the trees of the National Forest, past the fire station and at last out into the open on the brow of the hill. The great dome bursts upon us suddenly, its gleaming silver hemisphere like an up-ended dirigible; its faun-colored lower walls squat and substantial beneath. Over beyond, like a chick with a hen, is the tiny dome of the 18-inch Schmidt camera, and far away on an outer ridge, the dome of the 48-inch.

The air is cool and clear, the sky deep blue; the Sun beats down gorgeously. The field to the east of the observatory is scattered with wild flowers; beyond it the power house nestles against the farther rise, flanked by its family of silver water tanks.

A high wire fence encloses the dome, and through this, having parked our cars, we are permitted to pass. So completely enclosed is the Giant that at first we can see no entrance; then around on the northeast side we discover an austere little door, hardly larger than the door of a house. Over it, some day, they say, will be the legend: "The Hale Observatory."

Ours is the privilege of a specially conducted visit past all barriers and into the forbidden rooms and compartments surrounding the 200-inch telescope. Russell Porter will be our guide.

The foyer inside the main entrance is obviously Porter's handiwork, with its New England simplicity. There is a small rotunda here, very plain and fine, with elliptical arches supporting a miniature dome above. Hidden red and green lights behind the cornice give the place a soft illumination which prepares one for

the quiet of the great spaces beyond. Up to the left swings a
wide curving staircase, paved in green rubber, and the floor beneath our feet is of rubber parquet also. The room has dignity
and charm.

Porter leads us through a little door at the side and abruptly
we are in the midst of the machinery. Here is the foundation of
the telescope; vast steel beams rise above us into the shadows.
The base of the instrument is built of girders two feet square,
braced and cross-braced with the strength of a Golden Gate
Bridge. It rests on four massive concrete piers; one corner is
fixed in a big steel ball-and-socket joint, the other three are
mounted on oil jacks for accurate leveling. Horizontal screw-
jacks are added, for adjusting the telescope exactly north and
south.

Again we pass through a door and come out into a circular
corridor flanked on both sides by the astronomers' quarters; neat
and plain but highly organized. There are rooms for computing,
with desks and chairs and shelves; lounging apartments where
the astronomers may snatch a few hours' sleep; lunch room and
kitchen, shining in white porcelain and monel metal; and a long
row of photographic dark rooms with every conceivable wrinkle
that science can add. In one of the compartments is a large air-
conditioning unit for the whole building, with motors, com-
pressor and refrigerating mechanism all mounted on rubber
pads and springs to kill vibration. Nothing, no matter how trivial, has been forgotten.

Back in the rotunda we climb the stairs to the mezzanine; here
are the switchboards, rows and rows of them, all automatic and
all enclosed behind roller screens of sheet metal. Overhead the
wiring goes out in steel pipes just as in a ship; some to the power
house, some to the telescope, and some to a nest of trolley wires
to supply the dome. Five hundred circuits will be needed for the
telescope alone, fed to it through flexible cables wound on a
drum on the polar axis. This was Jerry Dowd's contribution; he

spent two years braiding them up out of fine copper wire by hand.

In the mezzanine we realize again how generous the astronomers will be to the visitor. Here is a good sized lounge with rest rooms adjoining. Walls of buff with green trim; indirect lighting, smooth rubber floors, drinking fountain—everything for comfort and a cordial welcome. In this reception room Porter intends to display the complete history of the 200-inch in drawings and photographs, pending a more elaborate plan to establish a separate astronomical museum on the grounds outside. Science has no wish to remain mysterious, so long as the public respects its privacy farther on.

Another short climb on the stairs brings us abruptly to the end of the road. Here, in a tightly enclosed space with double walls and ceiling of glass the visitor's penetration is ended. He will not be allowed on the observing floor itself. This gallery is fully ventilated and air-conditioned, so that the heat of the crowds will be pumped outside where it cannot affect the perfect balance of the mirrors.

Through the glass we get our first view of the Giant. Almost vertically overhead it towers into the vague silver arch of the dome—vast beyond all description, yet magnificently simple in outline. There before us are the north and south pedestals, coming up through the floor like the arms of an Atlas holding aloft the world. There is the yoke, its two huge cylinders bigger than the bodies of locomotives, their ends carried in the tilting horseshoe at the north and the spreading wing of the box girder at the south. And there is the telescope tube within, resting easily in its trunnions, pointing upward toward the sky. The Giant is silent and still, yet an indescribable sense of motion pervades it all. One can almost see those massive bearings push upward with the force of five hundred tons, straining and grunting as they hold.

Away up in the soaring spider work in the dome a tiny figure clings to the catwalk, encased in gloves and a helmet like a visiting Martian, and surrounds himself with a shower of sparks. This is Jock Clogston, the veteran welder, putting on the safety railings one hundred feet above the floor. Here and there on the flanks of the Giant other workmen are connecting cables, lining up mirrors, adding the last touches before the voyage begins. The 60-ton crane is dangling its hook down between the jaws of the horseshoe with a man swinging to it like bait on a fishhook. Arching up toward the zenith runs a thin soaring quadrant of rails and on it a shining monel-metal platform held in mid-air by a tubular arm. This we are told is the astronomer's flying carpet, to carry him to the mouth of the tube. It is attached to the dome and can follow the instrument wherever it goes. Down on the floor beneath there is a clutter of toothpick-sized planks, toy construction machinery and a dwarf or two; all made miniature by the bulk of the instrument above. We look inquiringly at Porter—is it possible that we can stand out there—just for a moment? He nods; today the rules may be broken.

Around through a series of doors and passageways liberally marked "No Admittance," and we come out in the central space under the dome. Presently we are standing directly beneath the tube, its lower end fifteen feet above us. There is a great empty hole there now, for the mirror is still in Pasadena. But we can see where it is to go, when it finishes its long journey by trailer. When the disk arrives downstairs a piece of the observing floor will be removed, and the glass raised up through by the crane.

A pair of rails set in the concrete lead off to one side to a circular steel tank as big as a battleship turret. This is Strong's new aluminizing outfit. Near it a low platform car on wheels stands ready to transport the disk. This is permanent equipment. On the rare occasions when the mirror needs a new reflective coating, the tube will be put in a vertical position and guyed to the floor with sturdy steel rods. Then the glass will be let down in its cell by cables fixed to the tube itself, the mirror will ride off to the tank, receive its new aluminum and come back and be hoisted into place, all in the space of twenty-four hours or so. For lifting light objects such as the Cassegrain spectrograph and observation platform below the mirror, a small hydraulic hoist is built into the floor at the center. The observer, it is planned, will be jerked up into place in a bucket.

Porter now leads us over beyond the south pier to the coudé room. This is a big cavern that slants down for a distance of thirty feet into the walls, heavily encased in concrete. Here a beam of light from the most distant of nebulae will arrive through a tube in the south bearing itself, after reflection from five different mirrors. With the aid of the Bowen "image slicer" it will be delivered into the high-dispersion spectrograph and concentrated upon a supersensitized plate as a spectrum. So delicate is this operation that room and instrument must be held at perfectly constant temperature and without the smallest vibration.

Following Porter again through the maze of machinery, we cross the floor past the little control desk between the legs of the north pier and up a long flight of stairs to the balcony. We come out on a wide, ring-shaped deck that passes around the whole hall, at the base of the dome. From here up, everything is carried around on those thirty-two trucks. We are on a level now with the bottom of the telescope tube. Two men are at work there assembling the leaves of the iris diaphragm—the "stop" for the mirror, which will close down over it during the day to protect it and help keep it cool. The leaves are shaped like propeller blades and stand nearly ten feet high. They slip so smoothly upon one another as the men test the operating motor that they make a nearly air-tight funnel that is perfectly circular on top in any position.

We walk around the deck, examining it. It consists of two rings, matching closely at the joint, the outer one turning with the dome, the inner one anchored to the foundations of the building. Even when the dome is revolving one can step across the line without danger, the motion is so smooth. The stairs, of course, belong with the inner portion, and at the south side there is an elevator, too—a little automatic one for the astronomers to come up from below. When they have arrived here they simply change cars to the flying platform and go on up to work in the telescope.

By and by we screw up courage to ask our guide if we may take a ride on that platform, or at any rate stand on it. He shakes his head. It is not in service yet; but if we insist on going up, says Porter, we may *climb*. On the back of the girder that carries the platform is a steep iron stairway, leading up almost vertically, then disappearing around the curve at the top.

"If you really want to see how it looks from above," chuckles Porter, "you can shinny up that. . . . No, I'll wait down here. It's no novelty to me any more." He unbuckles a chain swinging across the handrails bearing the sign: "Positively No Admittance," and stands aside. We hesitate, look at each other. Then —why not?

The ascent begins straight up, like the engineroom ladders in a big ship. We grip the handrails hysterically at first, then more calmly as things seem to go all right.

After thirty feet or so the steps begin to flatten out imperceptibly: we are moving outward now over the abyss. We pause for breath; climbing over flying steelwork like this is no light exercise on the top of a mountain. All around us the smooth aluminum panels gradually converge as they rise to the apex. Just behind us is the opening in the dome, and the two great shutters have been rolled aside so that we can see out into space. But it is not wise to look that way just now. . . .

The shutters themselves are double-skinned like the walls, and ride on three sets of rails built into the dome at the bottom, half way up and at the top. Heavy toothed racks are set into the moving parts, and electric motors fitted with pinions roll them open and shut. The joint where they meet is provided with heavy gaskets of rubber hose; pressed together they will be wind- and weather-tight.

Part of the opening is blocked with the canvas wind-screen; men above us are rigging the steel cables over a train of pulleys, which will unfold it upward to cut off the night air when the telescope is pointing high toward the zenith.

With a final burst of courage we finish our climb, the steps shelving off to a flat runway at the top. Breathlessly we hoist ourselves onto the bridge, one hundred feet above the floor. With white knuckles we grasp the rail and look over. There below us is the Giant of Palomar, spread out in all his massive grandeur.

We are looking down almost directly into the mouth of the observer's cage—a steel cylinder six feet in diameter and twenty feet long, supported by thin vanes coming out from the rim of the tube. Men are working in there now, connecting up the main Cassegrain mirror and the two smaller ones which will be swung into place by motors for long-focus observations. This will be a vast improvement over the 100-inch, where the changing of the mirrors takes several hours.

As we stand gazing down at the extraordinary complication of the apparatus we cannot help remembering what one of the workmen back at Pasadena was saying the other day: "They've got so many gadgets on that telescope they won't have time to look at the stars." But we know that they will; the remarkable co-ordination of every pound of steel and copper and glass guarantees that the telescope *will* work as planned. The astronomers will be too busy even to remember that the gadgets are there.

Over behind us the welder has just made his final shower of sparks and is laying down his torch; we edge along the bridge and speak to him, curious to know what he thinks of all this. "It's a job, isn't it?" he asks. But by the way he runs his hand over the work he has just finished we know that it is more than a job. It's a welder's paradise. "I've been here nearly four years," he tells us proudly. "Me and the family. One of the girls was pretty sick when we moved up here. Now she's fine. There she is now." He points down at the observatory floor. "Jacqueline. She's brought in my lunch."

Below a man with a hammer has walked over to an acetylene tank; he strikes it a smart series of blows which ring through the dome. Gradually the sounds of construction die off and a deep silence follows.

"That's the signal to knock off," says Jock. "I guess I'll go down if you don't mind." And, casting off helmet and gloves, he grasps the handrails and fairly shoots off into space down the ladder.

Ten minutes later, somewhat unnerved, we have completed the descent ourselves, and are once more on the solid deck of the gallery. Porter takes us outside, now, to the promenade around the dome. It is a circular iron balcony forty feet from the ground, and as we walk around it we see the whole outlay of Southern California beneath our feet. Westward the county road slips gracefully down the Rincon grade into a wide valley; north, the earth curves off into a blue-brown haze toward Elsinore; south, the shoulder of Palomar undulates gradually downward to be lost in the shimmering stretch of the Imperial Valley. And to the east, set against the dark blue backdrop of the sky, are the towering snow peaks of the San Bernardino range.

"One of those old fellows is twelve thousand feet high," says Porter proudly. "It's an inspiring place here for an observatory, isn't it?" As if extra inspiration were necessary for men about to embark on a voyage a thousand million light-years long!

Suddenly the whole landscape begins to move; imperceptibly at first, then more and more swiftly, the earth beneath us turns. Hurriedly we grasp the rail. Is this some trick? Or are we actually caught in a premature voyage through space? We run around the balcony; by skipping along fast we can just keep up with the landscape. By and by the whole thing stops as abruptly as it began, then starts without warning to roll the other way. Porter, waiting by the door, is convulsed with laughter. We come panting to rest beside him.

"They're trying out the dome drive," he says. "Don't worry. The ride is free." Cautiously we follow him inside. "You don't want to be like the girl they had up at Mount Wilson once," he chuckles over his shoulder. "She got caught outside on the balcony when they turned the dome and they couldn't get her to come in for love nor money. Finally they had to get her down the outside with a ladder."

Inside it is just as bad. The dome, the platform and ourselves are standing perfectly still; the telescope, like the world outside, is turning around. Or *seems* to be turning around. We know well enough that the five-hundred-ton Giant is firmly anchored to the earth and can't be moving. But try as we will, we can't imagine ourselves turning instead. Porter holds us back against the outside wall. "It'll come to rest in a minute," he says, and gives us a final anecdote to believe or not as we like.

They got Professor Einstein up at the 100-inch observatory one time, it seems, and then started the dome revolving around over his head to see what he would do. He did what everyone does—hung onto the instrument for dear life and gasped out that it had begun to move.

"It can't be! It can't be!" he kept wailing. "But it is!"

To heighten the effect the others made believe to hang on, too. Above the din someone shouted: "It's just relativity, isn't it, Dr. Einstein?" But the Professor was too dizzy to see the joke.

"Please, please," he begged them, "shut off the motors and let us come to rest."

# CHAPTER XXXVIII

## SCIENCE AND THE CITIZEN

AND now as the voyage begins we must make ready to step ashore and let the pioneers take their places. From now on there will be no room for outsiders—not an inch of extra space for deadheads.

Nevertheless, the spectator cannot be left on the dock, forgotten. His relation to the 200-inch observatory will always be an important part of the project. The average citizen is bound to demand a share in the great adventure. What is to be the extent of his privilege?

The Observatory Council is in a difficult position. It has concentrated vast amounts of skill and money in the largest astronomical machine in the world. Its primary obligation is to make good that investment to the utmost and to use every moment to greatest advantage.

But Palomar will be one of the big show places in America. Many thousands of people will flock there to see this new wonder of the world, expecting to have it explained and demonstrated. The Council therefore must compromise, endeavoring to make the public understand the situation and not expect too much.

It is plain that a modern telescope is not an instrument to be looked through. With the 200-inch it will hardly be *possible* to look at the stars. It would be no more useful to gaze at them in the great mirror than it would be to watch the propellers in action underneath a steamship. In fact, the observatory is like the engineroom of a liner, which must be denied to the casual visitor in order that the ship's machinery may do its work unhampered.

Photography will be the beginning and the end of the Giant's work, and photography cannot be shared with outsiders. So tremendously delicate are the measurements which the telescope will take that every condition which surrounds it must be under the most complete control: temperature changes, vibration, air currents, even sound must be eliminated if reliable results are to be obtained.

That is why all visitors will have to be confined within a glass show-case at one side.

Mount Wilson Observatory has had nearly forty years of experience with the public and the astronomers have learned how difficult it is to make visitors understand what they are trying to do. "People often do not distinguish," says Dr. Adams, the Director, "between an observatory and a planetarium. They have the idea that nothing goes on at Mount Wilson when they are not there."

Years ago Dr. Hale decided to establish as cordial a relationship as possible with the 75,000 visitors who came there every year. So a museum was built to display exhibits of the work the Observatory was doing; in a lecture hall adjoining, free talks are given once a week and an opportunity provided for asking questions. An assistant astronomer is on duty here every day. In addition, people are conducted through the 100-inch observatory for a half hour each afternoon and the guide moves the telescope and dome and explains fundamentals. Then, one evening a week, the 60-inch reflector is taken out of service till ten o'clock and people may look through it at certain well-known stars and nebulae. "The most revealing thing about that," said one of the astronomers, "is that the visitors have to stand in line and the majority of them get tired and go away."

On Palomar such privileges cannot be allowed, for the same reason that visitors are kept out of the operating room of a hospital.

The Mount Wilson staff has met the public more than half way all along. But it has been difficult to provide as generous a welcome as they would like and still protect their work. There

are always a few who insist on writing their initials on the walls
of the observatories. For a long time the 60-inch dome was particularly favored as an autographer's paradise. In the end the
Institution stopped it very gracefully by painting the place
with a mixture of varnish and sand which would break the
toughest pencil made.

(*Courtesy of the Saturday Evening Post*)

"I SEE THE NIGHT PLANE TO CHICAGO HAS A NEW STEWARDESS!"

Nor are the questions which the visitors ask always encouraging to the men who are doing their best to explain astronomy.
"One lady," said the lecturer, "asked me some quite lucid questions and I really laid myself out to give her clear and careful
answers. Finally she begged me to answer just one more and I
said I'd be glad to. 'Well,' said this lady, 'if the stars are all those
millions of miles away how did you ever get to find out their
names?' "

With the new—and unfortunately named—"Highway to the
Stars" Palomar Mountain will be almost as accessible as Niagara

Falls. What worries the astronomers is how to make the visitor understand that it is not Niagara Falls but a highly intricate scientific laboratory. The public would be perfectly willing to understand this if it could. But it finds itself up against a blank wall. To the layman a telescope has always been something to look through, and a 200-inch instrument, he feels, ought to give one a pretty good look. How shall the astronomer disabuse him and still remain on friendly terms?

It would help considerably if the visitor could be educated beforehand by a well-informed press. But that is not always possible. The scientists have not had time to explain what they are doing clearly, and the newspapers have rarely bothered to verify what they print.

Thousands of words have been published about the 200-inch telescope but few have been both interesting and accurate. From the earliest days at Corning the great mirror has been reported as a "lens," even by the Santa Fe Railroad, which carried it. One of the most reputable newspapers in the country lavishly referred to it as the "Cyclopean Eye," and said that the telescope would cost twelve million dollars.

When Marcus Brown began cleaning up the back of the glass with small grinding tools, a widely circulated popular science magazine published a picture of the men at work and informed its readers that they were "removing the heavy ribs which were left on the mirror so that it could be handled safely in shipment." And when the much-celebrated glass got to Pasadena a near-by editor unaccountably welcomed it as the "Hundred Inch Disk."

Lay editors are not the only ones. Russell Porter once made a sketch of an astronomer observing on the 100-inch at Mount Wilson, to go with an article in an astronomical society publication. With his penknife he picked out a dozen stars in the strip of sky in the background. When the engraving was printed the stars were gone; the editor had had them carefully touched out, thinking the drawing had been damaged in the mail.

Far more irritating to the astronomers than stupid mistakes are the fallacious reports of what the Giant will do. They object to the persistently printed statement, for instance, that the telescope will "bring the Moon within twenty-five miles of the Earth." It will not. They dislike to be quoted as boasting that they will "predict the weather on Mars." It makes them sick to read that "if there's a skyscraper on the Moon, regardless of its disguise, it can't remain hidden now." At the Lowell Observatory, where most of the world's work has been done on Mars, the 24-inch telescope is almost never used at full aperture. The most revealing pictures of the planet ever made were taken with a lens stop not more than eighteen inches in diameter. The 200-inch glass would be criminally wasted on such work and the pictures it took would be inferior anyway. Besides, there is not enough atmosphere on Mars to produce weather, and it is a thousand to one (to be conservative) that there are no skyscrapers on the Moon.

So the astronomer is confirmed in his impatience with the public, who, crammed with misinformation and not understanding in the least the real work ahead for the telescope, prepares to visit Palomar some day to spy on the inhabitants of the planets. The march is already on, in fact, and the curious are pouring up the mountain in ever increasing numbers. Not a day passes but Anderson and his colleagues are deluged with letters and telephone calls asking when the "fun" will begin, what star will first be chosen and who the lucky man will be to "put the telescope to his eye." Most of all, people want to know about the dedication. When will the ceremony occur? Who will be there—Einstein? Senator McAdoo? Joan Crawford? And will the President start the telescope on its first voyage by pressing a golden key in the White House in Washington?

The scientists turn all these queries off as kindly as they can, for they don't want to disappoint a public that sincerely expects something wonderful is going to happen. But when a broadcasting company offers to build a costly cable line to the top of the mountain in order to put Palomar astronomers on the air every week in authentic, red-hot stories of their discoveries, *while they are being made,* Anderson and the others get a little pale. And when two bottling companies fight for the privilege of donating a bottle of branded champagne for the prettiest girl in California to smash over the telescope's bow as she is launched into infinite space, the scientists withdraw entirely and cry "Enough!"

It is in the hope of lessening such misunderstandings even by a little that this book has been written. If it succeeds at all in its mission, those who read it will go to Palomar with a broader viewpoint, expecting to look *at* the great instrument and not through it, accepting the opportunity not as a right but a privilege. It is even possible that someone, more understanding than the rest, will offer his services in support of the work the astronomers are trying to do.

George Ellery Hale is dead and able Max Mason is in his place at the head of the project. But there is still need for Hale's talents in firing lay enthusiasm, for the work that the telescope will do still depends on money to come. Like all great scientific advance, the voyages of discovery that will fit out on Palomar are not for profit or for any other possible purpose than the world's own good. They must be subsidized continually by men far sighted enough to invest in a future they will not see.

What Hale said in 1928 is just as true today: "Lick, Yerkes, Hooker and Carnegie have passed on, but the opportunity remains for some other donor to . . . satisfy his own curiosity regarding the nature of the Universe." And it will always be true.

What the problems of this new search may be, I shall try to show in the remaining chapters of this book.

# CHAPTER XXXIX

## WHITHER AMONG THE STARS?

Six million dollars worth of the best scientific and engineering skill in the world was spent on the 200-inch telescope because its builders believed that it was justified. What, then, is the purpose of the great instrument? What will it do?

The Palomar Giant is the world's newest and largest precision instrument for the enhancement of physical knowledge. It is, says Dr. Mason, "the springboard from which the philosopher may leap ahead toward the solution of the problem of the Universe."

"Its construction," writes Arthur S. Eddington, in response to my request for a statement, "is of immense importance for astronomy. I am not expecting any *immediate* sensational results from it. What I do expect is that during the next decade our knowledge will be advanced just one step forward along the whole frontier of stellar, nebular and perhaps other branches of astronomy. Much of this advance may be humdrum; but here and there that one step will be what was needed to let us see round a corner."

"It will be very valuable," says Harlow Shapley, "as an inspiration." Implying, of course, that other men will be spurred on to invent other instruments and develop other techniques of comparable importance to astronomy.

Einstein, whom I questioned also, is inclined to be reticent. But it is certain that he is watching for results from the new telescope with eager interest. That is proved by the delight he showed at the Westinghouse dedication. This same reticence is rather general throughout the world, for astronomers everywhere are waiting to see what will happen before they commit themselves. Scientists are very cautious people, and abhor positive statements about anything. And they rarely become professionally excited, which is natural enough; men working in terms of the ultimate Universe can afford to be mild about a mere 200-inch telescope.

But astronomers, like other men, are sometimes a prey to envy; an envy the more lively because professional etiquette requires that it be rigidly suppressed. Here is a fortunate group of colleagues possessed of the world's most spectacular laboratory equipment. The men in other observatories would be less than human if they did not tend to underplay the new instrument's importance, being unable to command it themselves. Yet this envy is in most cases diluted by the fact that the telescope will be offered for the use of any man who genuinely needs it.

Science today is not as chaotic as the rest of human activity but it is by no means without its perplexities. No matter what he does the modern laboratory man cannot keep pace with the theorist. Experiment is infinitely more expensive and time-consuming than the development of mathematical hypothesis, and the man with the pencil, having made the most he can of discovered fact, has to bide his time till proof or disproof of his position can be worked out in the laboratory.

For three hundred years after its birth science occupied itself with exploration, applying every discovery as rapidly as possible to the actual uses of mankind. Natural phenomena lay about in such abundance that the scientist could devote a lifetime to invention without concerning himself very much with pure research. But by the end of the Nineteenth Century most of the surface had been spaded, most of the simple applications had been made; it was time to dig deeper into fundamental causes and begin to make voyages of discovery for their own sake.

George Hale was among the first to draw large fortunes to the advancement of fundamental research, and in pursuit of this produced the science of astrophysics. In the search for basic knowledge in chemistry and physics laboratory men were already badly hampered by experimental limitations. A study of the atom, for instance, could not be completed unless matter could be viewed under a wide range of temperatures and pressures—a range quite impossible to achieve on earth. Hale showed that the stars were in reality great cosmic laboratories, which offered the very testing ground that was lacking. Conditions in the outer Universe ran the gamut from millions of degrees and millions of pounds per square inch to absolute cold and a sparsity of matter thousands of times thinner than the best man-made vacuum. At both these extremes, he foresaw, atoms and elements would be found to exist in states never observed on earth—states which would explain the secrets of the constitution of matter. The window through which science might look in on these laboratories was the telescope.

In twenty years Hale furnished the world with two great observatories and inspired many more by his example. The work they have done has helped immeasurably to repair the lack of experimental data. But the more information they have gained, the more complicated the puzzle of the physical world has become. Instead of solving all problems the cosmic discoveries have shown that far more intricate ones lie beyond.

It soon became necessary to divide physics into two parts, the one dealing with the atom and its constituents, the other with the Universe as a whole. Man had evidently been set down by the Creator in the middle of a vast structural scale; the units of matter about him seemed to go on getting larger and smaller without end. Just where in this scale he stood, and just how far it reached in both directions, he must find out before he could hope to understand the nature of the physical world.

The astronomer now found himself half in one camp and half in the other. He was expected to supply observational data to both. Like a circus rider he was standing on two horses at once, and the animals were not going the same way. Not only were his spectroscopic discoveries in the stars in demand for the atomic researcher, but his measurements of the Galaxy and the distribution of the nebulae were needed by the cosmic theorist who was devoting his time to solving the riddle of the Universe. And like all laboratory men, he was woefully short of money and time. From the beginning it was impossible for him to keep up the pace.

The lag between experiment and hypothesis reappeared. With men like Einstein, Eddington, Jeans, De Sitter and Lemaitre on one side and others like J. J. Thomson, Bohr, Chadwick, De Broglie and Dirac on the other, theories of the Universe and of its building material were developed which were not compatible. Einstein led off with Relativity and on the basis of this Eddington developed his theory of the Expanding Universe. Their opposites pursued the microcosm through the atom to the electron and beyond to the neutron, the photon and eventually to the barytron, and developed the theory of Quantum Mechanics. They were worlds apart and yet all of them knew that somehow one uniform law must be found for all.

While theorists wait they are always busy, and the scientific scene has been enlivened all along with controversy. None of them has had enough evidence to prove anything and in its absence one hypothesis has been about as good as another. As Jeans remarked five years ago: "The advance of knowledge is at present reduced to what Einstein describes as 'extracting one incomprehensible from another incomprehensible.'" And Mathematics, to keep up with the parade, has steadily been supplying more and more complicated symbolisms in which the arguing could be done. Relativity, whose four dimensions used to be understandable to only twelve people in the world, is now spoken of in college classrooms as tame, "classical stuff." Today, I am told by a professor of physics, the graduate student plays handily with tensor analysis, indeterminism, and quantum electrodynamics, which use for their mathematical tools a "Hilbert space of a countably infinite number of dimensions." It is an involved world indeed, and none the less so for being entirely on scraps of paper.

Yet out of all this welter of symbols and theories and "apparent reality" there still comes the same cry from all sides: "Give us facts! More facts!" And it is this cry that astronomy, armed with such modern engines as the 200-inch telescope, is striving to heed. Hale's concept of an earthbound science drawing upon a whole universe for its experimental data, is more valid than ever. The Giant of Palomar is needed and needed badly. "More light!" was his theme, and more light is what the Two Hundred will give.

The work its owners intend to do will be less spectacular, perhaps, than some astronomers are willing to admit. They agree with Eddington that its operation will be largely humdrum. But they are satisfied that there may be, eventually, some important corner it alone can turn.

The program of the 200-inch telescope, says Dr. Adams, will be divided into two equal parts. Very extensive spectrographic work during the two weeks when the Moon is shining; photometric and nebular work during the dark of the Moon. The spectrograph can work during moonlight because the spectrum of the moonlit sky is rarely strong enough to affect the plates and interfere with the stellar impressions received. Direct photography of stars and nebulae, and even spectrographic records of the nebulae must be done when the heavens are completely dark because the telescope will be so fast that stray light will fog the plates.

The General Education Board early explained the purpose of the instrument which it was endowing. It would make further studies in the size and structure of the galactic systems, the distance, radiation and evolution of stars, the spectra of the brighter stars under high dispersion; it would give much new information on the separation of binary stars, and on many other phenomena bearing directly on the constitution of matter.

Probably the most dramatic work the telescope will do is to seek a solution to the problem of the Expanding Universe. This theory was based on the discovery of Slipher, Pease and Wolf that the spectral lines of the spiral nebulae were displaced toward the red end. The logical explanation was that the nebulae were moving away from us so fast that the wavelengths of their light were actually stretched out a little, and made longer, or redder. It was found that the farther away the object was the greater the shift in its spectrum. The astronomers applied the test to nearly a hundred nebulae and found that they were moving away from the earth in every direction, all at speeds roughly proportional to their distance from us. Hubble and Humason

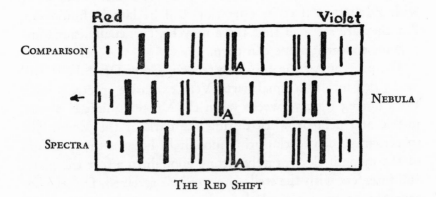

THE RED SHIFT

added to this brilliant observations indicating that the nebulae are evenly distributed in space at least as far out as the astronomical eye can reach. Eddington then took this data and constructed a theoretical picture of the Universe out of it. Applying Einstein's General Relativity Theory he arrived at a conception of space filled with billions of island universes rapidly scattering.

The interesting question was where did they start from and how far are they going? The answer would be very close to the fundamental one of how the world came to be born. Eddington and others began to work back then toward the beginning of things, and arrived at a tentative historical picture of fourth-dimensional space filled with elemental material which condensed into nodules of stars. These repelled one another and began to expand—and are still expanding, even Eddington does not dare say where or how far. Totally beyond the mind's ability to conceive, the whole thing depended on mathematical jugglery which may only be valid until a new and still more abstruse symbolism is invented.

Hubble and other astronomers meanwhile discovered further cosmic evidence which did not fit any too well with the Universe Eddington based on the red shift. They found that his conception was too small to suit their data. So again astrophysics landed itself in a muddle. And that muddle is at its height today.

If the red shift does not mean that the nebulae are flying away from each other, what does it mean? Astronomers do not know. There is no other cause so far discovered to explain it. Now comes the new telescope, with many times the power of any previous instrument. What will it say? If it corroborates the earlier hypothesis, then the Expanding Universe will have a powerful confirmation. If it disproves the theory of the red shift, then, as Adams says, "everything is unexplained and we are entirely at sea."

Perhaps it will prove neither. Perhaps the Universe is far too big for man ever to measure and describe it accurately. Perhaps the 200-inch will only do on a larger scale what the 100-inch did twenty years ago—ask a score of questions for every one it answers. At any rate the eyes of the world are upon it and the excitement is intense.

Another investigation of great interest is the work already begun by Fritz Zwicky on the supernovae. His problem is to explore the entire heavens in order to see just how common an occurrence the supernova is, and to study its life cycle in detail. For this purpose he is at present using the 18-inch Schmidt camera and will soon have the 48-inch, many times as powerful. These cameras are in effect finder telescopes for the 200-inch, capable of exploring the sky quickly in order to turn up important new objects for the big instrument to analyze in detail. Without them the 200-inch would be at a serious disadvantage. Its field of view is so limited that it would require 27,000 photographs to cover the sky—many lifetimes of work. But the Schmidts, with their extraordinary wide-angle plates and mirrors, can do the same thing in a single year.

Eventually there may come from Zwicky's work the answer to what makes a star shine—what keeps its fires fed over so many millions of years. These supernovae are the freaks of the stellar world. Like a pathologist in his laboratory, this physicist lately turned astronomer may gain an insight into stellar life through a study of stellar disease.

Zwicky and the Schmidt cameras have also embarked upon another interesting research, begun by others many years ago but always hampered by lack of light. This has to do with the gravitational fields of the nebulae and gives promise of providing a new proof for the Theory of Relativity itself. This theory is at the foundation of the whole present concept of the Universe, but it has not yet received adequate experimental test. What is needed is a demonstration of the apparent fact that light from a star is *bent* as it passes through the gravitational field of another star. Observations have been made during total eclipses, using our own Sun to produce the field, and a star lying close to its rim to furnish the light to be bent. But the quantities involved are too small to yield conclusive evidence. And the probability of two stars lining up correctly, even among the billions at the astronomer's disposal, is nil. "Perfect tests of General Relativity," said Henry Norris Russell, "are thus unavailable."

It has been known for a number of years that the nebulae themselves may act as "gravitational lenses," bending the light from other nebulae that passes close by, and thus offering a chance to check the Einstein theory that the stars themselves cannot give. On the photographs of the 18-inch Schmidt camera Zwicky has found a surprising number of these gravitational lenses, some of which focus the light of distant nebulae behind them upon our own Earth. On every plate there is at least one tiny nebular image with a mysterious ring around it. This ring is the light from a galaxy so remote that no telescope no matter how big could ever see it—without the "lens" effect. And because the nebulae are so gigantic, the gravitational force is many times larger than that of a mere star.

The research will be a long one, for hundreds of plates must be exposed in the Schmidt and hundreds of hours spent in the office analyzing images so small as to be indistinguishable except under a magnifying glass. But when he has finally found them, Zwicky can go back to Palomar and train the 200-inch mirror upon them again, and actually make spectrographic analyses which may possibly prove once and for all whether Einstein is right or wrong.

The Glass Giant of Palomar will by no means confine itself to investigations billions of light-years out into space. Its great light-gathering power will be used here at home in our own little world of the Milky Way. Almost every investigation on the stars that is now in progress can be carried much further with the new mirror. Faint stars will become bright and bright ones will approach the intensity of the Sun. Thus Sirius seen through the high-dispersion spectrograph at the coudé focus will yield a spectrum almost as detailed as the one we now get from the Sun.

The study of the physical constitution of the stars has an enormous future. It leads ultimately to the knowledge of how stars are born, how big they are and how hot, and how long they live. In the firmament around us there are millions of examples of stars in every conceivable state. The work already done by other instruments has proved that stars fall into a few distinct classes and that the members of each have a definite life-cycle. With the 200-inch telescope it is hoped to make this picture far more complete, and by that means to answer such questions as the actual age of our Sun, predict how much longer it will burn, and thus make a guess at the length of our stay in the Universe.

The work in this field may prove quite as important as explaining the Universe as a whole. Certainly it is more personal to us. As Eddington points out, the human race is an interloper in creation. We are here because one chemical element out of the whole ninety-two—carbon—happened to be able to combine with others in thousands of different ways. But we are here as a freak of nature, the product of conditions of temperature which seem to be very nearly unique in all the Universe. We cling to a tiny rock at just the right distance from just the right sun; around us the vast bulk of cosmic material is either fiercely burning at temperatures of millions of degrees, or else lying dispersed in unutterable thinness in the cold of absolute void. A slight deviation in either direction from our happy medium— from any cause—and we would be snuffed out in an instant.

Could anything be more important to us than to learn how we suffered that lucky chance? Is there any speculation more fascinating than to ponder our probable end? Or any investigation more thrilling than the one which will determine whether we are in fact alone upon the face of the deep, or accompanied by a handful of other freaks like ourselves?

And even the stars are not to be the nearest neighbors which the 200-inch will look into. Some work may be done on the planets. It will not be what the man in the street expects; it will be wholly scientific searches into the conditions which exist, say on Venus, Mercury and Mars. So far no one has ever seen the surface of Venus, nor does anyone know for sure what the lower layers of her obscuring clouds may be. Spectrographic analyses with the new telescope may answer that question. Radiometric measurements of surface temperatures on Mars may explain the controversial canals.

All this will not lead to any new theory of inhabitants on the other planets, but eventually it will help toward the solution of a much bigger problem: how was the solar system made? That matter is still in a chaotic state. Observational data does not add up to any one tenable theory, and it is still one of the most troublesome problems in all astronomy. The Giant of Palomar may, if it has time, bring new light.

These few examples will serve to indicate the kind of work the new telescope will perform. Because it is the largest instrument in the world people are apt to believe that it will supersede all other telescopes. This of course is not true. Shapley points out that not more than one-third of all astronomical advance is made with large instruments. Hundreds of small telescopes will always be needed for the spade work behind the distant voyages of discovery, and for scores of basic researches that large instruments are not suited to perform.

The 200-inch is a specialized piece of equipment, just as an ocean liner is a specialized means of transportation. No one would think of using the *Queen Mary* for a ferryboat across the Hudson River, though she would no doubt serve. Nor will anyone ask the Giant of Palomar to investigate the details of the Moon, when a dozen smaller instruments can do it as well. The primary function of the big fellow is to gather light, and in researches where light is not the prime requisite, it will not be used.

In the long train of investigation ahead the 200-inch will in general be available to all who require its help. Just as the 100-inch at Mount Wilson has served astronomers all over the world, so will the new instrument be offered from time to time to visiting scientists whose problems it alone can solve. And whether it be pioneer investigation or follow-up work on stellar detail, the Glass Giant of Palomar will always belong to the men who are explorers in spirit—who take risks and spend money that others at home may know more of the world and live better upon it.

Brave adventurers have been going to the polar regions for

nearly a century. They used to get there on foot or with sledges. Now they do it by airplane. The 200-inch is to Cal Tech what the airplane was to Admiral Byrd—simply the modern way of traveling into the Unknown.

Let those who complain that too much money is being spent on abstract knowledge while people are starving remember this: the alternative to knowledge is savagery. Their very existence as stowaways on the voyage of civilization is owing to advances in science which permit some to live without doing their share of the work. Let them be tolerant, then, lest by encumbering the useful ones they destroy the thing which keeps them alive!

## CHAPTER XL

## OPEN SEAS AHEAD

THERE remains only the privilege of waving the astronomers farewell on their voyage to the stars—in imagination riding with the Captain on his bridge down the bay till the pilot takes us off and puts us ashore.

It was, let us say, the dark of the Moon on Palomar, and on the walk over from the Residence we had to pick our way carefully along the narrow path cut between high banks of snow. It was scarcely six o'clock, and there was a long stretch ahead. Our astronomer (whom we shall call Mr. Bennett) was working on the first shift, from six to twelve. In these long winter nights the 200-inch telescope could serve two groups of observers comfortably.

Soon we were inside the little rotunda and following Bennett around the circular corridor to his private office. It was prettily fitted out, with a desk, cot and startlingly gay blue-and-white lounging chair. Bennett had a whimsical streak about him, it seemed.

But the office was far from frivolous. On the desk, piled helter-skelter, was a magnificent jumble of photographic plates, prints, open books, slide rules, scratch pads, pencils, erasers, magnifying glasses—all leavened with a scattering of yellow sheets covered with scrawled computations. An adding machine peeked out from one corner, and an empty coffee cup out of another.

Bennett was apologizing for the mess.

"I was working in here till four this afternoon," he said, "and I didn't have a chance to clean up. Somebody said that an astronomer is a fellow who works all night and does arithmetic all day—I guess that's about the story."

"When do you sleep?" we asked.

"Oh, between times. Back in Pasadena mostly."

There was a knock at the door and the Night Assistant appeared—a tall young fellow about thirty. He was introduced as Mr. Stanley, or "Stan."

"Ready to go, Cap?" he asked, jauntily.

"Just about," said Bennett. He went to a locker and dragged out a handful of heavy clothes—an aviator's fleece-lined suit, helmet, ear muffs, heavy mittens and scarf.

"You'll need 'em," laughed Stan. "I just took my readings. It's ten above zero exactly. Barometer up and humidity down. One of those crystal clear nights when the stars fairly crackle—"

"And the doggone seeing's about Two," said Bennett, wriggling into the flying suit. "Oh, by the way," he added, to us, "you'll need something warm to put on."

"Never mind us," we said. "We don't feel the cold. We're only here in imagination, you know. We've left our sensations behind."

"That's fortunate," said Bennett. "It would be rather crowded up in the cage for three people."

Stan had gone out and come in again with a thermos bottle of hot coffee and a package of sandwiches from the kitchen. Bennett thanked him and stuffed them into his pockets. Then he pawed through the papers on his desk and fished out a sheet with some figures scrawled on it.

"Here you are, Stan," he said, handing a list of the star positions over to the assistant. "All short exposures tonight. Let's go."

We went out in the corridor again and Bennett ducked into the refrigerator room and returned with an armful of plate-holders. He had supersensitized the emulsions with ammonia just before supper, he explained, and they had to be kept cold so as not to fog.

Soon we were in the little automatic elevator going up, and

in a minute stopped at the main floor. Stan got out, bound for
the control desk under the north pier. A blast of frigid air came
in at the door and we were glad that we had decided not to mind
the cold. Standing there for five hours at ten above zero wasn't
going to be so comfortable for Stan. But he didn't seem to mind.

Up we went again, and soon came out on the balcony. We
stopped for a moment and gazed around the vast shadowy
place. One or two hooded lights in the walls cast dim pools of
illumination discreetly downward. Above, the silver arch of the
dome could just be made out, sweeping off into space. The shutters were open, and out beyond we could see a faint band of in-
digo sky and a star or two—ships ahead on the open sea.

Then, among the shadows around us we began to make out
the great telescope, its vague outlines criss-crossed against the
blackness of the night, its horseshoe reaching out toward us, as
if offering the tube. Away up almost out of sight where the
tube ended was the little car in which we were to ride. It was
breath-taking and vast. Could this be a telescope? Like a lion
it seemed to be poised for its leap into space and we looked about
nervously for something to grip. Then indeed it did begin to
move—imperceptibly, like the first moving of an ocean liner
as it leaves the dock. The tube began to come over toward us,
leaning farther and farther down to the south. There was not
a sound—only the velvet stillness of the night and the sensation
that we were in the midst of tremendous action—which in truth
we were. Then the tube came to rest above us.

Bennett had already climbed the short iron stairway to the
loading bridge and was calling to us to follow. We dashed up
after him. With a quick pressure on a push button he brought
down the flying platform along its curved track; in a minute
it had come abreast of our foothold and we walked out upon it,
over the abyss. It was narrow and bent, held in space by a stout
round arm.

Bennett closed and locked the little swinging gate at the inner end, pressed another button and up we began to go, the driving motors humming quietly below. Never a child in the nursery has ridden a magic carpet like that; never a pair of adults have felt more hushed than we, as we gripped the railings of the platform and soared upward and outward toward the mouth of the giant tube. Skillfully Bennett brought us alongside. At last we were about to climb aboard the great ship bound out for its voyage among the stars!

Bennett dropped down inside the cage and we followed. The steel shell was as big as a cistern: circular, with a curving bottom and an instrument desk coming up through the middle. Around the inside wall ran a series of pipe rails and we helped ourselves down by these hand over hand, to the deck.

"As long as you don't take up any space," said Bennett, falling in with our fantasy, "I won't offer you accommodations. If you'll just stay still and watch now—"

He picked up a small telephone instrument from a bracket on the wall.

"Stan? Hello, Stan . . . O.K. Give us the first star." He hung up the instrument. "Voice-power phone," he explained. "It generates its own electricity when you talk into it. Saves complications."

The original telephone! Mustn't Bell be proud to see his first little "talking telegraph" at work in the Giant of Palomar! And Galileo, what he must be thinking as he watches real men being carried around in the mouth of an instrument whose ancestor he once held in his hand!

We were moving. The floor under us was tipping and one of the walls was coming around beneath. We gripped the handrails tightly and waited. Bennett paid us no attention. He opened the drawer in the central pedestal and put his plates in it, then seated himself in a curious kind of chair that rolled around the little compartment on rails. He drew a small notebook out of his pocket and consulted it, then stared across at the opposite wall where a bank of little instruments with dials was busily recording the changing position of the telescope. Slowly the hands traveled across the numbered faces like the hands of the clocks in a radio studio. Then all at once they came to rest.

Bennett had the phone to his ear again and we could faintly hear Stan's voice saying: "On!" Then he leaned over the center of the pedestal and with handscrews began adjusting the plate-holder frame. Swinging a small eyepiece into place at one side he stared into it for a moment, and said: "Yep, there she is"; then took out a plateholder and slipped it in place. "Have a look?" he offered.

We bent down over the eyepiece. There it was—the thing he was after—a faint blue-green blotch of light, picked out with tiny bright dots here and there. A nebula, he explained, seven hundred million light-years away.

"H-how do you know it's the right one?" we stammered.

"It has to be," said Bennett confidently. "The telescope's set on the right place in the sky. Look."

And he pointed at the dials and showed us that they read the same as the figures in his notebook.

As simple as that. . . .

"All right, Stan," he was saying into the telephone, "here we go!"

There wasn't a jerk or a jar or a sound, yet we knew we had left the harbor and were headed out for the open sea. Bennett's two mittened hands twisting the adjusting wheels back and forth, back and forth as he stared in his eyepiece, gave the only sign.

"Seeing's not as bad as I thought," he muttered, and looked up at us and smiled. "Well, there you are. That's all there is to it. We're under way."

We smiled in return and hung on.

Hours later, we walked back alone through the crackling night to the Residence. Our trip down the harbor was done.

THE END

# WHITHER THE READER?

THUS ends the account of the building of the Glass Giant of Palomar. It is admittedly incomplete, for no one not actually connected with the project could list every detail and be sure that none was omitted. Nor is it likely that the astronomers themselves could cover the subject thoroughly and at the same time with a detached point of view.

Moreover, the history, even of the building, is not yet complete. It will probably not be finished for five or ten years; perhaps never, for there will always be improvements and innovations, some of them revolutionary in importance.

So it must remain an unfinished story and one which my readers, I hope, will follow with interest in times to come. A portion of them, perhaps, will even wish to go further, seeking additional light on astronomy in general from some of the great authorities both in America and abroad. The books suggested below will help to further this quest. And they will make it possible for anyone who is ambitious to become an amateur astronomer himself and so take part in actual voyages to the stars.

HARLOW SHAPLEY: *Flights From Chaos.* This in my opinion is the most exciting book on general astronomy that one can read. Dr. Shapley, who is the Director of the Harvard Observatory, has a passion for cosmic order and has devoted his life to the sober task of arranging and cataloguing astronomical data which the world has been collecting for a century. The book is here and there slightly technical, but is written with extraordinary clarity and covers the whole gamut of material things from the sub-sub-electron to the macrocosm which may be God. One should, I think, read it first, to get a sense of order established and to appreciate the vastness of the field in which astronomy is making its snail's progress.

SIR JAMES JEANS: *The Mysterious Universe*. This is a dramatic, slightly fanciful account of modern physics and astronomy. Jeans always takes the larger view and here his thesis is that "God is a mathematician; the universe was not created for human beings at all." Like Shapley, he shows how vast the cosmos is and how insignificant are man and all his troubles.

There are many other books by Jeans of similar interest, which may be obtained at any good library. Among them are *Through Time and Space*, and *The New Background of Science*. All make inspiring reading.

SIR ARTHUR EDDINGTON: *Stars and Atoms*. This great English astronomer and sometime opponent of Jeans is quite as lucid and fully as dramatic as he. He is less of a visionary, perhaps, and takes more time to explain, with charm and clarity, the procedure by which astronomy has moved ahead step by step.

Eddington has a long list of titles in many libraries. Among them is a rather humorous lecture, *Science and the Unseen World*, once given before a Quaker organization, which nicely expresses the scientist's view of man's relationship to God. For those who insist on following Eddington into theoretical physics and cosmology, *The Expanding Universe* will meet their fondest hopes and conquer all but the die-hard who is determined to punish himself in the fourth dimension.

GEORGE ELLERY HALE managed to add a good deal of writing to his already overcrowded life, some of it remarkable for its clarity and popular appeal. For several years he published accounts of the work under way at Mount Wilson in *Scribner's, Harper's* and the *Atlantic Monthly*. Later on he gathered the material together and expanded it into four little volumes which may be obtained at good libraries. They are charming and direct and well illustrated, and tell a vivid story of the astronomers who are at the center of many a great project. Their names are: *Signals from the Stars, Beyond the Milky Way, The Depths of the Universe*, and *The New Heavens*.

HENRY NORRIS RUSSELL: *The Solar System and Its Origin*. Over one hundred years ago Laplace advanced his Nebular Hypothesis to account for the birth of the solar system. Ever since then astronomers have been trying to make it fit with observed data and have finally abandoned it. They have also abandoned many another theory built up to take its place and are at present quite at sea as to how the planets came to revolve around the Sun. Russell is a contributing editor to *Scientific American* and his account of what is going on in our own astronomical back yard is illuminating and untechnical.

J. EDWARD PENDRAY: *Men, Mirrors and Stars*. This is probably the most comprehensive history of astronomy and telescopes so far offered to the layman. It begins at the beginning and goes right on through the development of optics, the telescope and astronomy to the 200-inch instrument and beyond. The book is full of pictures and diagrams and should be read by anybody who has decided to study the stars seriously.

JAMES STOKLEY: *Stars and Telescopes*. Much less inclusive than Pendray's book, this one rapidly covers astronomy from the earth to the nebulae and gives a competent picture of the whole. It is rather more readable than Pendray's, and more popular. Stokley is the Director of the Buhl Planetarium in Pittsburgh and knows just how much the public can stand.

CLYDE FISHER: *Exploring the Heavens*. Dr. Fisher heads the Hayden Planetarium in New York and like Stokley understands how to present a generalized description of astronomy to the public. The book is copiously illustrated and gives a rapid glance at the Universe, and particularly at the insignificant portion of it near by.

For those who wish to build their own telescopes and take up star-gazing in earnest, there is only one book, *Amateur Tele-*

*scope Making*—a veritable bible for the enthusiastic amateur. It is staggeringly complete and if a man (or woman) has it in him (or her) to make a telescope, this book will bring it out. "A.T.M." is fathered by Albert G. Ingalls of the *Scientific American,* and god-fathered by Russell W. Porter, the patron saint of the telescope fans. It may be bought for three dollars and, with the addition of five dollars worth of glass and grinding compound, is all that anyone needs to start a telescope of his own. The qualities required to *finish* such a telescope must come from within. Before embarking upon the project, the candidate is advised to consult with his wife and be sure everything is going to be all right. There are several thousand "glass widows" in the country already.

There are hundreds of books on astronomy and its allied sciences, many of them no doubt as useful as the ones I have mentioned. Anyone who is seriously interested in the stars may readily make up a list longer than he can read from the catalogue of any good library. But to cap the climax and restore one to a state of complete bewilderment, he should not fail to read Einstein's own popular account of his work: *The Evolution of Physics.* It is deceptively simple, with not a single mathematical equation to be seen anywhere. But somehow one begins to fall behind toward the end of the book and at the last page thoroughly understands the difficulty of solving the problem of the Universe.

With a salute to Dr. Einstein for his courage in attempting to explain himself to the layman, I leave the reader to rescue himself from the effects of my own book as best he may.

# AFTERWORD—1948

THE 200-inch project is so huge that no history of it can be complete, for there will never be an end to the fascinating saga of the world's largest telescope. One can only set an arbitrary date and bring the story down to that, leaving the rest to future historians. This I did in 1939, when the instrument was far advanced, and within a year or so of the end of the long pull. But war intervened, and that year's work has been spread over seven. This chapter, then, is to tie up the ends and bring the telescope to the point where it can actually photograph the stars.

It is a sad commentary on human affairs that an undertaking so valuable to mankind should be stalled so many years, and that so many of the men whose lives had gone into it should have grown old waiting to finish their work. The only compensation for this is that the researches will be so tremendous in scope that they will make those lost years seem brief. A few decades from now, it will have been forgotten whether the 200-inch telescope went into service in 1942 or in 1949.

At the time this book was published the major elements of the instrument had been built and cast and there remained only two principal tasks: the completion of the mirror surface and the final installation and running-in of the machine to determine errors and get all parts working together. Today, both of these jobs are virtually done. On January 18, 1948, the first test observations were made; the mirror actually gathered light from the heavens and recorded it upon photographic plates. With what humility we can imagine, men who knew every detail of the theory and construction of the instrument crowded into its prime focus cage and gazed upon the image of a star cast clearly upon a ground-glass plate. Living for twenty years in a world of imagination and forecast, on this night they actually entered into the bosom of this glass-and-steel monster and saw that it worked. Before their eyes there shone out the proof that twenty years of planning and labor had achieved what Hale had said it would achieve.

What we have to catch up on now is, mainly, the completion of the reflecting surface and the mirror's move to the mountain.

First of all, what became of the telescope project during the war? It blacked out, almost complete. For the skill of every scientist and artisan was needed to devise new means of warfare. Soon after Pearl Harbor all men and all facilities were deep in military manufacture and experiment, most of it top secret. Eventually it developed that Cal Tech had had a large part to play in the research and design of rockets. Meanwhile, the famous Optical Shop was working under high pressure turning out range-finder prisms for the Navy and large parabolic mirrors, some of them three feet in diameter, for use in military wind tunnels.

For Dr. Anderson and Marcus Brown this meant little change in the familiar routine; actually, a lowering of the pressure and responsibility they had been accustomed to bear with the Big Glass. Wind tunnels, by the way, need optical mirrors because the best way to study in detail the flow of air around airfoils is to introduce smoke or colored gas into the slip stream and then observe its behavior with a telescopic system set crosswise to the tunnel's axis.

Like everybody else in war production, "Brownie" had to employ many untrained people to do skilled work. He found himself in charge of a crew of young girls, to replace his original men in white. These he instructed in a short time to run the grinding and polishing machines, and the work they turned out was excellent. He himself, with Dr. Anderson, did the testing and inspection.

Of all the war jobs that the telescope project did, perhaps the most interesting fell to Russell Porter, who soon found himself working full time for the Navy. Just as he had done for so many years, he made himself invaluable with his pencil. Scores, sometimes hundreds, of different designs were made up for rocket launchers and other ordnance devices. Every time something new came off the drawing boards, Navy technicians called in Porter to make one of his famous three-dimensional cutaway drawings so that the "brass" could visualize what they were going to have. He spent days and nights at Camp Pendleton, near by, helping the Marines to prepare themselves for tough landings in the far Pacific. And he spent many more days at the Navy's Inyokern testing grounds, sketching everything, much of it from the air. Around Washington he was affectionately known as "The Cutaway Man," and his drawings were a standard part of much that was new in ordnance.

The bombs of Pearl Harbor had scarcely shaken the world when the entire Pacific coast began to believe it saw fleets of Jap submarines lurking offshore, and to wake at midnight to the imagined horror of aerial attack. There was a rush toward black-out and defense, and a mounting concern for the many treasures of art and antiquity of the region. Among other things, people began to worry about the 200-inch mirror, sitting unprotected in its Optical Shop. Alarmed scientists everywhere urged the Observatory Council to move the great disk away into the mountains and bury it so deep that no bomb could reach it.

Anderson and his colleagues considered the matter thoroughly, and computed the chances of disaster. They finally decided to leave the mirror where it was. To move it and bury it could not possibly be done without massive handling equipment that could not be obtained. And they felt that elaborate protection on the spot would be a foolish waste of effort. It was better to run for luck, lock the observation gallery against all visitors, and cover the mirror with stout planks to protect it from flying fragments if the laboratory should receive a chance shot. Nothing could possibly be done to save it from a direct hit.

Actually, the invasion scare was over in a few weeks, without a single authenticated case of bombing by the enemy. The mirror was never in any real danger. Once this period was over, they even thought, wistfully, that they would like to continue work on the glass at a reduced pace. It seemed a pity not to, for the surface was partially parabolized and within five-thousandths of an inch of correct. Anderson knew well the many hundreds of hours that must still be spent to get rid of that tissue-thin layer of glass in exactly the right places over 30,000 square inches of area. He hated to see the time go by, unspent. But he had no choice. Supplies had dried up, clearance on the project could not be secured; the shops were filled with war orders and labor was unobtainable for non-war-connected work. It was a case of wait, and hope.

Not till six months after the war ended could the shops be cleared and the polishing and testing machinery reconditioned, so that the project could be resumed. The only progress in four years had been the intermittent operation of the 18-inch Schmidt camera near the big dome on Palomar. Here Dr. Zwicky and his colleagues had made important observations on supernovae and had taken photographs which showed the gravitational fields of the distant nebulae. It was certain that the little Schmidt, and the larger 48-inch, planned but far from finished, would be invaluable "feeders" for the Giant.

And now it was time at last to bring the main project through to the end. The planks were cleared away from the mirror, the whole place scrubbed till it shone, the pitch laps resurfaced and the test stands wheeled into position. It was a happy day for Anderson and Brown when, in late January, 1946, they could begin again to work their glass.

The task to be done was of a most exacting kind, and could proceed only with utmost deliberation and care. Brown took on no more than six men to help him, for the final runs were to shorten steadily, and the tests to become more and more frequent. And so they began, using the finest rouge and small lapping tools—and *worked for a year* on that five-thousandths of an inch of glass. On March 1st, 1947, they had polished the whole surface to within one wavelength of a perfect paraboloid at every point. That is one fifty-thousandth of an inch.

As the critical moment came closer the team increased its caution. The slightest mistake in bearing on too hard or polishing too long without check might wear some part of the surface a shade too deep, and then there would be no remedy but to lower the entire mirror surface to conform—months, perhaps years, of extra work.

Anderson now began to apply a modified form of what optical experts call the "Hartmann Test." This is simply a method for checking up on small specimen zones throughout the mirror, choosing them in pairs along various diameters of the disk, and comparing the exact points where each zone of a pair brings a light source to a focus. The Foucault knife-edge test is used at the receiving end, as in former methods. The zones are created by placing the mirror in a vertical position and masking it with a wooden cover supplied with rows of holes arranged in the form of two crossing diameters. There are twenty-six holes along each, giving thirteen zones when they are paired off. Only one pair is used at a time, the remainder being shielded with paper.

The purpose of the zonal test was to arrive at the "Hartmann Criterion" for the mirror—a mathematical expression of its state of perfection in terms of diameter. Translated, this means the actual size of the image, or blurr, created at the mirror's focus, of a distant point of light, measured in seconds of arc. The knife-edge, carefully calibrated, indicated this in a few moments, for any pair of holes in the masking screen.

The significance of the criterion is fundamental, since it gives an index of the sharpness of focus, or resolving power. A perfect parabolic mirror, if untroubled by the wavering of the earth's atmosphere, should form a star image so small that it cannot be measured. Anything less than perfection will expand that point image to a disk of light, and the size of the disk is what is measured in seconds of arc and called the criterion. Somebody asked Anderson one day in that spring of '47 how much longer he expected to keep on and how accurate he hoped to have the mirror in the end.

"Well," he said quietly, "not much longer. February was a very successful month for us." He consulted a chart on which he had been plotting curves showing the gradual approach of the various zones toward perfection. "On February 8th, you see, our Hartmann Criterion stood at 0.54; on the 12th it was at 0.44 and by the first of March only 0.40. That means that the diameter of an image disk would only be eight-tenths of a second. Another month or two, if we are careful, *and* lucky . . ."

"But how far are you going?"

"I hope," he confessed, "till we reach one-hundredth of a second. Of course, the average blurr—tremor disk—produced by the atmosphere upon a star image, is about a quarter of a second, even under the very best seeing conditions. But—" and here was his professional pride coming out—"we want to beat the best mirror ever made—the one—well, I won't say where—and I think we can."

And he did, but not until the first of October, 1947. It is a pity that his mirror can never make full use of that perfection because of atmospheric limitations entirely beyond its control. But Anderson knew that Hale would have wanted it that way.

The most daring optical job ever attempted by man (said the California Institute of Technology for publication on October 3rd) was completed today at 2 p.m., after checking and double-checking tests made earlier this week. As the goal was approached, Dr. John A. Anderson . . . and other members of the Observatory Council met more and more frequently to watch and discuss progress of the final polishing. They devised new methods of testing the mirror. This was done to check on the methods that had been used earlier. These new methods confirmed the accuracy of previous ones, and assured Anderson and his fellow scientists that the readings they were getting were as accurate as man can obtain with the instruments of today.

And very reassuring tests they were, too, for the investment in man-hours and materials—and in hope—represented in the finished surface could scarcely have been calculated in dollars, even in six figures. But the final, conclusive tests would not come till the mirror had gone down to the mountain and had been clamped for good in its supports in the telescope tube. "There is some slight chance," Dr. Mason had said a few months before, "that after it is installed the mirror will be found imperfect, and will have to come back to Pasadena for further work." That unhappy thought was virtually wiped out now. No one doubted that this giant would perform as the tests and computations had predicted.

The very day that the polishing was done, plans were begun for the final move.

All concerned had been thinking of this for some time, especially Bruce Rule, the engineering manager of the project. The first problem was to build a completely protecting box for the mirror and its cell. This was done with heavy beams and 2-by-12-inch planks, with a layer of aluminum foil inside the cover to delay temperature changes, as well as seal it against possible rain. The box took several weeks to build. When the mirror and cell were finally packed in, the whole assembly weighed over 39 tons.

But before the packing could be done, it was necessary to remove the big glass plug that had been cemented into the center hole of the disk back when grinding began. This plug, the reader may remember, had been lowered into the hole on a cake of melting ice. Now, Brown had devised a heavy timber saw-horse with a protruding horn, to be pushed into the latticed back of the plug to bear its weight while the mirror itself was moved away from it by the overhead crane.

Brown was fully aware of his crushing responsibility with this near-priceless mirror. With utmost care his men suspended the disk at just the right height while the cement that held the plug was chipped away. Then, inch by inch, the crane man backed the glass along so that the protruding horn of the saw-horse fitted into the back of the plug.

"Slack her away, now!" Brown shouted. "Easy—ea-sy!"

The weight of the plug was transferred presently to the

wooden support as the mirror dropped a fraction of an inch. Then—

"Walk her along, now. Careful. Take it slow, very slow-w-w—"

The crane man began to move the disk imperceptibly along the floor and, as Brown had hoped, the plug stayed with its new support and started to withdraw. Gradually it came out until two inches of it showed. Then, suddenly, it slipped and slid back into the disk. Brown and everybody stood transfixed, as that ton weight of glass, slightly wedged in shape, glided along the greasy wooden horn toward its old home in the disk.

"I sweated out a year's growth in that fraction of a second," Brownie admitted afterward. "I knew that plug had an enormous wallop in it, even if it was just barely moving. Well, it rammed itself home in the center of the mirror and hit with such a blow that the whole disk rang like a bell. The whole thing swung a little and then hung quiet, waiting for us to go and see what had happened."

For an instant Brownie was afraid to go round front, for fear he would find a crack that would mean the end of all those years of work. Then he shrugged and went. There was no crack. There had not been quite enough momentum in the plug to burst the rim of the hole. The next time Brownie picked up the plug, he had it well lashed against its support, so that slipping back was impossible.

As the day drew near for transporting the disk to Palomar, Bruce Rule worked diligently on arrangements. He had been conferring for some time with the State Highway Department and with county engineers and local police officials. The whole idea was that the disk should be moved as secretly as possible, to avoid traffic tie-ups and the danger of accident that would go with a crowd of spectators. It was decided to follow as many back roads as possible, and this resulted in a route through many small towns to the southeast of Pasadena, a short stretch along main coastal highway 101, and then a long swing from Oceanside up through the hills back of San Diego and thence to the mountain. In this way the shortest route of about 130 miles would be lengthened to 140 or more. They hoped they could negotiate it in two days.

The same Jack Belyea who had moved the disk in from Lamanda Park in 1936, was to provide the same mammoth drop-center trailer and power unit that had made the earlier move. It was estimated that the trailer and its freight together would weigh about 60 tons. Even though this huge load would be distributed on 32 separate wheels, it would be too great for some of the highway structures along the way. Rule and the officials spent many hours over engineering maps and records, sizing up the situation, altering the route here and there to avoid as many bridges as possible. Byron Hill, coming down from Palomar, helped work out the strengthening requirements and factors of safety. There turned out to be five culverts and three bridges that might be too weak. Plans were made, therefore, to send out crews in advance to shore up the spans with heavy timbers, or to lay planking to spread the load just before the truck passed over them. In the case of a railroad overpass near San Juan Capistrano, the only practical way to assure safety would be by adding wheels to the truck itself.

Meanwhile Cal Tech officials had been doing some worrying about the pressure of publicity. As complete secrecy was impossible, it was decided to hold a press party well in advance and to get the reporters on their side, appealing for help in delaying the story till the move was well under way. To heighten the effect of this party, Russell Porter built a full-size wooden replica of Newton's original reflecting telescope, and this was displayed, resting in the center hole of the big disk, and eagerly photographed. The little model was scarcely ten inches long. The comparison was just what was needed to insure co-operation. Every newspaper man agreed to hold back his story of the move till noon of the day the trip began. This would get the disk well beyond the populated section around Los Angeles and prevent the trip being mobbed.

When at last all preparations were complete, on November
16th, Belyea's men backed the giant trailer through the arch and
the swinging doors into the Optical Shop. He had welded two
large I-beams across the trailer bed and the box, lowered onto
them, fitted perfectly, except for a slight misalignment of holes
between box and beams. This was quickly righted by drilling more
holes. Then the great box was securely bolted to the bed, and
was ready to go. The loading took less than one day.

The following morning the crew assembled again and tackled
the problem of getting the trailer out of the building. The box
was twenty feet square and the trailer extended ten feet or more
front and back. Although the architects had planned the archway and doors for exactly this moment, it turned out to be a
snug fit indeed. Belyea's strategy was to back and fill with the
trailer, a foot or two at a time, thus gradually negotiating the
right-angle turn from the inner doors of the Optical Shop
through the archway to the short ramp down to California
Street. Toward night it became evident that it would take
pretty complicated maneuvers to jockey the load through the
opening, and this might delay the take-off. So it was decided
to knock a corner off the archway and allow the box to swing
around in one final arc that would get it clear. By dark on the
evening of November 17th the trailer and its freight stood ready
in the open.

It is to the great credit of the California newsmen that they
did withhold the story of the last move of the Palomar mirror,
as they had promised, for they could easily have aroused the
countryside that dark morning and produced a traffic jam novel
even in California motoring history. But when truck driver
Lloyd Green backed his tractor in at two-thirty on the 18th,
not a soul was around but Brown and Rule and the handful of
helpers needed to start the disk on its journey. At three o'clock
the cavalcade rolled out into the deserted avenue. A couple of
motorcycle policemen headed it, followed by a radio car, then

the truck, another radio car and a final police escort. Very gingerly they began their trip, for the mirror inside its box rested solely upon the supports of its cell, just as it would in the telescope. The lever-and-weight actions had been partially blocked, but allowed enough freedom so that they would give the disk a spring-like ride. Rule did not know just how fast the mirror might travel without starting a suicidal bounce. That remained to be seen.

To watch this every minute, several gauges had been installed inside the box. Two were placed at the back, visible through a small door, reading both vertical and horizontal displacement. A third was fitted in front, between glass and box top, indicating by electric wires on a dial in the driver's cab. Brownie took up his station at the rear of the trailer, a flashlight in hand, his eyes glued to the needles through the little door.

The first five minutes were slow and painful indeed. At every intersection, Green crawled across the rain dips that cut through California Street, then eased his tractor into the haul with a notch at a time on his throttle. Nothing happened. The Glass Giant rode as smoothly as if she had been doing this all her life. As the miles gradually stretched out behind them, they gained confidence; little by little the driver, a veteran of fifteen years' moving tremendous weights for Belyea, built up his speed, till they were actually traveling ten, sometimes twenty miles an hour. Brown, at the back, relaxed and rolled himself a cigarette. Rule, in the cab, sighed and lay back against the stiff cushions.

As they followed their allotted route the bridges and culverts, well prepared, bore the load perfectly. Here and there, after daylight had increased the traffic, the motorcycle escort went ahead to block entering highways and hold them till the mighty load was safely past. Finally, they rolled up to the Garvin overpass near Capistrano—the bridge that needed the extra wheels. Here, the perfect planning paid off. Two more tractor units were waiting for them, with the extra "dollies." Swiftly they unloaded them and hauled the new wheels into positions prepared for them under the main trailer. Sixteen were added in all, till the disk rested on a grand total of forty-eight. Then, quickly, the load was pulled across the bridge. Down below, an ingenious county engineer had rigged a stick to the under side of the bridge beams, its lower end dipping in a pail of mud. With this simple device he measured the actual deflection downward as the load passed overhead. It was almost zero.

The entire maneuver at the Garvin overpass, including unshipping the dollies afterward, took thirty minutes.

Noon that day had been the press deadline. No sooner had the sun crossed the meridian than the air was alive with reports of the great event. Taken entirely by surprise, school teachers along the route hastily declared a holiday and thousands of children lined the highway to cheer the disk's safe passage. By now the motorists, too, had caught on, and a long cavalcade of the curious followed the mirror. But the police saw danger in this, and from time to time stopped the truck and made the public pass on ahead and keep moving.

That night by five the disk wheeled quietly into the up-country town of Escondido and came to a stop outside the police station, in a street that was quickly cleared and blocked at both ends. Here the local forces took over and stood armed guard all night, while the weary drivers and engineers dispersed to hotels. Rule and Brown drove on to Palomar to bring the good news of the uneventful passage.

November 19th started off thick and rainy, and the state police held up the take-off till 5:30, afraid the roads might be too slippery. But Green said he could do it and Rule, back down from the mountain, assured them that there was nothing too bad ahead, so they began to roll again. Now came the real work of the expedition, negotiating the hard pull up to a mile of altitude. The two extra power units were hooked on behind as pushers, and the final climb began. The main grade up the mountain had been permanently blocked till the mirror had passed.

Anderson, Mason and Porter started out from Pasadena that

morning early, to be on the mountain in good season to receive their beloved glass. As they reached the area they were much worried, for it had begun to snow and the wind was rising to a gale. What would happen to the disk on those whiplash turns made treacherous by ice and slush and hidden by fog? They hastened up a little used road on the north side of the mountain, and arrived just at noon. Porter swung his cramped legs out into the snow and cold as the car pulled in behind the dome.

"Well! What do you know!" he cried. "The darn thing's here already!"

The mirror had been on the mountain a full hour, having beaten its schedule by nearly half a day. There hadn't been a single hitch worthy of the name.

\*     \*     \*

And so the 200-inch mirror came to Palomar, after eleven years of devotion on the part of every man.

It is as difficult to end the story here as it would be to end it a year from now, or ten years. We can only say that, so far, extraordinary success has come to every new phase of the mighty project. Not a foolish, trouble-free success, but one that was always earned by hard work and minute planning and elaborate precaution. Time and again they had found themselves up against what seemed to be a serious difficulty, only to discover some very slight misadjustment that a little straight thinking could fix.

Such a hitch occurred the day after the mirror arrived, when Byron Hill tried to lower it into the aluminizing tank that John Strong had designed for it. The tank was too small by a fraction of an inch. A simple machining job—a few days' delay—and it was all clear.

It happened again when the mirror finally rested in its cradle in the telescope and the first test observations with a new Hartmann screen were made. There seemed to be serious distortion in the glass. It was Anderson who sweated this one out. What he found, shortly, was that the "earthquake stops," meant to restrain the mirror in case a shake should try to dislodge it, were encroaching too heavily on the cell. A quick adjustment remedied that, once the cause had been thought out.

Or again, a mysterious "hunting" action turned up in the right-ascension drive, which prevented the telescope from accurately following its first star. The trouble here was discovered to be in a slight backlash of the worm drive. Once more a matter of alignment. Measured against the vastness of the project as a whole, insignificant ailments all.

And against them can be put the remarkable success of the aluminizing chamber. Strong had come out from his new post at Johns Hopkins to do the job, and expected to take many weeks to get the bugs out of this twenty-foot vacuum tank, the like of which had never been attempted before. But one night early in December, when he had succeeded in cleaning the mirror by making it "uniformly dirty" with lanoline baby oil, then rubbing off the sludge with special chalk, he found everything ready.

"Let's make a trial run and see how she works," he had said. So that evening they began pumping the chamber down with the oil diffusion pumps supplied them by the Army. All night they pumped and in the morning she was down, way down—a millionth of a millimeter of mercury on the gauges—very nearly a perfect vacuum. Three hours more, and they had "fired" all 360 wire coils bearing the aluminum, spraying it evenly over the whole surface in a film four millionths of an inch thick. Then, with the vacuum killed by increasing the leaks, they had uncovered the disk, to find that they had a virtually perfect reflecting surface over the entire expanse.

John just grinned.

Like small boys, whose minds dart from one unlikely adventure to another on the spur of the moment, they had decided to put the mirror into the telescope and try it. And there she rides today, with her "experimental" coating of aluminum so nearly perfect that it will be used for all the tests and probably for years thereafter, until some super-delicate work comes along that requires the very highest possible accuracy of reflection.

And now will come tests and more tests; adjustments, trials, a celebration or two, a proud showing to special friends, and then, as quietly as possible, a beginning of the vast voyagings so long planned. The least obtainable notoriety, the greatest attainable number of chilly hours in the distant star-fields of the universe.

How proud George Ellery Hale would be—perhaps is—to walk along the asphalt path unseen among a summer Sunday's visitors, and read over the massive doorway to the dome the simple words,

## THE HALE TELESCOPE

Twenty years, almost to the day, have achieved the result that he sought, that he planned for, suffered and died for, not knowing surely that it could be accomplished.

He might have known that it would be, for men and time and money can do anything, when objectives are clear and determination strong.

# PALOMAR'S NEW CONTINENTS

*(See photographs following page 174)*

THE great telescope on Palomar Mountain has been in regular service now for several years, and has long since settled down to its own special routine, taking its place as the most sensitive star camera in the world. It is no longer a spectacular news-maker, for the work of any precision instrument is bound to be quiet, steady and enormously detailed. It is simply one more fine tool the genius of man has been able to devise for disclosing secrets incredibly well hidden.

Highly specialized though it is, the 200-inch telescope does not work alone. There are various other smaller instruments on Palomar, also highly specialized. Most important among these is the 48-inch Schmidt Camera, at present engaged in mapping the entire sky visible from California, in a lengthy project sponsored by the National Geographic Society.

The 200-inch and the Schmidts (there are actually two large ones) work in close cooperation, the main instrument exploring in extreme detail single objects which the smaller ones turn up. With its huge spectroscope the 200-inch carries on studies which lead to new and better estimates of the nature of the nebulae, or "island universes," already known to exist, and it also reaches out into the profound depths of space to capture information impossible to any other instrument.

Not only do the Palomar instruments work together harmoniously; the group cooperates perfectly with the equipment on nearby Mt. Wilson, and as far as possible fits its program to others being carried out all over the world.

One overall scheme of research applies to the two California observatories, planned so that there will not be a moment lost in duplication. The astronomers, too, divide their time between the mountains, so that the integrated program becomes a mass attack upon the innumerable problems still unsolved in the sky.

Major jobs for the Palomar group are so technical that little of their work can be understood by any but scientists. A great deal of the program involves the spectrographs, yielding data which record the components of the light from stars and nebulae, and thus help to determine the nature of these bodies, their distances and motions.

But it is natural that many of the objects already familiar to astronomy through a century of observation should be looked at again and studied for detail formerly out of reach. The eight photographs which comprise this supplement to the Glass Giant of Palomar are mainly of this class. In some of them the detail is so fine that individual stars can be seen millions of light years away. Thus, proof is at hand for the first time that these star-worlds are in reality almost identical to our own Galaxy, though they are totally invisible to the naked eye.

These great systems reach out into space, apparently, in limitless numbers, being no different a billion light years away than in our own neighborhood. They are still there in vast quantity at the extreme limit of even the 200-inch telescope, so that, at present, there seems to be no end to the universe.

But the astronomers humbly admit that it is much too soon to be sure.